EDWARD PALMER:

Plant Explorer of the American West

EDWARD PALMER

Plant Explorer of the American West

ROGERS McVAUGH

Norman: University of Oklahoma Press

By Rogers McVaugh

Edward Palmer: Plant Explorer of the American West (Norman, 1956)

Ferns of Georgia, with Joseph H. Pyron (Athens, 1951)

The publication of this volume has been aided by a grant from income on the endowment of the Horace H. Rackham School of Graduate Studies of the University of Michigan.

Library of Congress Catalog Card Number: 56-11234

Composed and printed at Norman, Oklahoma, U. S. A., by the University of Oklahoma Press.

First edition.

INTRODUCTION

Development in the biological sciences, as in other spheres of human endeavor, has always been dependent upon proper co-ordination between the men who have gone afield in search of new things and those who have worked at home to evaluate, describe, and publicize their discoveries. This co-ordination is particularly important in taxonomy and other branches of biology which are partly descriptive and partly analytical. Conclusions in these branches depend in some measure upon materials supplied by explorers and collectors, and upon the field data relative to these materials. In recent years, scientists have shown increasing appreciation of the value of first-hand knowledge of plants and animals as they grow in nature, and many workers have chosen to supplement their laboratory work by periods of study and active collecting in the field. This has not always been true.

The second half of the nineteenth century was the heyday of the professional collector in North America, a period when a relatively small number of laboratory biologists worked unceasingly to keep abreast of the tide of new materials that poured in upon them. The great West was being opened up and made relatively safe and accessible, but travel was slow and arduous, not to be lightly undertaken by the busy medical men and teachers who were the botanists and zoologists of a hundred years ago. Opportunities for travel were not entirely lacking, however. Long before independent travel was feasible, every year saw organized parties setting out on the long westward trek. Military expeditions, railroad and boundary survey parties, and exploring groups of many kinds often included medical men who were interested in biology or men who were officially designated as naturalists. It is principally to these men that we owe our first knowledge of the flora and fauna of western North America.

The great collectors of this period were those who were temperamentally and physically able to continue the arduous life year after year, who were intellectually curious but lacked training or desire or ability to study and interpret their own collections, and who were willing to receive their rewards in praise and recognition of new floras and faunas brought to light, and new genera and species made known to science through their efforts. One of these great collectors was Edward Palmer.

Modern work in taxonomy stresses the importance of phylogeny, population studies, and variation within species. The interrelation of geography, geology, and the organisms under study are particularly important. Because of the emphasis placed upon these things, the value of a museum specimen *per se* is almost nothing, but the same specimen accompanied by a digest of what is known about its original habitat and source, associates, habits, abundance, variation, and other attributes, is immeasurably greater in value.

In striking contrast to this, biology of the year 1850, or 1875, was more likely to stress recognition of species and genera. Because of the great areas which were newly opened to scientific study between 1850 and 1890, many botanists of this period found their attention directed primarily to the descriptive phase of their science. Interest in these matters was intense in the mid-nineteenth century, especially in botany where the influence of John Torrey made itself felt at an early date and where Asa Gray became one of the leading figures of his time. "New" species were sought and expected, and collectors had little difficulty in disposing of their sets of specimens, not only to the few institutional herbaria then active, but also to the many amateurs who maintained private herbaria. Unfortunately many herbaria, particularly some of the large private ones, placed chief emphasis upon amassing the greatest possible number of species, and tended to discard, or disregard, additional specimens of species which were already represented in the collection. Such an attitude, of course, is similar to many a boy's first burst of enthusiasm for philately! Inevitably, where the name of the species was of the greatest interest, other information concerning specimens was often lost. The prevailing attitude toward documentation of specimens, even among the outstanding men in natural science, was a careless one by today's standards. Duplicate sets of collections were often distributed to the buyers without any information beyond the name of the species and a bare indication of the locality where the specimen originated. Information supplied by collectors was often condensed or suppressed in a way that today seems inexcusable. The modern student is often forced to consider old specimens which are historically important because of their geographical source or because of their status as nomenclatural types, but about which he has none of the information now held to be essential for critical studies.

The collections made by Edward Palmer between 1853 and 1910 were prepared with more care than those of most of his contemporaries. He was primarily a botanical collector, and his botanical specimens were exceptionally well documented for his time. Even in his earliest independent collections, made before 1870, his remarks on morphology, on dates, and on localities were set down methodically and in considerable detail. Only rarely, however, have his notes accompanied his specimens into the herbaria to which the latter were distributed. The specimens have been treated in various ways. They have been distributed with printed labels, with handwritten labels, and with almost no labels at all. Some have been sent out with generalized geographical information covering a whole year's work; some of the duplicates bear no information except an arbitrarily assigned serial number (not the same as Palmer's original field number); some have been misdated by as much as a year, and assigned to nonexistent localities.

This situation was partly Palmer's fault and partly the fault of his contemporaries. He was unwilling to attend to the documentation and distribution of his own collections, and preferred to entrust them for naming, sorting, and selling, to his friends and patrons—prominent scientists all. This was indeed the custom of the time. Nevertheless his reputation suffered in his lifetime, and has suffered since his death, from the occasional carelessness of these men. The men who worked over Palmer's plants, sorted them into species and genera, sometimes carried them to Europe for comparison, wrote his labels out in longhand, and finally packed the specimens up into sets and sold them, sending him the money, were doing this partly as a favor to him and partly to keep him in the field. They wrote his labels and transcribed his data in addition to their own researches and other work, and perhaps they should not be censured too harshly for hasty and superficial attention to the tedious details to which every modern collector must attend on his own account.

The present compilation was undertaken in an attempt to assemble and arrange, and make readily available, some of the widely scattered data pertaining to the life of Edward Palmer, and to provide documentation not for a single collection but for a collector—a field naturalist who gathered for the museums of the world more than 100,000 specimens of plants and uncounted thousands of archaeological, ethnological, and zoological specimens.

Palmer was responsible for many of the classical collections from the southwestern United States and northern Mexico. An estimated two thousand species of plants have been based, nomenclaturally, upon specimens which he collected, and one may find a Palmer specimen newly designated as a type in almost any current revisionary paper dealing with the West American and Mexican floras. A summary of the known facts about his collections and his travels has long been needed, not merely as a memorial to the work of an indefatigable explorer, but as a means of aiding and expediting research on collections of primary importance to systematic and geographical botany.

Readers who want facts will find many of them in the Geographical Index which occupies the latter part of this book and in the chronological account with which the book begins. It is to be hoped that these factual statements are in the main useful and even interesting.

Beyond the mere facts of Edward Palmer's life, however, consider the setting of that life, and the romance of it. Palmer's days began in the time of sailing vessels, and continued until the airplane was a curiosity; he went west across the Great Plains before the railroads had left Kansas City; he took part in the Pikes Peak stampede, one of the great gold rushes in our history; he was in mortal danger from the Comanches and Apaches who are peaceful citizens today; he saw Brigham Young and he knew Joseph Henry; Mexico was his second home in the golden days of the Díaz regime, when the stagecoach was the only means of transportation and the pines grew uncut on the great haciendas where the goats now graze; he was with the first party of scientists to penetrate the wilderness of Lake Okeechobee, and the first to call the attention of scientists to the destructive habits of the cotton boll weevil.

I have had the satisfaction, known to every taxonomist, of the orderly classification of the data which are set forth in the following pages, but most rewarding after all has been a vicarious acquaintance with this amazing man who, although small and frail, a hypochondriac, and often unfortunate in his dealings with other people, nonetheless overcame barriers of language and time and transportation in a fashion that has rarely been surpassed.

My own interest in Edward Palmer began about 1940, when I was a member of the staff of the Division of Plant Exploration and Introduction of the United States Department of Agriculture. While making an attempt to secure some additional information about a Palmer specimen in the National Herbarium in Washington, I discovered quite unexpectedly that in the files of my own Division was a nearly complete set of the collector's painstakingly written field notes, almost none of which had ever been filed in herbaria with the corresponding specimens. Further search revealed in the same voluminous files a collection of Palmeriana, manuscripts great and small, which had been assembled by the collector himself, and preserved and sorted with the collaboration of Commander W. E. Safford.[1] Finally, in the same files, was a manuscript biography of Palmer (some seven hundred pages long), begun by Safford but left unfinished at his death in 1926.

After examination of these sources, I found that there were still great unexplained gaps and discrepancies in the collector's career. As time permitted I explored the resources of the various government agencies in Washington, with encouraging results. The various divisions of the Smithsonian Institution, as might have been expected, were the richest sources, with the National Archives a close second. As the project expanded, I was able to visit the many biological libraries of Harvard University, and I found these scarcely less rewarding. Finally it transpired that all of Palmer's *remaining* documents—those in his possession at the time of his death in 1911—had been sold by the Merwin Sales Co., of New York, at public auction

[1] William Edwin Safford (1859–1926) was a botanist, ethnologist, and philologist, known to botanists chiefly through his published notes on economic plants. He began his career in the U. S. Navy, 1876; was vice-governor of Guam after the Spanish-American War, but soon resigned from the navy, and became assistant botanist, U.S.D.A., 1902, and economic botanist, 1915–26. It was through his influence that many of the extant materials on Palmer were saved from dispersal or destruction, and his unfinished biography remains one of the richest sources of information on some periods of Palmer's life. See *Dictionary of American Biography* (1937), XVI, 288–89.

in 1914, in three hundred separate lots. To my dismay I found that the sales records of the auction, if any had ever been kept, had long since been destroyed. To this day I have located only about one-third of all the manuscripts sold at the Merwin Auction in 1914, and some of the missing ones I should like very much to see. Even without them, however, it has been possible to reconstruct Palmer's life and travels in some detail.[2]

There is much published material dealing with the collections made by Palmer, as may be seen by reference to the appended bibliography. Biographical data, on the other hand, are relatively scarce in published accounts. Luckily for the biographer, Palmer left a remarkably complete, if inadvertent, record of his own life and travels. Files of his own correspondence were found at Yale University, at the New York Botanical Garden, at Iowa State College, at the Missouri Botanical Garden, and elsewhere, including Washington. He was a confirmed and verbose letter writer, a fact that has made it possible to follow him almost day by day over the nearly six decades that span his activity as a collector. Regularly upon arrival and departure, and often while on the way from one place to another, he sent word of his movements and activities, usually to his patron of the moment. About 650 of his letters have been examined, and many others have doubtless been preserved; Mr. Andrew Denny Rodgers, III, informs me that in his opinion no botanist or collector of our time, with the possible exception of C. C. Parry, was a more voluminous writer.

The greatest single source of Palmeriana, apart from the man's own letters, is the manuscript collection in the files of the Division of Plant Exploration and Introduction. This is invaluable because

[2] The public sale and dispersal of Palmer's notes seems never to have been satisfactorily explained. In his will (see Appendix V) he directed his executors to consult with J. N. Rose and L. H. Dewey, both of whom had worked with him in the study and arrangement of these notes, as to the best means of "utilizing the said papers and pictures." He directed further that if the executors saw fit, they were to use a sum of not more than $2,000 from his estate for the publication of his notes, which according to his estimate filled nine boxes and two trunks. As the monetary value of the papers was not large (the amount realized at the auction was about $450), the executors presumably allowed the papers to be sold after consultation with Rose and Dewey had convinced them that the collection was not sufficiently valuable to keep for reference at the Smithsonian Institution. This point of view is hard for even an amateur historian to understand.

of the part sorted and assembled by Palmer himself. At least a part of this sorting was done when he was an employee of the Department of Agriculture, appointed at the request of F. V. Coville for this very purpose, from 1899 through 1901, and at intervals during the rest of his life. The collection includes original letters, newspaper clippings, ticket stubs, hotel bills, transcriptions of travel diaries, and many other items. Much of the material almost certainly was obtained by Safford after the Merwin Auction of 1914, but individual items as listed in the auction catalog have been so dispersed that it is now impossible to establish their identities.

Safford's unfinished biography, also referred to above, was begun as a semipopular account of the collector's life and travels, combined with an account of the economic plants of Mexico. It is valuable to the historian chiefly because of the many quotations from Palmer's diaries, which seem to have been available to Safford, but most of which are now apparently lost. The quotations as recorded by Safford are somewhat idealized because they have been edited in an attempt to improve Palmer's style of writing (which was, to say the least, highly original). They do furnish, however, in many cases, valuable clues to routes and localities. Safford also makes, on his own authority, many statements that have not been confirmed; references to these will be found below under discussion of individual localities.

The account which follows could never have been completed without the wholehearted co-operation which I received on every occasion from the many persons who are responsible for the care and keeping of the scattered Palmer manuscripts. Materials in the custody of the United States National Archives, the several divisions of the Smithsonian Institution, and the United States Department of Agriculture have been made freely available by those in charge. I am also much indebted to the authorities of the Missouri Botanical Garden, the Yale University Library, the Iowa State College Library, the New York Botanical Garden, and the Taylor Museum of the Colorado Springs Fine Arts Center for permission to study manuscripts in their possession and for aid in locating and in some cases copying these manuscripts. The University of Arizona generously loaned for my study much valuable manuscript material which had come into their possession after the Merwin Auction of 1914. Special mention should be made of Harvard University, where the Museum of Comparative Zoology, the Peabody Museum of American Archaeology and Ethnology, and the Houghton Library all contain valuable items that have been freely consulted. The staff members of the Gray Herbarium spared no pains to put before me all possible documents that might prove useful in this study.

Of the many friends who have contributed their time and efforts, I want to mention especially Mr. Donald D. Brand, whose knowledge of Mexican geography and history have been freely made available; Mr. Joseph A. Ewan, who through the years has sent me scores of notes and new findings of Palmeriana and who has checked carefully the parts of the present work which have to do with Colorado; Mr. Ivan M. Johnston, who first called to my attention the existence of the Merwin Catalog of 1914 and who has made helpful suggestions in other ways; and Miss Muriel H. Wright, who has been generous and patient with my questions about the Indian Territory and its history.

It is also a pleasure to acknowledge the help of those who have made my research in Mexico more pleasant and more fruitful. They have been most helpful to a stranger in a strange land. Especially I would thank Señores Moisés Martínez, of Chihuahua; Rodolfo Sánchez S., of Saltillo; Bulmaro Valdes Anaya and Blas Rodríguez Ibarra, of Torreón; Nereo Rodríguez Barragán, of San Luis Potosí; Agustín Gómez y Gutiérrez, Ricardo Lancaster-Jones and Alberto Lancaster-Jones, of Guadalajara; and Maximino Martínez, of Mexico City.

Last of all I want to express my appreciation to the present and former heads of the Division of Plant Exploration and Introduction,[3] of which division I was a member from 1938 to 1946. During all this period Mr. B. Y. Morrison, who was then in charge of the unit, gave his support to the project and made it possible for me to continue it except as it was interrupted by the war. Mr. C. O. Erlanson, who has been in charge of the Division since Mr. Morrison's retirement from government service, has continued his early interest in the work and has facilitated in many ways the job of bringing it to an early conclusion.

The real hero of the book has been my wife, who has been called into service as proofreader, prepublication critic, research assistant,

[3] Now officially called Plant Introduction Section, Agricultural Research Service. This organization is mentioned in various places in the following pages, always under the name of Division of Plant Exploration and Introduction. The name of the Division was often abbreviated to PEI.

and simply listener. At times she has come, with some justice, to feel that Edward Palmer was becoming a permanent member of the family. She has followed his trail with me over the desert plains of San Luis Potosí and has puzzled with me over his letters. I hope she will recognize some of her own work in these pages and will accept my gratitude for her help.

ROGERS McVAUGH

Washington, D. C.
July 10, 1956

TABLE OF CONTENTS

Appendices

ILLUSTRATIONS

MAPS

EDWARD PALMER:

Plant Explorer of the American West

I THE FIRST YEARS

It is not difficult even today to reconstruct the facts of the life of Edward Palmer. The prosaic details of comings and goings, meetings and partings, collections gathered and salaries paid are matters of record for those who have the patience to unearth them. The physical likeness of the man has been recorded photographically, and his height and weight are known. Far more difficult to reconstruct, however, is his personality. Few living people remember him, and most of these remember him from chance meetings only, when he was advanced in years, a "nice old man" puttering around the Smithsonian Institution. His own letters record his doings but rarely express his opinions or his fully formulated thoughts. Contemporary estimates of his character are conflicting and are perhaps an expression of the paradox of his personality.

Here is a man who could neither express himself clearly nor spell his words consistently, but who corresponded regularly on an equal basis with the leading scientists of his day. He performed prodigious feats in accumulating, packing, and safeguarding collections of all kinds of fragile materials and he prepared copious data sheets to accompany the specimens, yet he rarely succeeded in keeping his records free from errors and hardly ever managed to distribute his specimens with the data he provided. He was small and frail and passed hardly a year without some incapacitating accident or illness, but when he was seventy-five years old he was still able to take in stride a week's trip on horseback in the rough mountains of western Durango. He inspired liking, or at least loyalty, in such men as Spencer Baird and John Torrey, and provoked violent dislike in other men in similar positions.

A few traits stand out even after cursory study of Palmer's career. First and foremost he was a man who did his best work for others. Who his real friends were, I do not know, but the scientists with whom he corresponded were his patrons, who encouraged, directed, and usually subsidized his work. He did not hesitate to suggest and discuss policies in his letters to responsible officials, but he looked to those officials to suggest new fields for his own work, to aid him in all possible ways to reach his objectives, to receive and care for his collections, and to express sympathy for his real and imagined ailments. This almost filial attitude on Palmer's part was apparent in his relations with Joseph Henry, for nearly twenty years with Spencer Baird, and successively with D. C. Eaton, Sereno Watson, and J. N. Rose.

Perhaps as a result of many lonely years, Palmer's thoughts often turned inward. His letters abound in references to his own ailments, both major and minor. He complained of various wrongs done him by his associates, some of which were perhaps real, some fancied, and some partly his own fault: He entrusted an early collection to Elliott Coues, who was on his way back to civilization, and through some error (perhaps on the part of George Engelmann to whom Coues gave the specimens), Palmer received no credit for his part in the affair until he had stirred up the botanical world by his protests. Later he left a collection for safekeeping at an active military post in Arizona, and was incensed when he returned after some years to find it had disappeared. He resolved never again to collect with another botanist, after C. C. Parry sent a full set of the joint San Luis Potosí collection, gratis, to Kew, thus depriving the partners (and Palmer in particular) of a part of their revenue from the sale of the specimens. When he was in Indian Territory in 1868, he was dismissed from his medical duties, ostensibly because of his excessive devotion to his collecting; he thought privately that the Indian agent, his superior, had harbored a grudge against him because of his protests against the illegal storage of the agent's "medicinal" whiskey in the tent set aside as a dispensary.

It seems that many of his troubles could have been avoided by a little more forethought and by a somewhat more realistic view of what was happening around him. He was often intensely—and often briefly—interested in details, but he seems less often to have understood the larger picture. He was at times extremely objective, as I have mentioned elsewhere; a dead Apache child was to him a specimen and nothing more, and throughout his life, like a census taker, he put all women, young and old, into a category which he designated as "females." It may have been that his thoughts occupied themselves with these logical and statistical details to the exclusion of other things until at last they returned to himself. It may have been logical and virtuous, for example, for him to have objected to the agent's whiskey in his closet, but it seems curious that he would not realize that such a protest might not endear him to the agent. He seems not to have understood that Parry's act in sending a set of their specimens to Kew was intended to accomplish what it actually did, that is, to make their collection one of the most notable ever to have come from central Mexico, because of its enumeration by W. B. Hemsley in the *Biologia Centrali-Americana*.

Although various contemporary reports, and his many specimens, attest that Palmer was an indefatigable collector, I have a feeling that he really did not enjoy collecting for its own sake. In the course of his career he accumulated not only museum specimens in biological and other fields, but also such varied things as coins, old newspapers, selected clippings on various subjects, and chips knocked off historical buildings and monuments. Most of these seem, however, to have been the results of desultory and sporadic attempts at accumulation, rather than sustained efforts to make scientifically valuable collections. He became known in his lifetime particularly as a collector of botanical and anthropological materials, and some of his collections along these lines were among the most valuable ever made. Almost without exception, however, they were made in the line of duty. When he was in the prime of life, for example, he worked for two extended periods on nonbotanical pursuits. For three summers (1871–73), he worked on the New England coast as an assistant in the Commission of Fish and Fisheries, and later (1881–84), he worked almost continuously in the Mississippi Basin for the Smithsonian's Bureau of American Ethnology. During these periods he collected almost no plant specimens, although he must have had numerous opportunities to do so. The impulse that took him back to the field again and again must have been not a liking for collecting itself (which is, after all, rather disagreeable and arduous work), but little more than a liking for travel and for strange places, a feeling that by his work he was contributing to science, and a willingness to accept commissions to collect certain classes of materials in return for the opportunity to go out again. He seems to have had relatively little feeling of his own obligation to complete the work of documentation and distribution of his collections. Instead, he packed off his bundles to his patron of the moment and asked for money to enable him to begin to collect again.

In one class of objects, however, his interest never lagged. From the time of his first expedition, that to Paraguay in 1853–55, he never overlooked an opportunity to accumulate notes and specimens pertaining to aboriginal and other local uses of plants. His first and only important published paper, *Food Products of the North American Indians,* is a pioneer effort which has been much quoted and reprinted, and has been translated into German. On all his trips, but particularly from 1865 to 1870 and from about 1895 until the end of his life, he devoted much attention to this specialty. His field notes, prepared to accompany his Mexican collections of the years from 1895 to 1910, abound in references to local names and uses of plants; in these same years, when he was becoming too old for much strenuous field work, he spent a great deal of time in the city markets, especially in Saltillo, San Luis Potosí, and Durango, and amassed a multitude of notes on plants which were offered for sale there. His notes on economic plants and ethnobotany in general have been extensively used and quoted by Safford, Standley, and other writers on Mexican plants.

The archaeological and ethnological collections made by Palmer (other than the ethnobotanical material mentioned above), include several very important series. His pioneer work among the Indians of the Southwest, his archaeological investigations in southwestern Utah, and his explorations in northern Mexico from 1878 to 1880, all rank high in this field of investigations. It was primarily as a botanical collector, however, that he excelled, and it was in this field that he did the most work and has secured the most recognition.

His collections from Arizona, Utah, and Sonora (1865–70), Indian Territory (1868), peninsular Florida (1874), Guadalupe Island (1875), San Luis Potosí (1878), Coahuila and Nuevo León (1880), western Chihuahua (1885), and Jalisco (1886) either were the first from the areas in question or were the first comprehensive series secured for American herbaria. In the last fifteen years of his life he made a trip to Mexico in almost every year, and on each trip he made a large collection. The plants he collected over his whole career included a total of approximately 100,000 specimens, distributed among about 20,000 separate collections, of which nearly one-tenth have been regarded as new to science. Of all botanical collectors in America in the nineteenth century, only Charles Wright[1] and C. G. Pringle[2] can be compared with Palmer as to the extent and value of their work.

We know very little about Palmer's early life or about what early associations may have turned him toward his career in natural history. He was born in England, probably in 1831, near Wilton in County Norfolk. Safford tells us that he was the son of Mary Ann Armiger, and William Palmer, a "commercial gardener" or florist.[3] The records of the General Register Office, in London, show that when Edward Palmer was married in 1856 he gave his father's name as Robert Palmer and his father's profession as "farmer." Tradition has it that young Edward was interested in plants from earliest youth and worked in his own garden under his father's tutelage. Our first actual knowledge of him is after his arrival in America, when he was newly come of age.[4]

[1] *Charles Wright* (1811–85), Botanical explorer. A graduate of Yale University, 1835. Botanist of the Mexican Boundary Survey, 1851–52, North Pacific Exploring and Surveying Expedition, 1853–56, and explorer of Cuba, 1856–67. See *Dictionary of American Biography* (1937), Vol. XX, 545–46, and for a readable account of Wright's early life, Samuel Wood Geiser, *Naturalists of the Frontier* (Dallas, 1948), 172–98.

[2] Cyrus Guernsey Pringle (1838–1911). Universally respected botanical explorer of Mexico, said to have distributed over half a million specimens, and to have brought to light more than 1,200 species previously unknown to science. See Helen Burns Davis, *Life and Work of Cyrus Guernsey Pringle* (Burlington, 1936).

[3] Quotations and statements attributed in the following pages to Safford, without further citation, are taken from the manuscript biography in the Palmer Collection of the Division of Plant Exploration and Introduction. See References and Sources No. 123b.

[4] I have not been able to secure documentary evidence of the date or place of Palmer's birth, or of the names of his parents. At my request the rector at Wilton, the Reverend D. F. Page, in 1953 searched the parish registers for the period in question, in the churches at Wilton and Hockwold, but was unable to locate the desired records. General registration of births and deaths was not required in England until 1837, and the parish registers ordinarily contain no dates of birth but only dates of christening. It is of course possible that Edward Palmer's family had their children christened in some church other than those near Wilton.

At various times during his life Palmer was required to state his age or his date of birth, or both, and according to these statements he may have been born as early as 1830 or as late as 1839. His birthday was invariably given as January 12. The year of his birth was probably 1830 or 1831. The earliest records available to us, namely the medical records of the *Water Witch* (1853), and the passenger list of the *Amazon* (1856), suggest that the year was no later than 1830, and I am inclined to accept these records, for certainly one is more likely to give his own age correctly at 20 or 25 than in later years when memory begins to fail.

According to Safford's published accounts of Palmer's life, the latter was born at Hockwold cum Wilton, near Brandon, County Norfolk, on January 12, 1831, by error printed 1821 in *Popular Science Monthly*, Vol. LXXVIII (1911), 341. Sargent, basing his statements upon information furnished by Palmer about 1890, gave the latter's birthplace as Wilton and the date as January 12, 1833. See References and Sources No. 106. Various conflicting statements in regard to this matter are tabulated below:

Date of Record	*Nature of Record*	*Palmer's Age as Given*	*Palmer's Date of Birth as Given*	*Presumable Year of Birth*
Nov. 7, 1853	Medical records of *Water Witch*	24		?1830
May 20, 1856	Passenger list of *Amazon*	26		1830
Jan. 4, 1864	Army enlistment	28		1836
Feb. 28, 1870	Passenger list of *Henry Chauncey*	34		1836
Mar. 17, 1879	Passenger list of *Comet*	40		1839
Mar. 13, 1886	Stated by Palmer in Veterans Administration	55		1831
?1890	Palmer's letter to Sargent		Jan. 12, 1833	1833
Jul. 1, 1899	Statement by Palmer		Jan. 12, 1883[!]	1833
Jul. 11, 1900	"		Jan. 12, 1833	1833
Oct. 30, 1901	"		Jan. 12, 1832	1832
Sep. 11, 1905	"		Jan. 12, 1833	1833
Oct. 30, 1907	"		Jan. 12, 1837	1837
Jan. 11, 1911	Pension Bureau, Statement by Palmer	80	Jan. 12	1831

II EARLY LIFE IN AMERICA, 1849–59

THE FIRST DOZEN YEARS of Edward Palmer's life in the United States must be reconstructed from pitifully small bits of evidence. A youth of eighteen, in a strange country, leaves few traces that last a hundred years for a biographer's attention. This particular youth came to America in 1849, "with a family of friends."[1] He landed in New York and later went to Cleveland, Ohio, where he became the personal attendant of John W. Taylor[2] and came under the influence of Dr. Jared Kirtland,[3] who gave the young man the use of his library and encouraged him in his biological bent.

Near the end of the year 1852, Palmer came to Washington and was enrolled as a member of the expedition to Paraguay which left the United States the following February, under the command of Thomas Jefferson Page.[4] Safford tells the story in Palmer's words:

[1] See References and Sources No. 106.

[2] John W. Taylor (1784–1854). U. S. Congressman from New York, 1813–33. Twice speaker of the House. Nationally prominent because of his active opposition to slavery. Moved to Cleveland, 1843. See *Dictionary of American Biography* (1937), XVIII, 335–36.

[3] Jared Potter Kirtland (1793–1877). M. D. Yale, 1815. An early associate of Eli Ives, Benjamin Silliman, B. S. Barton, Benjamin Rush. Moved in 1823 to Ohio and became prominent in biological and medical circles. In 1843 helped found the Cleveland Medical College, and held a professorship there until his death. Was an active editor and the author of many zoological and other publications, and one of the most respected and influential men in the Midwest. See *Dictionary of American Biography* (1937), X, 438–39.

[4] Thomas Jefferson Page (1808–99). Naval officer and explorer. See *Dictionary of American Biography* (1937), XIV, 140–41.

When I heard of the proposed expedition to Paraguay, I was eager to join as a collector. Mr. Taylor approved of my plan and gave me a letter of introduction to the Comptroller of the treasury. I went to Washington and presented this letter to Mr. Whittlesey, who received me kindly and gave me two letters, one to Mr. Brackenridge,[5] who was at that time superintendant of the newly established Botanical Garden, the other to Lieutenant Page. . . . When I called on Lieutenant Page and explained my mission, he held up both hands and exclaimed: "You are the very man I have been looking for for the last six months." He told me to report to him at the Navy Yard the next day. I did so and was enlisted as hospital steward. In addition to caring for the sick and dispensing medicines under the direction of the ship's surgeon I was to collect plants and take care of all other collections made by officers of the expedition.

The story of the South American collections made by the members of the La Plata Expedition under Captain Page, and the itinerary of the *Water Witch*, has been related elsewhere,[6] and Page himself, in a charming account of the expedition, described the country and its resources and people in a very thorough and graphic manner.[7] Palmer played no more than a very minor part in the activities of the expedition. There seems to be no contemporary record of his navy service, and presumably Captain Page engaged his services semi-officially, as was customary, so that Palmer served as a civilian, but under navy orders on a navy vessel.[8] His name is nowhere mentioned in Page's long published account of the expedition, and Page himself has usually been credited with the collection of most of the biological specimens which were brought back for the Smithsonian Institution. It is now known that Palmer collected most of the plants sent home

[5] William D. Brackenridge (1810–93). Remembered chiefly for his work on the ferns of the Wilkes Expedition. For accounts of his life and work see *Journal of the New York Botanical Garden,* Vol. XX (1919), 117–24; *Proceedings of the American Philosophical Society,* Vol. LXXXII (1940), 673–79.

[6] See References and Sources No. 42.

[7] See References and Sources No. 52.

[8] I searched among the archives of the Navy Department in 1943, but could not find any record of his having been officially enrolled in the Navy. His name appears incidentally on the medical records in the log of the *Water Witch.* The pension records of the Veterans Administration state that he enlisted in the Navy on December 15, 1852, but I could find no other record of this.

by the expedition, and a considerable proportion of the zoological material as well.[9]

Safford quotes occasional revealing or appealing excerpts from diaries which are now lost, and one such quote from the La Plata diary reveals Palmer at twenty-four to have had the same supreme detachment and naïveté and as little sense of humor as he was later to exhibit as a septuagenarian: He had some trouble persuading the Paraguayan Indian women to let him measure their enormous breasts, which far exceeded anything of which he had previous knowledge. It was the same Palmer who, ten years later, calmly walked into an Apache village and began measuring and collecting specimens in the wake of an army detachment which had just wiped out the population of the village.

Another, and equally strong, personality trait which Palmer never lost can be inferred from happenings on this expedition. This was a complete disregard for personal frailty. Although in later years he grumbled about innumerable complaints brought on and aggravated by exposure and life under primitive conditions, it seems never to have occurred to him to consider any other life. After nearly two years in South America, he became seriously ill for some months and was under treatment for "intermittent fever" (that is, malaria). After his recovery he was discharged from his duties on board the *Water Witch,* and he returned to the United States at his own expense. Upon reaching Washington in June, 1855, the young enthusiast at once offered his services to the Smithsonian Institution as an explorer. His trip to South America had confirmed his liking for travel, and set him upon the career that was to be his life for the next fifty-five years.

The following letter, the first of a long series which Palmer wrote to Joseph Henry[10] and to his successor, Spencer Baird,[11] is reproduced here because it shows its writer exactly as he was to remain: anxious

[9] See *Annual Report of the Smithsonian Institution,* 1856 (Washington, 1857), 14.

[10] Joseph Henry (1797–1878). Physicist, and first secretary (1846–78) of the Smithsonian Institution; in great part he was responsible for the early growth and prestige of that institution. See *Dictionary of American Biography* (1937), VIII, 550–53.

[11] Spencer Fullerton Baird (1823–88). One of the great naturalists, editors, and administrators of the nineteenth century. Assistant secretary of the Smithsonian Institution, 1850–78, and secretary, 1878–88. U. S. Commissioner of Fish and Fisheries, 1871–88. See *Dictionary of American Biography* (1937), I, 513–15.

for opportunities to travel and collect, but without organizing ability to direct his own expeditions; sincere in his devotion to the prosecution of science, but not realizing his own limitations; willing to let his work as a collector speak for itself, and proud of the work, without understanding that the collections in themselves were not enough to make him the intellectual equal of such men as Henry and Baird.

WASHINGTON CITY June 13th—1855

DEAR SIR
I beg to lay before you an application for an appointment in any expedition that may be formed.

I have just returned from the Exploriseing expedition to the Laplat River and the success which have attended my labours may be judged from the quality of the specimens collected. In the preservation of birds—insects—fish quadrupeds and botanical specimens I take great interest.

Intending to spend my life in the prosecution of science and trusting my qualifications be found sufficient to meet with your favourable consideration.

I remain, your obedient survent
Edward Palmer[12]

TO PROFESSOR HENRY OF THE SMITHSONIAN INSTITUE

Failing in his initial attempt to secure a place with the Smithsonian Institution, Palmer returned to Cleveland for a few months to work in Dr. Kirtland's library. He collected a few grasshoppers during the summer but did not settle down to any steady employment, and in September he set off on a trip to England to see his mother. His visit to his old home lasted six months, but after his taste of travel and exploration he was not content in England and, in April, 1856, he returned to New York and Cleveland, this time a married man, but still seeking a position in Washington.

Palmer's marriage and its aftermath remain among the most intriguing incidents of his life. His letters before and after the fact give few clues. When in September, 1855, he wrote to Professor Baird about his impending trip home, he noted that "All my immediate friends have died except my mother." After his marriage he seems to have been rather surprised by it himself; he wrote Baird again "You may wonder but so it is I was married on the 29 of March." His wife

[12] Smithsonian Archives, Letters Received, Book 71, p. 436.

was but twenty years old when she arrived in New York, and so could not have been more than twelve or thirteen when Edward first left home. We can imagine a whirlwind courtship and a honeymoon voyage on the great ship *Amazon,* which was competing for the transatlantic record on this westbound run. But Dinah Riches, the young wife, vanishes from view as she leaves the *Amazon* at New York. To my knowledge she was never mentioned from that day to the end of Palmer's life, and we can but suppose that she came to an early and untimely end, for certainly she did not accompany her husband on his later wanderings.

Perhaps the newly acquired responsibilities of a family made Palmer abandon temporarily his dreams of an explorer's life, for in November, 1856, we find him attending lectures at the Cleveland Homeopathic College.[13] The following February he was still at the college, but in April he moved to Highland, Kansas—to practice medicine! Perhaps it is fortunate that we know so little about the results of his medical practice for the next two years. Actually we are not even sure that he did practice the profession for which he had prepared himself by two years of service as hospital steward on board the *Water Witch* and a few months of lectures at Cleveland. It was common at this period, however, for medical men to assume the title (and the profession) of "Doctor" with no more training than Palmer had experienced aboard the navy vessel.

The Kansas years are extremely sketchily documented. All that is known of the life of the young naturalist is contained in four letters to Baird and in meager bits from the contemporary reports of the Smithsonian Institution. Probably Palmer's medical work did not occupy him very much of his time; how he was able to support himself is a question. He was still preoccupied with natural history, and

[13] D. H. Beckwith, *History of the Cleveland Homeopathic College from 1850 to 1880* (n.d.). The first part of this pamphlet (pp. 1–24) bears Beckwith's name as author, and is entitled *The History of the Western College of Homeopathic Medicine from 1850 to 1860.* The college began instruction in 1850, with work in medicine, surgery, anatomy, materia medica and jurisprudence, chemistry, and physical science. There were about sixty students. The first graduates, twelve in number, completed their work on February 7, 1851. Requirements for graduation included three years of study in a medical office, followed by two courses of lectures at the college, or one course after ten years' practice. The name of the institution was changed to Western College of Homeopathy in 1856. Palmer's name is not included in the list of graduates of March 11, 1857, and presumably he never completed any formal curriculum.

he was much pleased with the environment in which he found himself. His first year in Kansas, 1857, he found time to send one box and one can of specimens to Baird.

We know that he left Highland and settled near Leavenworth early in the year 1858. Early this same winter he made a rather long survey trip through northeastern Kansas and into Nebraska, but found the weather prevented him from collecting anything except minerals and fossils. He did not like Nebraska: "A more inhospitable country was never seen." Apparently the Smithsonian Institution received nothing from him in 1858, but the following year he sent three boxes of specimens from Kansas. The fate of all these early collections is unknown. I have never seen any of them cited in the literature, nor have any of them turned up among the collections at the National Museum. Safford states that Palmer made large collections which were subsequently destroyed by fire, but this is by no means certain.

Courtesy Smithsonian Institution

Edward Palmer as a Young Man
This is thought to be his earliest portrait,
made possibly before 1860.

DRS. ELLIOTT COUES AND EDWARD PALMER, No. 294

FORT WHIPPLE, ARIZONA, 1865. Apr 26

Corydalis montana Eng

fructu erecto

DR. EDW. PALMER..........SOUTHERN ARIZONIA, 1867. 245

Jatropha cardiophylla Mull

Mouzinna — Torr.

Bot Bound

Shrub, 3 feet high, many stems from running rootstock — female blossom white

Tucson Aug 10

~~346~~ 314 DISTRIBUTED BY THE SMITHSONIAN INSTITUTION.

Collected by

DR. EDWARD PALMER in the INDIAN TERRITORY, chiefly on the False Washita, between Fort Cobb and Fort Arbuckle, 1868.

Phyllanthus polygonoides —

(Above) *Labels typical of those which appear on Palmer's collections of 1865 and 1867, from the collections of the Missouri Botanical Garden. The handwriting is that of George Engelmann.*
(Below) *Label distributed with Palmer's plant collections of 1868.*

III COLORADO AND THE CIVIL WAR, 1859–65

NEWS OF THE DISCOVERY of gold fields near Denver began to spread widely in the late summer of 1858, and by the early spring of 1859 hundreds of gold seekers on their way west were pouring through Leavenworth every day. The trip on from Leavenworth to Denver took two weeks to a month, one of the longer routes leading across southern Nebraska to Fort Kearny, thence up the road along the Platte and the South Platte rivers. It must have been partly the excitement of the flood of emigration and the fever of gold that drew Palmer to Colorado along this southern Nebraska route a year after the rush began. We know that he reached Denver on September 26, 1859,[1] and we know that he lived there until August 6, 1861, but between these two dates we have to reconstruct his life from two letters, a series of field notes, and a few memoranda. Perhaps he made his living as a doctor in the raw, precarious surroundings of the gold fields. Almost certainly he did not spend his time in any serious search for gold. In spite of the lack of any financial compensation, however, he continued his interest in natural history. He "left for the mountains" on June 20, 1860, and it may be supposed that this was a trip for the purposes of collecting and exploring, but all we really know about his work of 1860 is in a letter which he wrote seven years later:

You will probably remember receiving from the Smithsonian Institute a box of plants collected by me in the Colorado Territory from the

[1] Note in Palmer's hand, in Merwin Item 87b. See References and Sources No. 45.

base of Longs Peak across the summit through Middle and South Park to the base of the mountains in 1860 but they were lost while enroute to Washington but three years after turned up . . . .[2]

The Annual Report of the Smithsonian Institution for 1863 records the receipt from Palmer of "Fossils, minerals, &c, Pikes Peak." Possibly these were the collections of 1860—less the plants which had been sent to Engelmann—which turned up three years late as suggested by Palmer in his letter. Actually it now seems impossible to establish the truth. Nothing else is known about the fate of the plants collected in 1860, if indeed any of them actually reached Engelmann. I have never seen any of them; if any still exist, they are doubtless to be found among the collections at the Missouri Botanical Garden.

For the next year, 1861, we have a few more definite bits of information. We know from a letter with the characteristic heading of "Denver City, Pikes Peak, K[ansas] T[erritory]," that Palmer was still in Denver in February. He met with a group of thirty-one other citizens on July 31 to discuss the desirability of forming an agricultural society.[3] Between these two dates Palmer spent a considerable amount of time in the mountains directly west of Denver. His field notes mention relatively few definite localities, but he makes many references to the mountains, mountain streams, and other features of the landscape. The earliest date noted is April 21; many collections were made in the mountains in May, June, and July, and apparently he traveled as widely as he could in what was then extremely primitive country. We know that he was at Golden at least once and that he made at least one trip over the old stage road to Empire and Central City.

In 1861, Palmer collected both plants and animals. The history of

[2] This was a letter to George Engelmann (1809–84). Engelmann was the most respected and able botanist west of the Alleghenies, and, after Gray, the leader among systematists. He was a medical doctor (Würzburg, 1831) who came to St. Louis in 1833 and began his practice in 1835. He was soon collaborating with Gray and also with Torrey, and became known as the greatest authority on various difficult groups of vascular plants. Many general collections from the Western states were entrusted to him for identification, including most of Palmer's plants from 1863 to 1867. See *Dictionary of American Biography* (1937), VI, 159–60, and a sketch by Asa Gray in *American Journal of Science*, Series 3, Vol. XXVIII (1884), 61–67.

[3] Alvin T. Steinel, *History of Agriculture in Colorado* (Fort Collins, 1926), 54.

these collections is an interesting one. The field notes for all the Colorado collections, as pointed out some years ago, had lain undisturbed in the correspondence files of the Smithsonian Institution since 1862.[4] When these were "discovered," about 1943, it was supposed that they pertained chiefly or entirely to material collected in 1862, the year in which they were forwarded to Professor Baird. Now, however, a closer scrutiny of what is known of Palmer's whereabouts in 1862 brings out the fact that most, if not all, of the plants covered by the notes (Nos. 1–165) were collected during the spring and early summer of 1861. Some collections actually are dated 1861, and others are from localities which Palmer in 1862 could not have visited on the days cited. A few collections only, particularly those made on the plains east and southeast of Denver, are dated 1862, and even these dates may be erroneous.[5]

Until recently not one single Colorado specimen of Palmer's collecting had been located in any herbarium. Since the finding of the field notes, however, Joseph Ewan has used them to identify, and subsequently locate in the National Herbarium, several of the specimens, apparently those collected in 1861. Among the species found are *Leucocrinum montanum, Anemone globosa,* and *Primula parryi.* Doubtless a more extended search will reveal the presence of others. None thus far found bears any information except the words "Dr. Palmer" and "Colorado Territory," these phrases written in a clerical hand during the early years of the Department of Agriculture Herbarium. That the specimens were identified by Asa Gray is attested by the tickets in Gray's handwriting.[6] As Palmer did not collect in

[4] See References and Sources No. 41.

[5] This is Smithsonian Accession No. 291 for 1863. Certain notes refer to specimens taken at Denver, July 30, and August 1 and 2, 1862. Palmer's outfit had left Fort Larned, Kansas, on July 25, 1862, and it seems impossible for him to have reached Denver in five days. He was in Denver on the above dates in 1861, however, and the collections may well have been made in that year.

[6] Asa Gray (1810–88). The greatest American botanist of the nineteenth century, and more than any other person responsible for the development of the science in this country. His herbarium became the basis of the Harvard University Herbarium (later Gray Herbarium). See *Dictionary of American Biography* (1937), VII, 511–14. About the year 1860, and for almost a decade thereafter, most of the botanical collections received by the Smithsonian Institution were sent for determination and sorting to Torrey and Gray, and most of the work of identification of the western American plants fell upon Gray. See A. D. Rodgers, *John Torrey* (Princeton, 1942), 265–69, and see *Brittonia,* Vol. V (1943), 65.

Colorado except in these early years, there seems to be no reason to doubt the authenticity of the specimens, and we may assume that there are (or were) more than one hundred sheets, dating from 1860–61, deposited in the National Herbarium.

After two years in Colorado, Palmer left Denver as suddenly as he had come. Perhaps he needed money and found it hard to come by in Colorado; perhaps he wanted to see new country. He himself said that he went to California to "convey a widow and her children to their friends." At this time overland travel by the new stage lines was possible, and passengers were hauled from Denver to San Francisco in a matter of three weeks, by way of Julesburg, Salt Lake City, the Humboldt Valley of Nevada, Donner Pass, and Hangtown.[7] A flavorful and apparently authentic remark made by Palmer here is preserved by Safford: "I visited [Hangtown] in 1861 as passenger by Ben Holladay's Stage[8]—took breakfast and washed it being customary not to wash until after the sink of the Humboldt was passed." Today it is difficult to imagine the conditions of travel which were then taken for granted—the horse-drawn stages ran on through the night in clouds of alkali dust past the sink of the Humboldt and the arid foothills south of Pyramid Lake, crossed the pass and dropped down through the Sierras to disgorge the dead-tired passengers for a welcome wash and a late breakfast.

Upon reaching San Francisco late in August, Palmer soon found work with the Geological Survey of California. This connection with the Survey has been somewhat overly stressed in published biographical sketches; actually he was no more than three and one-half months in the work, which involved the collecting of marine invertebrates in the vicinity of San Diego, where he went early in October. Almost nothing is known of the details of his work at San Diego. He worked under the direction of J. G. Cooper, who was in charge of the natural

[7] Now Placerville, California.

[8] Apparently Palmer left Julesburg, Colorado, on a stage of August 7, but no list including his name has been found. Denver newspapers of this year do not carry passenger lists as they customarily did in later years (Ewan, *in litt.*). Actually Ben Holladay did not assume control of the stage lines until 1862, but overland stages to San Francisco had run as early as 1858, at first making the trip from St. Louis in about twenty-four days. See J. V. Frederick, *Ben Holladay, the Stagecoach King* (Cleveland, 1940).

history aspects of the Survey.[9] Cooper mentioned Palmer as a diligent collector and named a new invertebrate species in his honor,[10] but later turned against him and had nothing but censure for the man and his work.[11]

The Civil War had broken out in April, 1861, and Palmer decided to go to Washington to join the Union Army. He chose what now seems a rather roundabout way; instead of crossing the continent directly, as he had come, he went by boat from San Francisco to Panama, crossed the Isthmus, and took another boat to New York. Actually he chose the quickest way to reach his destination; service on the Panama route was good, having improved in the last decade with the constant traffic to and from the California gold fields, and Palmer made the trip from San Francisco to New York in twenty-four days. The overland route was uncertain and often took longer than this, even for the part between San Francisco and Leavenworth.

After a week in Washington he set out for the West again, this time as a volunteer surgeon in the 2nd Colorado Regiment. His reason for joining this particular outfit is told by Safford:

> The morning after my arrival [in New York] I went to Washington, where I met J. H. Leavenworth, a recruiting officer who had just been authorized by Secretary Stanton to raise a regiment at Denver, Colorado. Colonel Leavenworth asked me to accompany him to Denver, promising that I should be appointed an assistant surgeon as soon as the regiment was formed.

It seems to have been by mere chance that Palmer first met Leavenworth, a colorful and somewhat stormy figure.[12] (The paths of the

[9] James Graham Cooper (1830–1902). Zoologist and naturalist, known especially for his work in the Western states. See *Dictionary of American Biography* (1937), IV, 406–407.

[10] See References and Sources No. 15.

[11] Letters from J. G. Cooper to Philip P. Carpenter, dated at San Francisco, December 4, 1863 and March 12, 1864, now among Carpenter papers at McGill University. These were called to my attention by Mrs. Katherine V. W. Palmer, of Ithaca, New York.

[12] See the sketch of his life by Carolyn Thomas Foreman, *Chronicles of Oklahoma,* Vol. XIII (1935), 14–29. Jesse Henry Leavenworth (1807–85), the son of General Henry Leavenworth, graduated from West Point in 1830, resigned from the Army in 1836 to become a successful businessman and civil engineer

two men were to cross again in 1868.) At their first meeting Leavenworth had been commissioned a few weeks previously and given power to select his own officers. He did not delay long in Washington, for soon after the first of June he led his Volunteers into Denver, to which Palmer returned after an absence of only ten months, but after more than 8,000 miles and nearly five months of travel!

Most of the year 1862 is rather well documented and it is possible to follow Palmer's movements in some detail. His life in the army was a busy one, but in spite of his duties as surgeon he did not forget his interest in natural history. After his enrollment with Leavenworth, he went at once from Washington to Fort Leavenworth,[13] Kansas, where the regiment was located for about a month before leaving for Colorado on April 26. It was a slow trip to Fort Kearny and up the Platte, and Palmer was able to do a bit of collecting even while traveling with the army detachments.

The Denver papers took ample note of the arrival of the troops on June 2:

The famous battery belonging to the 2nd Colorado Regiment arrived this morning and paraded through the principal street of the city,

---

in Chicago. When he was commissioned colonel on February 17, 1862 he headed the 2nd Colorado Volunteers, a cavalary regiment; he at once went west, by way of Leavenworth, Kansas, to Denver, where he kept his troops busy coping with various civil disturbances and minor Indian troubles. In August, he made a trip with the troops to Fort Larned to negotiate with a band of Pawnees. He made a good reputation during the summer of 1863, for his ability to deal with the restive Kiowas and Comanches; a part of his regiment, under a Lt. Col. Dodd, was detached and went east to take part in the drive to Fort Gibson in 1863. Leavenworth was suddenly discharged from the army in 1863, perhaps for political reasons. In 1864 he was appointed agent for the troublesome Kiowas and Comanches (a post he held until 1868), and in 1865 was one of the commissioners to treat with the Indians of the Upper Arkansas River. The Kiowas and Comanches continued unruly, especially along the Texas border, and in 1866, Leavenworth suggested the reoccupation of Fort Cobb to prevent more outrages in this area; there was much local demand for this early in 1868, and Fort Cobb was temporarily occupied pending the completion of Fort Sill. There was much resentment against Leavenworth's conduct, both from the Indians and the whites, but apparently he worked hard to prevent active outbreaks of ill feeling, and he is remembered for his efforts in securing the release of numerous white captives.

[13] Named not after Palmer's commanding officer, but for the latter's father, Gen. Henry Leavenworth (1783–1834), a famous frontier soldier.

attended by an immense supply train, it occupied near half a mile while on the march.[14]

Camp Weld, newly established at Denver in 1862 by Colonel Leavenworth, was the headquarters of the 2nd Colorado and was, likewise, Palmer's principal base for some months, though actually he spent much of his time in travel with the troops. On June 14, he went "with a detachment to assist the civil authorities to inforce the Law in the mountains." Returning from this trip, he was ordered with his unit to Fort Lyon, Colorado, to remain there "until the Indian troubles down the Platte were settled." After about ten days at Fort Lyon, however, the troops began a further march, this time a trip of twelve or thirteen days to Fort Larned, Kansas, followed by a quick return trip to Fort Lyon and Camp Weld. Palmer was sent to Fort Lyon again in September, this time charged with "overhauling and straightening" the hospital at that post, a task which occupied him until early in December. After a few weeks in Denver, he was sent again to Fort Lyon, where he was hospital steward for the first four months of 1863 before journeying eastward with the troops to take part in the active campaigns then brewing in the Indian Territory.

Collecting and storing museum specimens at an active army post on the frontier, while hampered by lack of time and lack of facilities for transportation, must have been a difficult problem indeed, and it is not strange that Palmer's collections of 1862–63 were not large. He managed to secure a few things on the trip out to Denver in May; he picked up a few specimens at the Gregory Mines in June, while accompanying a squad of cavalry on a march of a hundred miles in less than a week; a few collections came from rather vaguely defined localities between Denver and Fort Lyon: "edge of mts.," or "Arkansas River," or "100 miles north of Fort Lyons." In September, he shipped to Baird his collections of 1861 and 1862, together with all the field notes for 1861 and 1862, and in December he sent another box of recent acquisitions. While at Fort Lyon in the spring of 1863, he collected a few more specimens, both plant and animal, and even on the march eastward toward Fort Scott, in May, he says, "I rode in an ambulance with the sick, collecting on the way a number of plants." Some of the 1863 specimens are in the National Herbarium, and additional ones should be looked for at the Missouri Botanical Garden,

[14] *Colorado Republican and Rocky Mountain Herald,* June 2, 1862. (Ewan, *in litt.*)

for apparently George Engelmann received some of these specimens for determination,[15] contrary to the opinion expressed in an earlier paper.[16]

With the march to Fort Scott in May and June of 1863 began one of the few periods in Palmer's life when he was unable to find time to collect plants or indeed to collect anything. For almost two years he was involved in the battles of the Civil War and the aftermaths of these engagements. We have but little knowledge of his own doings during the second half of this year, but apparently he accompanied the detachments of the 2nd Colorado Cavalry that left Fort Scott late in June and marched southward as a part of General James G. Blunt's drive on Fort Smith;[17] they took part in the battles of Cabin Creek and Honey Springs, and were then stationed for a time at Fort Blunt, in the Cherokee Nation.[18]

[15] Engelmann wrote Palmer on January 12, 1868: "I am arranging . . . your plants of 1867 . . . I probably will take them, and the old collection of 1863 with me to Cambridge where I expect to be in April." Perhaps Engelmann received these from the Smithsonian Institution, for Palmer's collections were forwarded to Washington from Fort Scott in September or October, 1863 (his letter of January 28, 1864), and additional collections were sent to Washington from St. Louis on January 13, 1864.

[16] See References and Sources No. 41.

[17] This is a popularly little-known phase of the Civil War. The Confederate States, early in the war, had concluded treaties with the Five Civilized Tribes, including the Cherokees. Cherokee guerillas, under the leadership of Stand Watie, ranged widely in what is now eastern Oklahoma and well north into Kansas and did a great deal of damage to crops and stock. One estimate put the losses of stock among the Cherokees as high as 300,000 head. Several thousand refugees fled northward and put themselves under the protection of the Union forces. In the winter and spring of 1862–63 serious efforts at repatriation were begun. This involved successful military occupation of the Indian Territory, hitherto a Confederate stronghold. Union forces, under the vigorous leadership of General James G. Blunt, gradually pushed southward in the summer of 1863, in a campaign that culminated in the Confederate rout at Honey Springs on July 17, and the occupation of Fort Smith six weeks later. The campaign and its setting is discussed at length in Annie Heloise Abel's *The American Indian as Participant in the Civil War* (Cleveland, 1919). See also Charles C. Royce, "The Cherokee Nation of Indians," *Annual Report of the Bureau of Ethnology* (1887), V, 129–378, and maps.

[18] Fort Blunt is a name that does not appear on ordinary maps or in indexes, and so seems to deserve special mention here. Fort Gibson had been demilitarized in 1857 at the urging of the Cherokees, and when it was reoccupied and strengthened early in the Civil War it was renamed in honor of General Blunt, who then

In August, Palmer was ordered to Kansas City from his station at Fort Blunt, to be examined for a promotion (which apparently he did not get). He was with his unit at Fort Blunt until they moved on to Fort Smith in mid-September; they left this area in mid-November and reached St. Louis a month later. Palmer's health began to suffer from continued exposure at this time, and at the time of his discharge from the army the following year he was certified as disabled because of rheumatism and heart disease contracted during the march from Arkansas.

Palmer had served some twenty months in the army without either pay or formal appointment, but on January 4, 1864, we find him at Leavenworth, Kansas, formally enlisted as a private in the 2nd Colorado Volunteer Cavalry, with his enlistment and pay dating back to April 14, 1862, by order of the War Department. Safford says that Palmer had appealed for this directly to Secretary of War Stanton, after failing to get pay or appointment otherwise. At the time of his formal induction his papers describe him as twenty-eight years old, by occupation a nurseryman, with brown eyes, black hair, dark complexion, and standing five feet, six inches high. The photograph showing him in his army uniform was taken about this time.

The year 1864 ushered in for Palmer a protracted period of hospital service in the Kansas City area. He was on "detached service," separated from his regular cavalry outfit and acting as hospital steward first in charge of casualties at a field hospital at Pleasant Hill, Missouri, then after the first of March at Kansas City. The army order which took him to Kansas City requested his transfer from Pleasant Hill "if he could be spared." After his transfer, he found time in April to make a hurried trip to Washington, partly to try to secure a part in a proposed expedition to Minnesota. In May, his health began to fail badly, and he was hospitalized in Kansas City during May and June and again during September and October. Apparently because of this, he was released from all duty sometime during the summer,[19] and late in October we find him in St. Louis, announcing his intention "as a citizen leaving everything behind" to go on again to Kansas City and Leavenworth where he knew that numerous casualties urgently needed medical care. He was recovered sufficiently to accept a position as contract surgeon, with the status of a civilian, working

commanded the Union forces in this so-called "District of the Frontier." The new name was little used after 1863.

[19] His "Certificate of Disability for Discharge" is dated August 27, 1864.

for but not in the army.[20] He was in charge of wounded Confederate prisoners at the Kansas City General Hospital from November to March.

About the end of March, Palmer began to entertain plans for a trip to Arizona, but after the annulment of his contract he was persuaded to take for a time a post as examining surgeon of the Missouri state militia, to pass on the condition of persons claiming military exemption because of physical disability. This service, which lasted about a month, took Palmer to various places in the Kansas City area. By April 7, however, he had definitely decided to go to Arizona with a party including "several dignitaries of New Mexico and Arizona," and soon after the beginning of May he concluded his medical duties and completed his preparations for the trip.

[20] His formal discharge from the Army was dated November 30, 1864, but apparently because of his disability as certified the previous August, he was permitted to accept contract service, as acting assistant surgeon, U. S. A., beginning November 17, 1864. His contract continued until March 31, 1865, when it was annulled at his own request.

IV FRONTIER POSTS IN ARIZONA, 1865–67

IN 1865, ARIZONA was a new, raw country. Extensive discoveries of gold and other minerals, especially during the winter of 1862–63, had stimulated the growth of the population, and small communities were beginning to spring up as agricultural and commercial settlement followed the opening of the mines. The presence of so many new people was resented by some of the Indian tribes, particularly the Apaches, and to keep the Apaches in check and prevent their depredations, the United States Army maintained a number of military posts in the territory. To one of these posts, Fort Whipple, which was then hardly a year old, Palmer came in late July after a long trip by stage from Kansas City. Collecting was uppermost in his mind. At one point along the route, at Fort Dodge, Kansas, he noted that he had not had any chance to collect, because danger from hostile Indians had forced him to keep close to the main party. The principal route into Arizona led from Fort Dodge westward to Trinidad, Colorado, thence southward over Raton Pass and down to Albuquerque, and westward again.

When Palmer reached Fort Whipple he was welcomed by a fellow naturalist, Dr. Elliott Coues,[1] an army surgeon who had been already some months in residence. It may never be known what ar-

[1] Elliott Coues (1842–99). Army surgeon, 1864–81. A prominent ornithologist, general naturalist, psychical researcher, historian of exploration in the West. He was the possessor of an extremely able mind and a facile pen, a man who did not hesitate to speak his mind, and withal one of the gifted writers of his period. See *Dictionary of American Biography* (1937), IV, 465–66.

rangements the two men made, but evidently they collected together during the summer—Palmer devoting all his time to the work, and Coues what time he could take from his medical duties. Presumably because of the danger from Indians, most of the collecting was done near Fort Whipple, or while one or the other of the naturalists was with the troops on marches into areas as much as forty miles away.[2]

Coues and Palmer collaborated well enough during the summer, and when in early autumn Coues left Fort Whipple to return to the East, he was entrusted with the joint plant collections on condition that he submit them to the proper authorities for determination. Coues was a comparative youngster not yet twenty-three years old, but he must have possessed already the forceful and positive character that his later writings show him to have had. He was absorbed in ornithology and other branches of zoology and when, some months after his departure from Arizona,[3] he turned the plants over to Engelmann, he minimized or entirely neglected to mention Palmer's part in their collection. From Coues's negligence developed a situation about which Palmer was extremely resentful. His own version of the affair is given us by Safford:

Dr. Engelmann told me Dr. Coues presented the collection to him without the least mention of my name in connection with it. On finding out what had been done I wrote to Dr. Engelmann who added my name to the specimens with that of Dr. Coues. When I went to Arizona Dr. Coues had a few plants and other things collected. I went to work collecting everything vigorously, and as Dr. Coues was going to return to Washington I agreed to share the credit with him if he would take the collection through and have it worked up. He, on getting through, claimed the entire credit, not noticing me; even my Camp Grant plants, collected long after Dr. Coues had left, were by mistake credited to him.

[2] Some of the collections are marked "20 miles east of Ft. Whipple," "Rio Verde," "40 miles south of Fort Whipple," etc.

[3] Coues remained at Fort Whipple until at least the first of August, then went overland to Fort Mohave. During September he went by steamer down the Colorado River as far as Yuma, where he spent a few days before returning to Fort Mohave. He left Fort Mohave October 30, crossed California by the Mojave River route to San Bernardino and San Pedro, and spent some weeks on and near the coast as a guest of J. G. Cooper. He probably returned to the East Coast by way of Panama, and was in Washington by January 29, 1866. See *Ibis,* Series 2, Vol. II (1866), 259–75.

Apparently Palmer was correct in his claims that certain of his collections from Camp Grant and elsewhere, made in 1866 and even as late as 1867, were credited to Coues *and* Palmer even though Coues had long since returned to the East at the time the collections were made. This is suggested, for example, in the following note from Engelmann to Palmer (also quoted by Safford):

The collections made by you and Dr. Coues in 1865 and 1866 [*sic*] were, as you know, presented to me by Dr. Coues and are to the greatest extent incorporated in my herbarium. I can give you all the reference you wish, or even a list of the species, though I do not know how I have a right to dispose of this even, without the donor's, Dr. Coues', consent, as he wished it published separately.

Apparently because of Palmer's representations to Engelmann, all the collections of 1865 were distributed under the joint names of Coues and Palmer. Palmer may have felt that his ten years' seniority, his long war experience, and his previous work as a collector, all entitled him to primary consideration for the work of this summer, but actually the linking of his name with that of Coues probably added to his credit rather than detracted from it, for the collection includes not only plants collected during Palmer's stay at Fort Whipple, but also specimens which must have been collected by Coues alone, as much as three months before Palmer's arrival.

The collection made by the two men included at least six hundred numbered specimens, the numbers arranged more or less chronologically. No complete duplicate sets were collected, as far as known, and very few Coues and Palmer specimens are to be found except at the Missouri Botanical Garden, where there is a large series. This lack of duplicate material is hinted in a letter to Engelmann from C. C. Parry[4] in 1870:

[4] Charles Christopher Parry (1823–90). Explorer-botanist, friend of Asa Gray. Parry early came under Torrey's influence. He secured his M. D. from Columbia in 1846, and moved to Davenport, Iowa, where he made his home the rest of his life. He was one of the botanists of the Mexican Boundary Survey, 1849–53, and spent many summers in later years exploring in the West. He published little of importance, but many of his data, specimens and suggestions were used by Gray and others. He was botanist of the United States Department of Agriculture, 1869–71, and for several years, especially 1878, closely associated with Palmer. For the most informative materials on Parry, see A. D. Rodgers, *American Botany, 1873–1892,* (Princeton, 1944).

I suppose you have little in the way of duplicates of Palmer's (and Cous) [*sic*] except of common things: and being distributed in your collection they would be difficult to unearth. So they may as well stay to be hunted out by those who want to see them.

No published report on the collection was ever made, and apparently Engelmann did not even furnish a list of determinations for the collectors. This seems to have been implied by Coues's statement in 1867, in a paper dealing with his own collections of mammals made in 1864 and 1865: "The plants, collected jointly by Dr. E. Palmer and the writer, still remain in the hands of Dr. Geo. Engelmann of St. Louis, to whom they were transmitted for examination and identification."

In October, Palmer re-entered army service. His salary as acting assistant surgeon was $125 a month. He was sent at once to Camp Lincoln, on the Río Verde some fifty miles east of Fort Whipple. He tells of his first trip out to the new camp:

The command travelled to the descent of the Verde about 55 miles without any impediment. Before us was the valley of the Verde, the road down was not only new but steep and very crooked and extremely rough; the day was drawing to a close & it was found impossible to take the wagon down with its contents, so it was unloaded and the men packed everything on their backs, except the heaviest articles which were let down by ropes, distance down 1½ miles . . . . Because of the lateness of the hour & tired condition of the men, the wagon & desk containing the companies' papers were necessarily left behind until morning. The night was very dark and a very strong guard was placed around camp. At an early hour a detachment was sent to bring down the wagon & desk which were found in ashes. The Apaches had watched our movements. . . .

The post at Camp Lincoln was no sinecure, even aside from the danger from actively hostile Apaches. All supplies for the army posts in northern and central Arizona were brought by boat up the Colorado River to Fort Mohave, and freighted overland by mule teams to the individual posts.[5] The difficulties in transportation made food

[5] Beginning in 1866, the contract for hauling supplies to Fort Whipple and Camp Lincoln (later called Camp Verde) was held by W. H. Hardy (?–1909), a Mohave County pioneer who came to Arizona in 1864. He established Hardyville

rationing necessary, especially in winter. The troops at Camp Lincoln were a miscellaneous lot, including some white men, some Mexicans of mixed blood, and some Indians. There was discontent because of food shortages, lack of adequate clothing and shelter, and the persistent "intermittent fever"—doubtless malaria—that raged in the camp. The troops periodically undertook "scouts" against the Apaches; these were expeditions of several days each, on foot in enemy country, each man carrying his own pack for want of pack animals. Palmer's pack was heavier than that of the soldiers; he had to carry not only the pack of blanket and provisions, which weighed 28½ pounds, and the gun which weighed 7 pounds, but also his instruments, his medical supplies, and his collecting equipment. His own weight at this time was 143 pounds!

He describes one of the "scouts":

Feb. 11th [1866] . . . at 7½ P. M. with 5 days rations on our backs, & Lt. Gallegos in command, & myself as surgeon & with 45 men . . . we left Camp Lincoln and during the night travelled N.E. in front of Cathedral Bluffs; laid up all day & no fires lit as the smoke would betray us; no noise was made . . . . The second night travelled E. and by day lay up on the South Fork of Beaver Creek in a ravine. At evening trailers were sent out and espied the Indians. They returned at 9 P. M.; they had gone close enough to see their fires. . . .

Soon after their return, the party resumed the march over every species of hill, valley, smooth and rough. . . . Just before day dawned, we arrived at the edge of what the moonlight showed to be a very steep and rough descent to a stream of water, and there were fires distinctly seen.

The command was formed into 3 divisions, which suddenly assailed the foe, whom they found in caves arranged one above the other. The fighting became general on both sides. . . . Only 2 were seen to escape. The caves presented a horrible sight, as dead of all ages and sexes with household goods and provisions lay mixed with the dirt from the caves brought down by firing of the guns, while the blood of the dead freely mixed with all . . .

Feb. 15 at 11 A. M. the command marched with their prisoners back to camp.

as a river trading center, maintained a toll road from Hardyville to Prescott, and was a well-known figure in the early days of Arizona. See T. E. Farish, *History of Arizona* (8 vols., San Francisco, 1915–18), IV, 74ff.

Throughout his experiences on the frontier Palmer seems to have preserved a curious detachment which brought him unmoved through what were sometimes very dangerous experiences. In a way this objectivity made him regard everything as a possible museum specimen; he was insensitive to if not actually unaware of his surroundings except as they related to his collecting of things and information about things. (On the other hand he was fully aware of the many wrongs, major and minor, real and fancied, which were done him by his associates and the strangers with whom he came in contact.) His matter-of-fact pursuit of his work under unusual circumstances has been referred to before; the following incident from life at Camp Lincoln is another illustration:

An Apache child, wounded in the raid described above, died two days later. Palmer continues: "The females of the camp laid it out after their custom & covered it with wild flowers and carried it to a grave. . . . They hid it so completely that its' body could not be found, as I had a wish to have it for a specimen. . . . no persuasion could induce them to tell the secret, so I did not get the specimen."

While at Camp Lincoln, Palmer made at least two trips (of about four days each) to Fort Whipple for supplies. According to his account this was because the post commandant at Camp Lincoln "did not think it prudent to leave the post—One officer could not talk English the other could not be trusted. So I was the only available officer and if any business called for any one to go to Fort Whipple the commanding officer Issued special orders for that purpose." On returning from a trip to Fort Whipple about the end of May, he was thrown from his mule and received head injuries from the effects of which he never fully recovered; he was incapacitated at the time for some weeks. As late as July 13 he wrote: "Am able to be out now some."

The summer of 1866 was an unusually rainy one, and the "intermittent fever" was rife in the camp. As many as sixty men were down at a time, and the garrison was greatly reduced by this and by the departure of soldiers whose time had expired. No relief was sent from Fort Whipple, so finally all the animals at the post were returned to Prescott for want of men to care for them, and the few remaining officers and men appealed to the settlers in the Verde valley, some seven miles away, for transportation for themselves and their more valuable property. Palmer was greatly weakened by frequent attacks of fever and was cared for by one of the settlers, a Mr.

Ramstein. This unfortunate combination of circumstances, complicating the injuries received from his fall, made it urgent for him to return to Prescott, where he was confined to the hospital at Fort Whipple for some weeks. Officially he was stationed at Camp Lincoln until September 1.

It appears that all the collections made by Palmer at Camp Lincoln in 1866 were lost. I have never seen any botanical specimens collected by him in 1866, or mention of any such in the literature. The following quotation from his own account, written several years after his stay at Camp Lincoln, is self-explanatory:

On going to Camp Lincoln, which was situated in an interesting locality, I made every effort to collect in all branches of natural history. I made examinations among the numerous ruins near by, & from which many articles were discovered which had belonged to the former occupants.

At the time of my leaving the post, was so prostrated by fever that I could not take my collection away as I had no means of transporting them, there being then none but pack animals, but the new commanding officer told me not to give myself any concern that he would send them on at the first opportunity. Hundreds of opportunities offered themselves, for many an empty wagon went to Ft. Whipple, but the boxes never were sent. . . . On my visiting Arizona in 1869, I visited Camp Lincoln and to my sorrow found that no effort had been made to forward the collection, according to agreement. I was told that the things had been thrown away and the only thing that was recovered was a scrap book, so that the collection made around the Post and on 7 foot scouts, under adverse circumstances, was all lost by carelessness. . . . I had returned to the post with the intention of replacing the lost articles, but found that no escort could be had and so very little was done toward replacing the lost collection. Owing to Indian hostilities I could not travel without troops.[6]

These are apparently the same collections to which Palmer referred in a letter soon after his departure from Camp Lincoln: "Have two boxes of plants and seeds which I will forward to you as soon as a good opportunity offer."[7]

He mentioned them again a few months later:

[6] See References and Sources No. 45, Item 22.

[7] To Engelmann, from Fort Whipple, November 26 [1866].

Last summer collected two boxes of plants and seeds. . . . They were left at Fort Whipple to be forwarded to you but cannot here anything from that post as to there departure. . . . I left Fort Whipple in a great hurry had not time to make a copy of the notes belonging to the two boxes of plants. . . . The book is at that post.[8]

Engelmann received Palmer's collection of 1867 about the end of that year, and acknowledged this, implying at the same time that he had never received any shipments for 1866. Doubtless the collections were destroyed, as Palmer found at the time of his visit in 1869. There is cited occasionally in the literature a Palmer specimen from Camp Lincoln, and presumably a few of these were collected in 1869. Coues and Palmer also collected near the site of Camp Lincoln, along the Río Verde, in 1865, and some of these specimens are extant. Outside the field of botany there are known a few specimens from the Río Verde, as for example certain corals.[9]

Palmer's next, and last, post in Arizona was Camp Grant, which he reached late in the year 1866 for a stay of some seven months. His health was still poor, although he had been released from the hospital at Fort Whipple. Dr. Charles Smart saw him in Tucson, on the way to Camp Grant, "a very sick man."[10] While at Camp Grant he suffered

[8] Letter to Engelmann, from Camp Grant, April 20, 1867.

[9] See F. B. Meek's report in *Report of the Geological Exploration of the Fortieth Parallel*, IV (1877), 33.

[10] Pension records, Veterans Administration, U. S. National Archives. Smart (1841–1905), who was one of the many medical men of his period to take some interest in botany while stationed at army posts in remote areas. When C. C. Parry was botanist of the Department of Agriculture he noted that the National Herbarium had received nearly 300 specimens, "a very choice collection from Southern Arizona, collected by Dr. Charles Smart, while stationed as army surgeon in that district, in 1867."

Smart had an interesting career. He was a Scot, with degrees in medicine and surgery from the University of Aberdeen. He came to the United States in 1862, apparently with the primary intention of getting into the Civil War which was then in progress. He served with distinction in the Union army, and in 1864 was brevetted captain for meritorious service in the field. He continued in army service after the war. From July to December, 1865, he saw duty at the Presidio and at San Jose, California. From March, 1866, to July, 1867, he was post surgeon at Fort McDowell, Arizona, and following this he held the same post at Camp Lowell, Arizona until June, 1869. During most of this period he was chief medical officer of the District of Arizona. After a brief period of duty in the East, he was post surgeon at Fort Bridger, Wyoming (July, 1873, to June, 1876), and at Camp Douglas, Utah (June, 1876, to December, 1877). He became

greatly from malaria, and, as he said, "for weeks at a time I was unable to do any collecting." On March 31, he made formal request for his release from his contract, alleging ill health as his reason for the request. The request was granted without undue delay, but not until August did he leave Camp Grant.

During the spring and summer he was able to accompany the troops from Camp Grant on some of the "scouts" against the Apaches. One of these is described in detail in his notes: The party left camp on April 21, traveled up Arivaipa Creek, then north to the junction of the Gila and San Carlos rivers, and returned to Camp Grant on April 28, by way of the Gila, the "San Romickeo" and the San Pedro rivers.[11]

When leaving the post, about the first of August, Palmer went overland to Tucson, thence by the Southern Pacific Mail Stage line to Yuma and Los Angeles. In October, he went from San Francisco to Sonoma, in an attempt to find a cure for the malaria which still plagued him, and toward the end of this same month he set off again by boat for New York. This time, instead of crossing the Isthmus of Panama as he had in 1862, he crossed by way of Lake Nicaragua and Río San Juan, and took a New York boat from Greytown. He was back in Washington before the end of the year, looking for a new field of exploration.

Many of the collections of 1867 are from the vicinity of Camp Grant. They include mammals, about 100 bird skins,[12] and about 250 numbers of plants. The plants were numbered serially (at least in part chronologically) and were sent to Engelmann for determination. The principal series of these is at the Missouri Botanical Garden, and a few duplicates are at the Gray Herbarium and in the Torrey Her-

known for his work on military medicine, particularly on sanitation, and in 1879 was called to Washington for duty with the National Board of Health (1879–83). He assisted with the compilation of the *Medical and Surgical History of the War of the Rebellion,* and was the author of numerous articles on medico-military subjects. He served for some years as assistant surgeon general of the United States, and after the Spanish-American war he was appointed chief surgeon of the HQ Division of the Philippines. He retired on January 19, 1905, with the rank of brigadier general, and died three months later at St. Augustine, Florida. (Data from records of the Adjutant General's Office, U. S. National Archives. See also *Annual Report of the Commissioner of Agriculture,* 1870 (Washington, 1871), 108.

[11] Merwin Item No. 10. See References and Sources No. 45.

[12] U. S. National Museum, Division of Birds, Nos. 49,681–49,784.

barium at New York. A few were collected along the way between Camp Grant and Tucson, but I do not know of any collected between Tucson and Los Angeles. The small number of duplicate specimens is indicated by Engelmann's letter acknowledging the receipt of the collection:

Your welcome letter dated Dec 25 was received a week ago, and a few days after both boxes arrived in good condition. You have surprised me by the richness of your collection—pity that there are mostly only single specimens of the dried plants.[13]

Palmer's first important ethnological collections were made in this year, especially near Tucson and Yuma, from the Apache, Pima, and Papago Indians.[14]

[13] To Palmer, January 12, 1868; returned to sender, Palmer having already left for the Indian Territory.

[14] U. S. National Museum, Division of Ethnology, Cat. Nos. 5,507–67, and probably Nos. 5,629, 5,642, 6,016, 7,522–34.

V INDIAN TERRITORY, 1868

IN 1868, THE INDIAN TERRITORY was in a state of flux. Conditions and whole civilizations were unsettled, and tensions ran high. The Civil War was not long over. It was apparent by this time that the Indian nations were not going to be able to persist as isolated eddies in the stream of the westward march of European culture, but would inevitably be absorbed. The railroad was on its way south from Kansas City, but the muddy roads of the Indian country were still the only avenues of travel. The United States government was establishing Indian agencies and settling whole new tribes in the Leased Lands west of the Chickasaw Nation, in what is now southwestern Oklahoma.

Palmer came into this muddled situation not as a naturalist but as a medical man. His former commanding officer, Colonel Leavenworth, was the newly appointed agent of the Kiowas and Comanches, and had recommended Palmer's appointment as agency doctor. Leavenworth's first task was to locate a permanent headquarters for the agency. Palmer joined him in Kansas City, sometime after the middle of January, and went on with him to Leavenworth, Kansas, thence to Ottawa (the terminus of the railroad), and by way of Fort Scott to Fort Gibson, Arkansas. Fort Gibson was one of the principal points of departure for the west and south, and a good deal of military travel came this way. Apparently the Indian agencies on the Washita took advantage of this, for during the period of Palmer's stay all outgoing mail was postmarked at Fort Gibson.

Leavenworth's party left Fort Gibson, presumably traveling on horseback, soon after the first of February. Their road to Cherokee

Town (their first stopping place near the Washita River) lay westward, first crossing the Deep Fork of the Canadian River, thence turning southwest through the Seminole Nation. From the vicinity of Cherokee Town the party ascended the Washita River to a point some twenty miles below the site of old Fort Cobb. They reached this point about February 19, and camped for more than two weeks while Agent Leavenworth was deciding upon a site for a permanent settlement for his charge.

Palmer's letters indicate that he was busy from the first. From the time of arrival at the temporary camp he gave medical treatment to about fifty Indians each day. At the middle of March the permanent site was selected. Palmer wrote, "We shifted our camp to Eureka Valley . . . at the mouth of a canyon, commanding a fine view of the Washita River." Spring was evidently not particularly early this year, but Palmer was collecting birds as early as March 5, and his plant collecting began the middle of March.

Little more than a month after this, there was evidence of friction between Palmer and his superior officer. The agent, Colonel Leavenworth, in a formal complaint to the Indian commissioner, stated that although he had urged Palmer's appointment because of his good work in Colorado for the army during the Civil War, he was disappointed in his present attitude. Leavenworth referred to Palmer's lack of interest in the illnesses of his Indian charges, and his great absorption in collecting specimens, "skinning a skunk," etc. Palmer wrote in his own behalf to the Indian commissioner, defending his actions, and in this he was warmly supported by Major Henry Shanklin, who was in charge of the near-by Wichita Agency. In spite of this, Leavenworth, on May 4, as Palmer wrote, "officially removed me from the Kioway and Comanche Agency assigning as a reason that my time was wholly taken up with my Scientific pursuits."

Major Shanklin befriended Palmer and allowed him to move his effects to the headquarters of the Wichita Agency, which adjoined that of the Kiowas and Comanches. Whether Palmer continued his medical work, this time on behalf of the Wichitas, I do not know; it seems unlikely. In any event he did some plant collecting during the remainder of the month of May and made at least one six-day excursion to the site of old Fort Cobb.

Unwittingly, he became involved in the beginnings of what was to culminate in the Indian "uprisings" of the winter of 1868–69, which were quelled by the army after a troublesome campaign. One of the causes of the disturbance was the friction between the Kiowas and Comanches, both newly settled on the Washita, and the Wichitas and other tribes under the jurisdiction of Major Shanklin. Partly as a result of this friction and the trouble which it engendered, the Kiowas and Comanches were settled in 1869 at a new agency at Fort Sill.

Palmer's part in the affair is alluded to in a published report. In speaking of his own Indian charges, Major Shanklin had this to say:

> It was very unfortunate for these people that the former agent of the Kiowas and Comanches [i. e., Leavenworth] located in the immediate vicinity of their village, bringing into their midst between 4,000 and 5,000 of the very worst of the plains Indians, some having never before seen an agency. Their conduct was insolent and humiliating to the last degree. . . . Dr. Palmer, the physician of the district, and who made his home at the agency, had become a special object of hatred, to such an extent that threats were made that they would kill him. . . . Receiving information from one of their own tribe that they intended to burn the agency and kill the doctor, it was deemed prudent to move at once. The night after the building was burned with its contents . . . .

Palmer learned of this plot about the first of June. How the disclosure came about will probably never be told, but in Palmer's last will and testament he acknowledged his gratitude to an Indian, one Black Beaver, who had on one occasion saved his life. Black Beaver is a well-known historical character, a Delaware, who was friendly to the whites, and who was active in guiding and serving various government parties in the Indian Territory during the period of Palmer's visit. It is interesting to think that on this occasion it may have been Black Beaver who discovered the unfriendly intentions of the Kiowas and Comanches, and warned Major Shanklin and Palmer.

From our distance of more than eighty years in time it is hard to picture what must have been a hasty and disorganized departure on Palmer's part. Probably his plight was not a desperate one, for there was no general uprising of Indians at this time, but he lost no time in leaving Eureka Valley after the discovery of the extent of the feeling against him. Perhaps he had a military or other escort on the way down the Washita River. In any event he found opportunity to collect a few plants during the course of the four-day trip.

After reaching the comparative civilization of Cherokee Town, Palmer abandoned any plans to seek the permanent security of Fort Arbuckle, some fifteen miles to the south. Instead he made his headquarters in the vicinity of Cherokee Town until fall, and there pursued his natural history collecting. Late in June, he made a two-week trip over the wagon road to Boggy Depot, some seventy miles to the southeast. In mid-July, he made a shorter trip to the northeast, into the Seminole Nation, presumably over the road he had traversed the previous February. We know very little about what he did between the first of August and the middle of September. Apparently his last collections were made on September 10, for on the following day he was attacked by "congestive feaver." By the end of September he was sufficiently recovered to leave Cherokee Town, taking his collections with him. On October 10, he was back in Leavenworth after a long trip by carriage and train, "safe but in bad health."

The collections made by Palmer in 1868 were considerable. As noted above, his devotion to this avocation had brought about his dismissal from his medical duties. He is known to have collected ethnological specimens,[1] amphibians, mammals,[2] and birds.[3] He also collected plants, approximately 484 numbered specimens, in at least two sets.

The botanical specimens were sent for determination to the aging John Torrey,[4] who, according to the general practice of his time, arranged them in systematic order and assigned to them serial numbers in this order. These numbers, of course, bore no relation to Palmer's original field numbers, which were mostly in chronological order. Torrey never completed the work of naming the collection, and presumably it was returned to George Vasey, the then botanist of the Department of Agriculture, after Torrey's death in March, 1873. The specimens were then distributed with a printed label, such as shown in the illustration in this book.

The labels bear, in addition to the printed heading, the serial number assigned by Torrey, and his determination, if any. Neither

[1] U. S. National Museum, Division of Ethnology, Cat. Nos. 6,876–7,001.

[2] Safford refers to these as Nos. 9,248–9,304, Division of Mammals, U. S. National Museum.

[3] U. S. National Museum, Division of Birds, Nos. 52,986–53,068.

[4] John Torrey (1796–1873). Botanist and chemist. Principal American taxonomist of the early nineteenth century, and source of inspiration to many, including Gray. See Rodgers, *John Torrey*. Torrey's large herbarium was ultimately incorporated into that of the New York Botanical Garden.

specific localities nor dates are given on the labels, but in most cases Palmer's original field number is given, and the exact source can often be determined by reference to the field notes. The collection as a whole, which is potentially one of the most valuable ever to have come from the Indian Territory, thus has been little studied or cited because of the general lack of information about the specimens. There are apparently but two principal sets of the collection, one now at the United States National Herbarium and the other in the Torrey Herbarium at the New York Botanical Garden.

Since the publication of an account of the history of this collection,[5] Palmer's own field notes of 1868 have been discovered among the Torrey papers at New York. They are accompanied by Torrey's unfinished list of the collection, systematically arranged and numbered. Torrey's manuscript bears not only the numbers under which the specimens were distributed, but also the corresponding field numbers, so that one can determine the exact place of origin of any specimen. A copy of the field notes, together with an index to the numbers assigned by Torrey, comprises Appendix IV of this book.

The following summary is based on the botanical field notes, with some supplementary information from zoological collections and other sources:

Field Numbers	*Place Collected*	*Date*
1–114	Near the Kiowa-Comanche Agency and nearby along the Washita River	March 14–May 5
115–?74	Near Old Fort Cobb	May 19–24
?175–223	Near the Wichita Agency	May 26–31
224–38	Along the Washita River between the Wichita Agency and Cherokee Town	June 3–6
239–94	Cherokee Town and vicinity	June 8–12
295–441	Trip southeast to Boggy Depot and vicinity	June 20–July ?3
	Cherokee Town and vicinity	July 9–14
	Trip to the Seminole Nation	July 18–20
442–84	Cherokee Town and vicinity	August 6–September 10

It so happens that the printed labels on these collections are somewhat misleading. Whereas nearly half of the entire series came from the general neighborhood of Fort Cobb, only a mere handful of spe-

[5] See References and Sources No. 43.

cimens was collected "on the False Washita, between Fort Cobb and Fort Arbuckle," and apparently no specimens at all were taken in the vicinity of Fort Arbuckle itself, where Palmer seems to have spent very little time. We suppose that he was at the Fort on June 10, at least long enough to mail a letter which is postmarked from there, and perhaps again on August 6 (to mail another letter), but except for these two letters there seems to be no evidence of his having visited Fort Arbuckle.

Although some of Palmer's field labels on birds and other specimens read "Fort Cobb," it has not always been clear what locality was meant. The Kiowa-Comanche Agency and the Wichita Agency, to which he transferred after his dismissal by Leavenworth, were in Eureka Valley, which according to Palmer was seventeen miles southeast of old Fort Cobb. This military post had been abandoned by the federal forces at the outbreak of the Civil War and had subsequently been destroyed by Indians or by Confederate forces. It was reoccupied temporarily in the summer and fall of 1868, while the troops were preparing to move to permanent quarters at the new Camp Wichita, which was later named Fort Sill. Palmer also refers to Fort Cobb as being three miles up river from the Kiowa-Comanche Agency, and I cannot but suppose this to have been another temporary encampment. His specimens labeled as from "near Fort Cobb," or a certain number of miles "below Fort Cobb," probably came from somewhere along the Washita River, between the site of old Fort Cobb and the agencies in Eureka Valley, near present Anadarko.

VI ARIZONA, UTAH, AND SONORA, 1869–70

THE SUMMER OF 1868 marked the end of the first principal period of Palmer's productive years, and 1869 ushered in the second period, which was to continue to the end of his life. Heretofore he had been an amateur of natural history employed for the most part as a medical officer and managing to make his collections in his spare time. He had spent the past twelve years in frontier posts and in close contact with the Indian tribes, and his continued interest in collecting, and particularly in ethnology, made him the obvious choice in the United States to carry on botanical and ethnobotanical investigations in the West. He had earned the right to call himself "Doctor" by nearly six years of continuous service as a medical man in army camps. Now he was ready for the chance he had wanted since his trip to Paraguay, the chance to devote his full time to the "prosecution of science."

The great West was opening up. The railroads spanned the continent in the summer of 1869. It was apparent to men like Spencer Baird that a multiple purpose was to be served by botanical, ethnobotanical, and purely ethnological work in the Southwest: new crops or new areas suitable for familiar crops might be discovered, but most important of all was to record the vanishing culture of the Indian before it was modified or extinguished by the culture of the Europeans. With these purposes in mind, Palmer set out for Arizona in mid-March, as a general agricultural explorer, under the auspices of the United States Department of Agriculture, the Smithsonian Institution, and the Army Medical Museum.

From Sheridan, Kansas, the terminus of the Kansas Pacific,[1] he went by stagecoach to Santa Fé, New Mexico, and thence west to Fort Wingate. At this time he had been a little over a month on the road from Washington. He began in earnest his attempts to secure data and specimens relative to the Indian tribes; he visited the Acoma pueblo and the Navajo Agency, not forgetting to collect birds and plants in the meantime. On the first of June, he began a trip which has been repeatedly cited in botanical and other papers, namely the one on which he accompanied Commissioner Vincent Colyer to Oraibi and the other Hopi villages.[2] This was a hard trip through arid country west of Fort Defiance, but Palmer was able to collect, both along the way and at the Indian villages. He made a "large collection" of "Moqua Indian" materials, which he arranged to have freighted privately to the railroad instead of relying upon government transportation.

After returning to Fort Wingate to ship his accumulated collections, Palmer began his trip west again. He traveled with an army escort and a wagon train, by the usual road from Fort Defiance, which extended down the Río Puerco and the Little Colorado, crossed the latter near the mouth of Canyon Diablo and thence ascended to the west toward the San Francisco Peaks. Palmer climbed the principal peak to the snow line; I do not know how he persuaded his army escort to wait while he made this sortie, but perhaps because it was the Fourth of July they were off duty!

Nearly a week later the party reached Fort Whipple, the site of Palmer's first work in Arizona, four years before. Here he made his headquarters again for more than a month. He went with a cavalry escort on a ten-day excursion to Bill Williams Mountain; his account

[1] Then the Eastern Division of the Union Pacific Railway.

[2] Vincent Colyer (1825–88). American artist and humanitarian. Began artistic career with crayon portraits, turned to oil. Interested in interracial relations. During Civil War worked to better position of Negro troops. Appointed as a special Indian commissioner by President Grant in 1869 because of his known sympathies with the Indians. A controversial figure, who was not popular with the civil and military authorities in the Southwest because of his conciliatory tactics when dealing with Indians. See E. E. Dale, *The Indians of the Southwest* (Norman, 1949), 96–99; also Colyer's own account of his survey trip of 1869 in *Annual Report of the Secretary of the Interior*, 1869 (Washington, 1870), 512–38; also *Appleton's Cyclopedia of American Biography* (1888) I, 700. For an account of Colyer's character and behavior as the military saw it, see *Chronicles of Oklahoma*, Vol. II (1924), 18–25.

of part of this trip sounds like something that might have been written by any field botanist, ancient or modern:

> Set out the next morning to climb Bill Williams' Mountain. . . . I made a large collection. . . . The next morning we were to start back, [but] . . . midnight found me still at work, my plants all in good shape and ready for packing. . . .

It was at this time also that Palmer visited Camp Lincoln, to hunt for "Astect" ruins, and to try to locate his plant collections of 1866 which he had left there. He was unsuccessful on both counts and soon returned to Fort Whipple. Here he stocked up for a long journey, and late in August set out across the desert to the Colorado River.[3] He descended the river by boat, past Yuma to the old shipyard at Puerta Isabel near the head of the Gulf of California. In this year began his interest in the agriculture of the Cocopa Indians along the Colorado, an interest which was to bring him back here several times to study their food plants.

Not finding either plants or Indian materials to keep him occupied, he set off on a roundabout route which carried him back to Yuma, in a steamer towing fruit scows, up the Gila River to the Pima villages (near present Sacaton), where he made botanical and ethnological collections, thence overland to Fort Whipple again, and finally to Camp Date Creek, a few miles southwest. Here he stayed and collected a short time before undertaking a second trip to Ehrenberg, Yuma, and Puerta Isabel. This second trip was more successful than the first; he stayed more than two weeks and accumulated at least three boxes of specimens which he sent off before his own departure. Soon after the middle of October he returned to Yuma and went by stagecoach to Tucson. After a short stay here he took passage in a coach to Altar, Hermosillo, and Guaymas—all in Sonora. At Guaymas he was welcomed by Alexander Willard, the United States Consul there, who befriended him on this and later visits.[4]

[3] There are contradictory accounts of his route on this first overland trip. His own manuscript account described a trip over the same route to Ehrenberg which he followed on a second trip in September. In a letter from Fort Whipple on August 16, however, he stated his intention to cross to Fort Mohave and ship his collections from there, and in a letter of October 6 he mentions two boxes of specimens previously sent from La Paz.

[4] Alexander Willard (?–1892). Born in Philadelphia. U. S. Consul at Guaymas, 1867–92. At the time of his appointment to the position in Guaymas, had

From Guaymas, late in November, Palmer set sail in a small trading schooner for the mouth of the Yaqui River. His destination was the ranch of Don José Maldonado, where he was a guest for two weeks. On his return he chartered a dugout to take him and his collections to Guaymas; for nine days he walked along the shore, collecting as he went while the boat kept pace with him offshore; how his boatman must have marveled at the demented ways of the gringo!

Palmer concluded the field season with a trip by steamer to San Francisco. His ship anchored off Carmen Island one morning, and he managed in spite of a rough sea to land and collect a few specimens; evidently a whole strenuous field season had not lessened his interest in new localities. After a month in San Francisco, he entrusted himself and his precious twenty boxes of specimens to the Panama steamer for the twenty-four-day trip to New York.

It has been stated at various times that most, if not all, the specimens collected by Palmer in 1869 were lost at sea; Safford commented on this at some length in his biographical sketch read at Palmer's eightieth-birthday celebration,[5] and Palmer himself commented on the loss at various times in the later years of his life. It is now apparent that the losses were of relatively minor importance, and there is question as to whether or not any collections were lost.[6] Early collections from New Mexico and Arizona, made before Palmer's departure from Fort Wingate in June, were sent overland to the railroad, as mentioned above.[7]

---

been living in Mexico for nearly nine years and in Guaymas for two of these, and was appointed as from the state of California. He assumed office on July 4, 1868, and was several times re-appointed because of his outstanding abilities and character. He died at his post after twenty-four years of service. He was a good friend to Palmer, and it was at Palmer's request that the leguminous genus *Willardia* was so named by Rose. Data from Consular Reports of Guaymas in the United States National Archives. See also *Contributions from the United States National Herbarium* (1891), I, 97.

[5] See *Popular Science Monthly*, Vol. LXXVIII (1911), 345.

[6] Contemporary correspondence throws some light on this. On March 4, 1870, Parry wrote Engelmann that Palmer thought some of his boxes might have been on the wrecked steamer *Golden City*, "which ran ashore off South California last month." On April 5, Parry wrote again: "Dr. Palmer has advises [*sic*] that a large part of his collection was wrecked on the *Golden City*—probably a total loss." On May 23, however, Parry wrote to Gray: "5 boxes Palmers came to hand since he left [eight days before, on a new expedition to the Southwest] from the wrecked steamer *in good order! !*"

[7] Letters to Henry, Archives of the Smithsonian Institution, Letters Received, Book 89, pp. 158–59.

As has been pointed out elsewhere,[8] specimens collected during the early summer, between Fort Wingate and Fort Whipple, and in the course of Palmer's first stay at Fort Whipple (July to mid-August), probably all reached Washington in safety. In addition to plants collected at various places (Bear Spring, San Francisco Peaks, Hell Canyon, Bill Williams Mountain), the National Museum has bird skins collected along the Río Puerco on June 27, at Bill Williams Mountain on July 28, and at Fort Whipple on August 10. These collections may have been sent overland from Fort Whipple or, as seems more likely, from La Paz by river steamer.[9]

On October 6, Palmer shipped three boxes of specimens from Puerta Isabel, at the mouth of the Colorado. I have not seen any specimens or records dated between August 10 and October 6, and it is possible that these three boxes were actually lost. Presumably this included the collections made in August and September, between the first and second trips to the mouth of the Colorado. Even this much of a loss is doubtful, however, for there are existing specimens which may have been collected during this period (e. g., plants from Camp Date Creek and birds from along the Salt River). Safford states that the lost specimens were shipped from Ehrenberg, but I have not been able to confirm this.

All the specimens collected at Guaymas and on the Yaqui River were forwarded to San Francisco by steamer[10] and eventually reached Washington in safety. It may be that the twenty boxes which Palmer brought home with him included all his collections of the last two months of 1869. Most of the plant specimens in herbaria are inadequately labelled, so that it is often difficult to assign dates and localities to them, but the National Museum has a number of bird skins (Nos. 59,187–59,219), collected near Puerta Isabel in October, and also some from Guaymas (Nos. 59,221–59,234). The Division of Mollusks has collections from "Pinecate Bay," Cape San Lucas, and Guaymas.

Ethnological specimens received by the National Museum[11] early

[8] See References and Sources No. 41.

[9] Palmer informed Henry on August 16 that he intended to go from Fort Whipple to La Paz and ship his collections from there; on October 6 he wrote him again, mentioning two boxes previously sent from La Paz. It seems likely that these two different references are to the same specimens.

[10] Palmer, as quoted by Safford.

[11] Records of the Division of Ethnology.

in 1870, and so presumably collected in 1869, include Nos. 9,359–9,404 (from southern Arizona and Sonora, including articles from the Pimas and Maricopas, from the Salt River near Phoenix, from the Cocopas at the mouth of the Colorado, and from the Yaquis), Nos. 9,483–9,594 (mostly from New Mexico), Nos. 9,729–34 (from Montezuma Well, Arizona), and Nos. 9,969–89 (Arizona). Parry noted, "There is several nice parcels of plants from the mouth of Colorado River & Carmel [*sic*] Islands."[12] The National Herbarium has a considerable collection of plants from the Yaqui River and from Guaymas, and a few specimens from Carmen Island. Specimens from Camp Bowie, Arizona, and some collected between Tucson and Guaymas are known.

The total number of specimens was probably more than four hundred; Parry noted, probably early in 1870, that the plants "thus far received number about four hundred species."[13] He stated in his report for 1870 that the "numerous duplicates" would be distributed. This statement is open to question; except for the large series at the National Herbarium, and a few duplicates at the Gray Herbarium and at the New York Botanical Garden, Palmer's collections of 1869 do not occur widely in herbaria, at least in America.[14]

Immediately upon his return from the Southwest, Palmer began to lay plans for another trip. The results of his first agricultural exploration had satisfied his sponsors, and after a little more than two months he was off again for the same general region he had visited in 1869. One of Parry's comments before Palmer's departure gives the impression that governmental procedures were almost as ponderous in 1870 as they are now: "Palmer not yet got off—waiting for authorities to act. Rather disgusted."[15]

By the middle of May, however, all was ready, and he left Washington armed with official credentials from the Department of Agriculture, and their commission to "make collections of Natural History in the Western Territories of the United States." In this year of 1870, for the first time, one could cross the United States by rail, and Palmer availed himself of this for the trip as far as Salt Lake City. Here he

[12] Letter to Engelmann, March 7, 1870.

[13] In the report of the botanist in the *Report of the Commissioner of Agriculture*, 1869 (Washington, 1870), 93.

[14] As noted further on, however, it is probable that the combined sets of 1869 and 1870 were sent out to at least four herbaria in the United States and to at least four in Europe.

[15] Letter to Engelmann, May 4, 1870.

From a photograph in the Palmer Collection
Division of Plant Exploration and Introduction

Alexander Willard, United States Consul at Guaymas

Courtesy University of California

Edward Palmer in Army Uniform
From a photograph taken in Kansas City, 1865.

armed himself with a letter of introduction from the Mormon leader, Brigham Young, and set off to travel the length of Utah in the stage, a trip which he made, with stopovers, in a week. Collecting improved as he went south, and finally in the hot valleys near St. George he stayed about ten days and collected birds and plant specimens.

Beyond St. George, transportation was scarce, and the only means at hand when Palmer was ready was a threshing machine which was being hauled to St. Thomas. The road, which did not go beyond St. Thomas, followed essentially the route taken by today's highway from St. George to the southwest. Palmer's diary makes this clear:

June 17–1870. Turning to the left of St. George the road was very sandy & hilly for some few miles to the Clara Creek . . . leaving this place to the left for a few miles travelled entirely amid broken ridges with steep rough sides, to the mouth of a pass in the mountains here we leave water and as it was near night we camped. During the day by repeatedly jumping off & on I had secured many specimens. . . .

The following day travelled until afternoon through a pass in the mountains, rather rough but plenty of fine vegetation. I secured many good things. We soon emerged from the mountains to an open extensive plain covered with tree Yucca called "Joshua" by the Mormons. . . . Truly the sight was grand, before you was a vast level looking like a low forest surrounded on all sides by lofty mountains. . . .

. . . Our route lay across one corner to the left so as to strike the Virgin river where Beaver Springs empties into it, at which place arrived after night.

From this place to St. Thomas our road lay along the immediate bottom of the virgin river which was crossed and recrossed ever little while. . . . I had to walk nearly all the time which gave me a chance to collect.

June 20–1870 Arrived at St. Thomas. . . .

June 25–1870. There being no means of travel beyond St. Thomas, and only the mail carried on horse back . . . [I purchased] of Mr. Paddock a mule, saddle and bridle [and] packed on what food was necessary for myself for the trip . . . also 1 blanket and 4 feeds of grain for the mule. . . . My companion, the mail carrier, was similarily equipped. . . . We soon struck the Salt Mountains or Hills, a large irregular mass of salt entirely denuded of soil, of a pinkish hue . . . and standing a little back of the ridge, by the side of the Virgin river. . . . Journeying on for some miles . . . our trail left the Virgin River and entered an opening to the left, travelled to "Bitter Springs." . . . At noon we stopped at the only available spot where either water or grass could be found for many miles. . . . Our journey during the afternoon was slow. . . . Truly I can say that if ever any one suffered from fatigue and bad water, I did; filled with pain caused by the bitter dissagreable water creating a burning thirst . . . I had to ride on as best I could, and the thought of leaving my bones to whiten in this of all places fit to die in, kept up my determination to hold on, but when the trails led through deep ravines or between mountains the heat was so intense [that] when you turned to catch the south wind . . . [it was like] facing the mouth of a highly heated oven, nearly depriving you of breath; I was compelled to hold my broad brimmed hat over my face in order to breathe at all; thus we journeyed on nearly lifeless to dark, when the Mts. of the Colorado River were struck and we soon halted at Callville . . .

At 4 A.M. . . . our journey was resumed. . . . For some miles the trail was over the rough mountains and down the steep side, and along the edges of the Colorado River, sometimes so narrow that the least cause would hurl you and your animal hundreds of feet below. . . . Much of the first 8 miles had to be walked. . . . We struck the river again, halted, and fed the animals a little, made some coffee, filled the canteens, for we here left the river to strike it no more until night. . . . Hour after hour we journeyed on, riding but little of the time, as it was too steep and rough. . . . At last, sore in body and mind, I reached Eldorado Cañon . . .

. . . At an early hour we left. . . . We travelled all day amid the mountains, occasionally touching the river . . .

At last the mountains receded from the river a little, and the trail was over ridges and grassy river bottoms to Cottonwood Island, at which place we obtained food; this was a mail station; I slept soundly and by morning felt a little better. Started on over rough stony ridges, projecting spurs of mountains. . . . Arrived at Hardyville. Its owner, Mr. Hardy, received me kindly . . .

From Hardyville, Palmer went at once to Fort Mohave, whence he proceeded by mule, accompanying the mail carrier down the Colorado as far as Williams Fork. He then visited the copper mines[16] twelve miles up river and spent some time at a near-by ranch. At the

[16] Not otherwise named by Palmer. This was evidently the Planet Mine, which was worked from 1865 to 1873. See Farish, *History of Arizona,* II, 296–97.

mine, as he said, he collected "a good many specimens." His account continues:

I had come here from Ft. Mohave to this place to collect principally ripe fruit and seeds of the Cereus Giganteus, which for many years, had been wanted so much in the United States and Europe. I collected a great many nice ones. Having completed my collection returned to the ranch of Ogdale and Kearney. Here I was taken sick one night, and there being only one man at the ranch, the rest having gone away on business, and no medicine or doctor, I felt that I must die. I was in a bad way and it seemed uncertain one night whether I would pull through; but in the morning, I improved, but it was several days before I could ride my mule.

To Messrs. Hubbard [the manager of the copper mine], Ogdale, and Kearney, I will ever feel indebted for their kindness to me during my sickness. Returned to Murray's ranch.

From Murray's Ranch I went with the mail to Camp Colorado and was received by Lieut. Nolan [*sic*][17] and lady, also by Dr. Ames,[18] Post Surgeon; staid but a day or two. I sent off my specimens by mail, and my Cereus Giganteus fruit among the rest, but months after on my reaching Washington could not find this fruit or seed in the Dept. of Agriculture. In March, they were found in a shed attached to the green house, all damp and mouldy; some few were good and were distributed.

It appears from this account that Palmer worked at least a week and perhaps more along Williams Fork, and so may have reached Camp Colorado soon after the middle of July. Possibly he returned by river steamer to Hardyville, for he informs us that in that place on July 20, 1870, the air temperature stood at 117 degrees F., while the water in the river stood at 76 degrees! More probably he passed the second half of July, after his visit to Camp Colorado, at the Mohave Indian

[17] This was Lewis Nolen, 1st Lieut. 12th Inf., commanding officer of Camp Colorado during this summer. Nolen was about thirty years old at this time; he had fought in the Civil War as a volunteer from Delaware, and had served with distinction. After the war he re-enlisted in the regular Army, and was sent West in 1869. Data from the records of the Adjutant General's Office, U. S. National Archives; see also Heitman, *Historical Register and Dictionary* (1903), I, 750.

[18] T. M. Ames, acting assistant surgeon. His name is carried in the post returns from Camp Colorado (Adjutant General's Office, U. S. National Archives).

reservation a mile down river. Probably it was at this time that he obtained the "six boxes of things collected from the Mohave Indians" about which he wrote Baird.[19]

About this time, unfortunately we lose the thread of Palmer's travels. He was in Yuma in mid-August, and at the mouth of the Colorado soon after the first of September. The best contemporary account of his wanderings is the brief notice given by Parry only a year later:

In that year [1870] he went South from Salt Lake to the head of navigation on the Colorado. Thence down the river to the mouth and returned by way of Ehrenberg . . . across the Desert to Los Angeles.[20]

The date of the trip across the desert to Los Angeles is said by Parry to have been in September; the route was not the old Butterfield line which he had taken in 1867, but a slightly more direct one which passed to the northeast of the present Salton Sea. Even on this trip by stage he was able to collect an occasional specimen.[21] Then for the first time he made the trip from West Coast to East by the overland route, stopping in Denver after an absence of seven years to see some old friends,[22] and finally arriving in Washington soon after the first of November.

The collection of 1870 was probably smaller than that of 1869; Palmer was in the field approximately half as long in 1870 as in the earlier year, and some of his localities were "repeats," visited a second time for some special purpose, rather than with the idea of making general collections. The plants of 1870, like those of 1869, were distributed from the National Herbarium. Most of them are without definite locality data, but it may be inferred that most of them are from one or another of the following localities: Fillmore or St. George, Utah; St. Thomas, Nevada; Hardyville, Arizona, and vicinity; near mouth of Williams Fork, Arizona; or the vicinity of Puerta Isabel, Sonora. Safford says that Palmer collected at Canyon Springs, California, while enroute to Los Angeles, and it appears that collections were made at Whitewater on the same trip.

[19] Archives of the Smithsonian Institution, Letters Received, Book 101, p. 410. August 9, 1870, on board the steamer *Cocopah,* "steaming down the Colorado River."

[20] Letter to Engelmann, August 1, 1871.

[21] See Louis C. Wheeler, in *Rhodora,* Vol. XL (1938), 320–23.

[22] *Rocky Mountain News,* October 23, 1870.

It was perhaps unfortunate for Palmer, and for botany, that his collections of 1869 and 1870 were sent to the Department of Agriculture when they were. Both were received by Parry in his capacity as botanist of the Department of Agriculture, and at least the preliminary sorting of the collections was done by Parry. He was not particularly interested in the areas where Palmer had collected, however, and so failed to be enthusiastic over the specimens from these areas. His comment is typical: "I do not find much of interest in Palmers last set the Alpine plants are very meager."[23]

Worse than this, however, Parry was dismissed from his post as botanist in September, 1871, and the task of identifying and distributing the collections fell upon the new incumbent, George Vasey, who was ill-fitted because of lack of experience to perform the task.[24] Instead of identifying the material himself he sent out much of it to specialists, a practice now commonplace but then difficult because there were so few specialists! The process was a slow one; by the end of 1872 the naming of the collections was far from finished. Parry's note, the sour tone of which may have been due to his own position in the matter, describes the situation: "A letter from Palmer[.] Vasey is sending off his unnamed plants to be named and returned! and then he will publish a catalogue query? will he wait till he gets his things back? if so his catalogue will be good for the *next generation!*"[25]

A year later, however, Vasey wrote to Palmer stating that four "sets" of his plants had already been sent to Europe, and that sets were ready to be sent to D. C. Eaton,[26] and to Chicago, Philadelphia, and California.[27]

I have not been able to learn many details about the disposition of these collections. The four sets sent to Europe are presumably

[23] Letter to Asa Gray, commenting upon the collection of 1869, May 28, 1870.

[24] George Vasey (1822–93). Boyhood in New York, where he knew Knieskern. In 1848 moved to Illinois, where he practiced medicine for eighteen years, maintaining a steady interest in natural history. In 1868, accompanied J. W. Powell as botanist on an expedition to Colorado. Botanist, U. S. Department of Agriculture, 1872–93. Known especially for his work on grasses. See *Dictionary of American Biography* (1937), XIX, 229–30.

[25] To Engelmann, December 19, 1872.

[26] Daniel Cady Eaton (1834–95). Grandson of the pioneer botanist-teacher Amos Eaton. Studied at Yale, and later under Asa Gray. Became known especially for his work on North American ferns. His herbarium went at his death to Yale University. See *Dictionary of American Biography* (1937), V, 606–607.

[27] Letter of November 3, 1873, in answer to Palmer's letter of October 12.

still in existence, but have not been traced. I am equally in the dark about sets which may have been sent to California or to Chicago. The records of the Academy of Natural Sciences of Philadelphia, however, show that in 1874 a collection of Palmer's plants from "Arizona and southern California" was received from the Department of Agriculture, as a gift through George Vasey.

It is probable that the sets to which Vasey referred were made up from the combined collections of 1869 and 1870, although I have seen no direct evidence of this. No catalogue of the collection was ever published, and apparently not even a manuscript list has come down to us, if indeed any was ever prepared.

Ethnological collections sent to the National Museum included Nos. 10,319–53 from Fort Mohave, Nos. 10,440–47 from southern Arizona, and Nos. 10,668–79 from St. George, Utah.[28]

[28] Records of the Division of Ethnology; specimens entered in 1871, and presumably collected in 1870.

VII INTERLUDE, 1871–73

WITH THE YEAR 1871, a three-year period began in which Palmer made no important natural history collections.[1] After his strenuous Western trip of 1870, he made his home in Washington for three winters, spending the corresponding summers (of 1871, 1872, and 1873) on the New England coast as an assistant to Professor Baird, who had just added to his duties as assistant secretary of the Smithsonian those of the newly created post of United States Commissioner of Fish and Fisheries.

In February, 1871, Palmer had been appointed (as he thought) agent for the Pima and Maricopa Indians of Arizona; during April and May he was in Washington making plans to go west. Early in June, however, he found that his appointment was never to materialize. I do not know why; it may be that the appointment was given to someone else as a political favor, as Parry intimated.[2] Palmer himself wrote Engelmann that he had been "cheated out of" his appointment. Whatever the reason, he found himself without any employment, and he accepted the post under Baird for the months of July, August, September and October. For this work, which apparently consisted chiefly of the routine collection, cleaning, and preparation of marine animals (both vertebrate and invertebrate) and their parasites, he was paid $60 a month. He spent most of his time at Woods

[1] But see Records of the Division of Ethnology, United States National Museum, for a few collections. Catalogue Nos. 10,680–81; 11,416–36; 12,107; 12,113–16; 13,516–20, in part; 22,056–60; 22,097; 22,098; 22,118.

[2] In a letter to Engelmann, June 3, 1871.

Hole, Massachusetts, where the work of the Commission was centered in 1871. He made no large collections of plants or of anything else except as required by his official duties. The National Herbarium received a small series of plants which are labeled merely "Dr. E. Palmer, Woods Hole." The results of the summer's work are summarized in the formal reports of the work of the Commission.[3]

During the winter of 1871–72, Palmer worked at least part time, as he wrote, in "cleaning and putting in order the Smithsonian collection of fishes &c." The following summer he was again Professor Baird's assistant, this time in the vicinity of Eastport, Maine, at a salary increased to $100 a month. His work was similar to that of the previous year. We know from a note by D. C. Eaton that he paid at least one visit to Grand Manan Island and collected a few algae,[4] and the records of the National Museum show that a few ethnological specimens were received from Eastport and nearby Pleasant Point.[5] He was back in Washington in November and worked steadily at the Smithsonian Institution during the winter.

The summer of 1873 saw Palmer a member of a party which began work on Peak's Island, Maine, in July. This was also a project of the Commission of Fish and Fisheries. His salary had by this time increased to $150 a month, and his work was similar to that he had performed for the Commission in earlier years. After the termination of the work at the end of September, he went from Portland to Cambridge, Massachusetts, where Professor Louis Agassiz had offered him the task of "overhauling" the marine animals in the Museum of Comparative Zoology.[6] Presumably the work included routine assignments of filing, labeling, and arranging the bottled material in the museum's collection.

Agassiz died in December, and a month later Palmer wrote that "the shortness of funds compels the Trustees to suspend work in this Museum. . . . Notices was issued yesterday that after the first of April

[3] See References and Sources No. 124b.

[4] *Transactions of the Connecticut Academy of Arts and Sciences* (1873), II, 343–50.

[5] Division of Ethnology, United States National Museum. Catalogue Nos. 11,416–36; 12,107; 12,113–16.

[6] Jean Louis Rodolphe Agassiz (1807–73). One of the most distinguished naturalists of the century; instrumental in the development in America of the university ideal; noted for his philosophy, "Study nature, not books"; founder of the Harvard Museum of Comparative Zoology. See *Dictionary of American Biography* (1937), I, 114–22.

the work would stop." This sounds as if only the influence of Agassiz had kept the work going; the "shortness of funds" is suspiciously timely.

Palmer continues: "In consequence of this change am now arranging to go to Florida in two weeks will collect whatever I can that can be sold to pay my expenses . . . shall start from Providence by water with a party of gentlemen."[7]

[7] Letter to D. C. Eaton, January 14, 1874.

VIII FLORIDA AND THE BAHAMAS, 1874

THE "PARTY OF GENTLEMEN," of which Palmer was a member, took part in an expedition to the then all but unknown region of Lake Okeechobee in Florida. The trip was sponsored by the magazine *Forest & Stream* and was led by F. A. Ober of Beverly, Massachusetts, who in a series of letters to the magazine reported the progress of the expedition under the pseudonym of Fred Beverly.[1] In addition to Palmer and Ober, the party included E. J. Shores of Brown University and Colonel F. B. Van Buskirk of New York.[2]

After an uneventful trip to Jacksonville, the expedition left for Lake Okeechobee early in February. They made a quick trip by boat up the St. Johns River to a point opposite present Titusville, where they crossed to the Indian River to meet Ober, who had preceded them. He had made another, but unsuccessful, attempt to reach Lake Okeechobee (in 1872), and his description of the earlier passage down the inland waterways is illustrative of conditions in Florida at this time:

The steamer up the St. John's, from Jacksonville to Salt Lake, a distance of two hundred and seventy-five miles, and a portage of six miles will bring the traveller to the banks of Indian River, at Harvey's, or Sand Point, where boats and guides may be hired down the river

[1] Frederick Albion Ober (1849–1913), ornithologist and writer. His principal contribution to science was in ornithological exploration in the West Indies. See *Dictionary of American Biography* (1937), XIII, 606–607.

[2] Safford, MS.

to Jupiter, one hundred and thirty miles further. The cost of transportation from New York to Sand Point will be about sixty dollars. The visitor had better camp, and bring with him such articles of need as a camper-out appreciates.[3]

With the party complete, the expedition continued down the Indian River as far as Fort Pierce (St. Lucie), where they loaded boat and supplies on a wagon and set out overland. Ober's report from "Fort Bassenger Ford on the Kissimmee River" again provides a graphic summary:

We have walked sixty miles, have swimmed two creeks, and *waded over twenty miles!* The wheels upon which we hauled our boat have broken down twice, and, take it all together, the trip was a rough one. We were a week *en route,* though but four days actual travel. I have with me three companions, all from the north, gentlemen well fitted to endure the dangers and hardships. . . . Intend going in with a month's provisions, as the lake is said to be destitute of game. 'Said to be', but . . . according to the only resident east of the Kissimmee, there have been but three white men in the lake since the Indian war.[4]

The party found that a two-day trip down the swift Kissimmee River in their boat brought them to Lake Okeechobee, which they circumnavigated before returning to Fort Bassinger. They had failed to find any trace of ancient cities or marvels of plant and animal life which they had more than half expected to discover in the wilderness of Okeechobee. The trip had been hard; Palmer wrote:

It was with joy that we returned to Fort Bassenger, after an absence of eight days and nights. Our clothes were spotted with blood from the bites of mosquitoes. On the trip I had collected plants and insects. . . . A wagon drawn by oxen was once more hired . . . and we returned to St. Lucie.

They had been away from St. Lucie a month on the trip inland. Palmer was disappointed in the quality of the plant collections he had been able to make thus far, and when the expedition disbanded he extended his stay in Florida in order to get more worthwhile and sal-

[3] *Forest & Stream,* Vol. I (Nov. 20, 1873), 225.

[4] *Forest & Stream,* Vol. II (March 26, 1874), 105.

able specimens. He collected along Indian River until about the end of March, then returned to Jacksonville, crossed the peninsula to Cedar Keys by rail and took passage on a steamer to Key West, where he made his headquarters until July. In May, he began a three-week trip to the Bahamas to collect algae and sponges; Eaton was much interested in algae at this time, and Palmer had engaged to collect them for him whenever possible in these subtropical waters. As a result of his labors in this direction, he accumulated enough algal materials to justify the publication of a special paper by Eaton, dealing with this group alone.[5] Following his return to Key West and some excursions along the coast as far northeast as Miami, Palmer returned to Cedar Keys and Jacksonville and concluded his work in Florida soon after the first of September.

Most of the collections made by Palmer in this year were botanical in nature. The algae included at least 128 collections, reported by Eaton under 105 numbers,[6] for there were duplicates of some or all of the algal groups.[7]

The vascular plants included something over 800 separate collections, sent for identification to Gray, and distributed by him under 672 numbers,[8] assigned arbitrarily after the arrangement of the collection in systematic order. Almost one-third of the collections, according to Gray's list, are labeled simply as from "East Florida," and about the same number of specimens are marked "Indian River." About 65 numbers are labeled as from Biscayne Bay, and there are about as many from Key West. The remainder are distributed approximately as follows: Cedar Keys 23; Lake Okeechobee 12; New Smyrna 2; St. Augustine 1; South Florida 1.

In Gray's manuscript list, 48 numbers are noted as from both "East Florida" and "Indian River," with the evident implication that a part of the material under each number came from each locality. There are, in all, about 133 numbers for which more than a single locality is noted, including 11 numbers for which three localities are given.

[5] D. C. Eaton. *A List of the Marine Algae Collected by Dr. Edward Palmer on the Coast of Florida and at Nassau, Bahama Islands, March–August 1874,* (New Haven, 1875. 6 pp.).

[6] The same number was assigned to all collections of the same species, without reference to the source of the material.

[7] Eaton noted that No. 41 was marked 42 in *some of the sets.* (Author's italics.)

[8] These are listed, with localities, in Gray Herbarium *Miscellaneous Plant Lists,* Vol. I (MS).

Gray published a note on this collection offering for sale "four or five sets" at $8.00 per 100 specimens; the sets were said to range from 250 to 630 species each.[9] Set No. 5, now at the National Herbarium, included 407 specimens.[10] The total number of specimens distributed must have been in excess of 3,000.

[9] *American Journal of Science,* Series 3, Vol. IX (1875), 67–68.
[10] Watson to Vasey, Feb. 5, 1875.

IX GUADALUPE ISLAND AND THE SOUTHWEST, 1875–77

WHILE IN CAMBRIDGE, Palmer read a magazine article describing a commercial attempt that was being made to produce a superior strain of goats upon Guadalupe Island, off the coast of Baja California.[1] No biologist had ever made collections on the island, and because of its extreme isolation its flora and fauna promised to be interesting. With the encouragement of Sereno Watson,[2] he decided to visit the island before there was further destruction of the flora by the rapidly breeding goats. He reached San Diego in mid-January of 1875 and found that there was no regular transportation to the island; the Guadalupe Island Company, however, ran occasional supply boats, and on one of these he secured passage, taking with him a helper for his collecting. He reached the island about the first of February, expecting to stay six weeks and return with the company boat on its next trip. The boat failed to return in time, however, and he was forced to remain on the island until mid-May, when some of his friends in San Diego, alarmed at his long absence, hired another boat to take him off. In the meantime his food had run low and he and

[1] Buena Esperanza, "Guadalupe, La Isla de la piel de oro, sin duda alguna," *Forest & Stream,* Vol. II (July 9, 1874), 337–38. The author's name is, of course, pseudonymous.

[2] Sereno Watson (1826–92). Curator of the Gray Herbarium, 1874–92. At the age of forty, Watson studied chemistry and mineralogy and went to California to make his fortune. Almost by chance he joined the King Expedition as botanist, which resulted in his publication of the botany of that expedition, and his subsequent career. See *Dictionary of American Biography* (1937), XIX, 547–48.

his few companions had been in some danger of starving on the uninhabited island, with nothing to eat but goat meat and a few greens.

The botanical and zoological collections made on Guadalupe Island were reported upon in several special papers.[3] The plant specimens were distributed under 119 numbers assigned to them after their systematic arrangement. Palmer actually collected on the island under about 140 different field numbers, as recorded at the Gray Herbarium.[4] In addition to the set retained at the Gray Herbarium, duplicate sets at $15 each were distributed as follows (The name of the recipient as recorded by Watson is followed by the name in parentheses of the institutional herbarium where the specimens are presumably deposited):

Set Number

1 De Candolle[5] (Conservatoire et Jardin Botaniques, Genève)[6]

2 Maximowicz[7] (Komarov Botanical Institute, U.S.S.R. Academy of Sciences, Leningrad)

[3] Land Shells, *Proceedings of the Academy of Natural Sciences of Philadelphia,* 1879 (1880), 16; Coleoptera, *Transactions of the American Entomological Society,* Vol. V (1876), 198–201; Ornithology, *United States Geological and Geographical Survey of the Territories, Bulletin No. 2* (1876), 183–96; Orthoptera, *Proceedings of the Boston Society of Natural History,* Vol. XVIII (1876), 268–71; Plants, *Proceedings of the American Academy of Arts and Sciences,* Vol. XI (1876), 112–31.

[4] The numbers assigned by Watson, and those under which the collections were sent in by Palmer, are listed in *Miscellaneous Plant Lists,* Vol. 2 (MS).

[5] Alphonse [Louis Pierre Pyramus] de Candolle (1806–93), one of the most distinguished European botanists of the nineteenth century, author of numerous monographic studies of vascular plants and works on phytogeography, sponsor and author of the International Rules of Botanical Nomenclature. The De Candolle Herbarium is now a part of the holdings of the Conservatoire et Jardin Botaniques, Geneva. For a sketch of Alphonse de Candolle's life and writings see *Bulletin de l'Herbier Boissier,* Vol. I (1893), 203–34.

[6] Although Watson evidently intended to send the best set of this collection to De Candolle, there is no record of its receipt at Geneva. In 1954, through the kindness of Dr. Baehni, I was permitted to examine the very complete records of accessions to the Candollean herbarium, but could find no reference to any of Palmer's collections of this or any other year.

[7] Karl Ivanovitch ("C. J.") Maximowicz (1827–91), prominent Russian botanist; from 1852 curator of the Imperial Botanic Garden, St. Petersburg, and ultimately Director of the Museum and Herbarium of the Imperial Academy of Sciences. See *Proceedings of the American Academy of Arts and Sciences,* Vol. XXVI (1891), 374–76.

3 Canby[8] (New York Botanical Garden)
4 Redfield[9] (Missouri Botanical Garden)
5 Boissier[10] (Conservatoire et Jardin Botaniques, Genève)
6 Olney[11] (Brown University)
7 Engelmann (Missouri Botanical Garden)
8 Brewer[12] (Not located)
9 Carruthers[13] (British Museum, Natural History)
10 LeRoy[14] (New York Botanical Garden)

[8] William Marriott Canby. (1831–1904). Banker, and enthusiastic amateur botanist. His own large herbarium went to the New York College of Pharmacy, whose collections are now incorporated into those of the New York Botanical Garden. See J. W. Harshberger *The Botanists of Philadelphia and Their Work* (Philadelphia, 1899), 278–83. See also *Torreya*, Vol. IV (1904), 52–56; [H. H. Rusby], "The Canby Herbarium," *Bulletin of the Torrey Botanical Club*, Vol. XIX (1892), 336–39.

[9] John Howard Redfield (1815–95). Early interested in science. In transportation and machinery business until 1885. Conservator of Botanical Section, Academy of Natural Sciences of Philadelphia, 1870–95; modernized and organized the herbarium there, and presented many valuable sets of plants to the Academy. His personal herbarium was purchased in 1897 by the Missouri Botanical Garden. See *Bulletin of the Torrey Botanical Club*, Vol. XXII (1895), 162–71; Harshberger, *The Botanists of Philadelphia*, 211–19.

[10] Edmond Boissier (1810–85). Student of the botany of Spain, the Mediterranean region, and the Near East. Author of the *Flora Orientalis*. Possessor at his death of one of the best private herbaria in Europe, a collection now a part of the holdings of the Conservatoire et Jardin Botaniques of Geneva. See a sketch by Asa Gray in the *American Journal of Science*, Series 3, Vol. XXXI (1886), 20–21.

[11] Stephen Thayer Olney (1812–78). Commission and woolen merchant, Providence, Rhode Island. Amateur botanist, who was noted particularly for his work on *Carex*. At his death left his herbarium to Brown University and endowed a professorship of botany there. See *National Cyclopedia of American Biography* (1906), XIII, 35.

[12] William Henry Brewer (1828–1910). Member of the Geological Survey of California, 1860–64. Professor of Agriculture, Sheffield Scientific School, 1864–93. See *Dictionary of American Biography* (1937), III, 25–26. Brewer's personal herbarium is said to have been given to the United States Department of Agriculture; see *Rhodora*, Vol. III (1901), 207.

[13] William Carruthers (1830–1922). Keeper of the Botanical Department, British Museum, 1871–95. See J. Britten and G. S. Boulger, *Biographical Index of Deceased British and Irish Botanists* (2nd ed., London, 1931), 60.

[14] Peter Vincent LeRoy (1821–89). A native of New York City, one of the founders and the first secretary of the Torrey Botanical Club, and at this time curator of the Torrey Herbarium of Columbia College. The herbarium has since been incorporated into that of the New York Botanical Garden. See *Bulletin of the Torrey Botanical Club*, Vol. VI (1876), 128.

From the time of his return to San Diego about the first of June, Palmer specialized in botanical collecting, yet gave some little attention to ethnology. He was authorized by the Department of Agriculture to collect certain botanical materials for the Centennial Exposition which was to be held the following year. In addition to this, he collected several thousand specimens which were sold for him by the Gray Herbarium.

During the first part of the summer he worked in San Diego County. This involved a trip by coach to Soledad, another to Jamul, a long trip of a month to the Cuyamaca Mountains and Julian, the Diegueños Indians near Warner's Ranch, and the Indians in Coahuila Valley. His success in collecting may be judged from a newspaper notice which he received on his return to San Diego: "[Dr. Palmer] arrived here from Julian City yesterday, bringing with him two wagon loads of the curious things he had gathered."[15]

At this time, as soon as his collections were cared for, Palmer tried to get a pass to Fort Yuma and back, with the mail contractors. As far as we know he never went as far as Fort Yuma, but he succeeded in getting transportation a part of the way. One of the stage routes to Yuma from San Diego lay almost along the Mexican boundary, and on this he went as far east as Mountain Springs. Late in August or early in September, he set out from Campo, a station on the same road, on a trip into Baja California, his objective the "Tantillas Mountains." His companion on this trip was G. W. Dunn.[16]

Tantillas, or Cantillas, Canyon is one of Palmer's more famous localities. He made a collection of more than 60 numbers from the "Big Canyon" and from "Tantillas Mountains," including specimens of the genus *Palmerella* which was named in his honor. Although Charles Orcutt[17] made several trips in to the same locality in later

[15] *San Diego Evening World,* August 11, 1875.

[16] George W. Dunn (1814–1905). "An eccentric but indefatigable collector," particularly of insects. See *Madroño,* Vol. II (1934), 156–57, and E. O. Essig, *A History of Entomology* (New York, 1931), 605. Dunn claimed the credit for the discovery of a plant on this trip, the same which Gray dedicated to Palmer as a new genus, *Palmerella.* Dunn convinced E. L. Greene of the justice of his claim, and as a result Greene renamed the species as *Lobelia Dunnii.* Palmer, in a note published in *West American Scientist,* Vol. VII (1890), 8–9, protested this and gave his version of the incident.

[17] Charles Russell Orcutt (1864–1929). Natural history collector, known for his publication of the journal *The West American Scientist,* which he began in 1884. See *Madroño,* Vol. I (1929), 273–74.

years, and published various notes on his trips, no one today knows the exact location of Cantillas Canyon, beyond the fact that it must be one of the canyons on the desert side of the Sierra de Juárez, overlooking the Colorado Valley.

Returning again to San Diego, Palmer spent a few weeks working over and packing his collections, trying to finish before the end of September for a change of base, this time to Utah. He noted that on his "late trip to the desert" he obtained many Indian implements from the Spanish-speaking Indians, so apparently his interest in ethnology did not lag. He finally reached St. George, Utah, to start a new field season, about the middle of October.

Early in the course of his work in Utah, Palmer became acquainted with J. E. Johnson, with whom he maintained friendly relations for the rest of the time that Johnson lived in Utah.[18] The youngest daughter of the Johnson family, now Mrs. Rosemary Johnson Fox Johnson, remembers Palmer's early visits, and has sent from her home in Salt Lake City her recollections as we give them below:

Dr. Edward Palmer was a handsome, quiet man who came to St. George when I was about ten years old. My father, Joseph Ellis Johnson, turned over the library, which was in an adobe building apart from our residence, to him both for sleeping quarters and workroom. It had a fine large fireplace in it, with a high mantel upon which Dr. Palmer placed bottles and jars containing many kinds of snakes. On it also was an old silver-combed music box once owned by grandmother Julia Hills Johnson in Illinois[—a music box] which had been brought by the long ox-team journey across the plains. The doctor

[18] Joseph Ellis Johnson (1817–82). The Johnson family were among the very early converts to "Mormonism." Joseph and his family moved to Utah in 1861, and settled in a spot south of Payson which was named Spring Lake Villa by his wife, Eliza. In 1865 he was called by the church authorities to settle at St. George, where he began the development of a garden that was to become one of the show places of southern Utah. In addition to his work in horticulture he was interested in the native plants, and maintained contacts with botanists of his period, including Palmer, C. C. Parry, and Sereno Watson. In 1882, he was called by the church to a further service; with his brother Benjamin F. Johnson he made the arduous journey to the Salt River Valley of Arizona to establish at Tempe a base from which Mormon colonies in Mexico might be established. See *Heart Throbs of the West,* ?Vol. X (1949), 195–201; this is an account of the life and horticultural work of J. E. Johnson, by his son Rufus D. Johnson, who has also kindly furnished supplementary biographical data.

liked to turn it on and listen to its tinkling chimes while he worked. He had his meals at our house and was always very polite and interesting in his conversation.

Dr. Palmer taught us children to always carry a wide mouth bottle with a cork in it whenever we went out on the hills or down in the garden and to turn over rocks and watch closely for any interesting insects. Also we wore a strapped folder over our shoulder so we could pick and press any unusual flower or plant. We had an ox team which sometimes we drove out in the canyons and hills. We bragged about this outfit because *our* oxen could trot! One day some of the boys gave me a little black bat. I had to hold it by the wings so it would not bite me. I took it to Dr. Palmer and he showed me how to kill it without spoiling it. He held it with two fingers at its back with thumb tight on its breast until it stopped breathing. He also taught us how to catch and mount butterflies and not spoil the wings. He handled many cacti and naturally acquired numerous thorns in his hands. On several occasions he paid me twenty-five cents per half hour for working on his hands with needle and tweezers.

Occasionally the doctor had trouble with the Indians. They would bring all sorts of things to him, most of which were of no interest and when he refused to buy them the redskins would become very wrathful. One day an old Piute called "Limpy" (because of a crippled leg) brought in a long rope braided from rushes. When the doctor shook his head and said "No want," Limpy seized his knife and cut the rope into many small sections. These he threw at the doctor's feet and limped off in a rage, muttering no one knows what maledictions.

When father built a store at Silver Reef I went with him to keep house for him. Dr. Palmer visited us there. One day my father said he was hungry for a dried apple pie. I told him I didn't know how to make one. The doctor said, "Here, I'll show you how." So he pitched in and thus helped me make my first pie. It was pretty good, too! I was very sorry when he had done with the Indian mounds and went back east. I never did see him again, though father used to read his letters from Washington to me.

My eldest brother, Charles, helped in the excavations. He told me that Dr. Palmer watched like the proverbial hawk each removal of articles from the burial places. The boys never had the slightest chance to snitch any choice bit for themselves. The things were brought over from the Santa Clara fields to the library, where they were laid out on a long table. From here they were carefully packed and shipped by stagecoach to the railroad, the terminal of which was then a long way to the northward.

Ethnological collections made in 1875 before Palmer's departure for Utah include the following in the National Museum: Catalog Nos. 18,896–99 (California); 19,476–79 (San Diego); 19,726–83 (Diegueño Indians); 21,065–21,141 (San Diego); 21,779–97 (Coahuila Indians.)[19]

The plant collections made in California and Baja California in 1875 have been widely distributed. A series of wood samples intended for the Centennial Exposition, and one set of about 250 herbarium specimens, were sent at once to the Department of Agriculture with a full list of localities.[20] The numbers on this are the collector's original field numbers from 1 to 302, and it is supposed that Palmer selected the material with the wants of the Department especially in mind. The remainder of the collection, comprising about eleven sets, was sent for determination to Asa Gray and was distributed from the Gray Herbarium. It is listed in manuscript, a total of 462 numbered collections, in addition to about 30 duplicate, supplementary and unnumbered collections. The arrangement is systematic, according to plant families. The locality of collection is given for all except 23 numbers, the number of sets is given for each, and Palmer's field numbers are given in parentheses.[21] The field numbers in the Gray Herbarium list correspond except in a few cases with those of the Department of Agriculture set, and comprise the same series, 1–302. Notations made by Gray indicate that the sets were "spoken for" as follows (modern institutional herbaria in parentheses):

Set Number		*Number of Specimens*
1	Carruthers (British Museum, Natural History)	440
2	Rothrock[22] (Chicago Natural History Museum)	437

[19] Records of the Division of Ethnology. See also Catalog Nos. 54,965–55,482.

[20] This list, which was sent from San Francisco about October 10, 1875, is the principal source of information about the geographical location of Palmer's collecting localities during this year.

[21] Gray Herbarium, *Miscellaneous Plant Lists,* Vol. 2 (MS).

[22] Joseph Trimble Rothrock (1839–1922). In youth a special student of Asa Gray. M. D., Pennsylvania, 1867. Took part in Kennicott expedition to Alaska,

3	Clinton[23] (Buffalo Museum of Science)	434
4	Maximowicz (Komarov Botanical Institute, U.S.S.R. Academy of Science, Leningrad)	423
5	Redfield (Missouri Botanical Garden)	412
6	Canby (New York Botanical Garden)	398
7	Canby (New York Botanical Garden)	382
8	Boissier (Conservatoire et Jardin Botaniques, Genève)	363
9	Morong[24] (New York Botanical Garden)	343
10	Martindale[25] (Philadelphia College of Pharmacy)	329

The collections of 1875 were advertised by Sereno Watson:

Sets of Dr. Edward Palmer's recent collection of plants of San Diego Co., California, and of the Tantillas Mountains in Lower California, near the boundary, will shortly be ready for distribution. They will probably number about three hundred species, and will be sold at ten dollars per hundred.[26]

After his arrival in St. George in October, Palmer de-emphasized

and was botanist to Wheeler Surveys of 1873–75. Professor of botany, Pennsylvania, 1877–1904. Influential in the forestry movement in Pennsylvania from its beginning, and the first commissioner of forestry in that state. His personal herbarium was acquired by the Chicago Natural History Museum (then Field Museum) in 1909. See *Dictionary of American Biography* (1937), XVI, 188–89.

[23] George William Clinton (1807–85). Lawyer, jurist, enthusiastic amateur botanist who maintained a large correspondence with his contemporaries in this field. His large herbarium became the property of the Buffalo Museum of Science, Buffalo, New York. See C. A. Zenkert, *Flora of the Niagara Frontier Region* (Buffalo, N. Y., 1934), 11–13, and a sketch by Asa Gray in the *American Journal of Science,* Series 3, Vol. XXXI (1886), 17–20.

[24] Thomas Morong (1827–94). Ordained a Congregational clergyman in 1854, and continued in this work until 1888, when he undertook a successful botanical exploration trip to South America. Curator of Columbia College Herbarium, ?1891–94. See *Bulletin of the Torrey Botanical Club,* Vol. XXI (1894), 239–44. Morong's first published paper appeared in 1880, and his interest in botany seems to have been awakened even before this. His own herbarium was incorporated into that of Columbia College (now at New York Botanical Garden).

[25] Isaac Comly Martindale (1842–93). A banker, of Camden, New Jersey, whose avocation was botany. He amassed a large private herbarium, which became the property of the Philadelphia College of Pharmacy. See *American Journal of Pharmacy,* Vol. LXVI (1894), 251–54, and *Bulletin of the Torrey Botanical Club,* Vol. XX (1893), 98–100.

[26] *American Naturalist,* Vol. X (1876), 235.

plant collecting and spent more time on archaeology. "Palmer's work here represents the very first attempt at scientific investigation of Puebloan ruins in the Southwest, and his results have been characterized by Professor Holmes as 'the first collection of importance known to have been made by exhumation'."[27] A part of his work was to collect material illustrative of Indian life and customs, for the coming Centennial Exposition. He had also begun working for F. W. Putnam and the Peabody Museum, a connection that continued for some years to the profit of both parties.[28] Archaeological material collected in 1875 included at least 150 specimens from St. George and Kanab, Utah, and along Muddy River, Nevada. Palmer's system of numbering in this year is, to say the least, somewhat confusing. I suspect that he continued his field numbers through the year 1875, keeping but a single series for all collections instead of keeping separate series for plants, Indian artifacts, and so on. The numbers for his early collections from California and Baja California ran up probably almost to 600. The following additional series are known, but their relation to the main series of numbers has not been determined up to the present time:

Nos. 600–69 (with many numbers missing). These are plants, from St. George, Utah, November–December, 1875, listed in field notes in the PEI files. I have not seen these, and do not know under what numbers they were distributed.

Nos. 606, 621–52. Seeds, collected at St. George, October to December, 1875, listed in Smithsonian Accession 4,790.

[27] Neil M. Judd, "Archeological Observations North of the Rio Colorado," *Bureau of American Ethnology Bulletin No. 32* (1926), 40–41. This article summarizes the work of Palmer and others in this part of southwestern Utah, and describes the sites and the archaeological situation in general.

Records of the Division of Ethnology, United States National Museum, show the receipt of the following: Catalog Nos. 20,926–21,064 (from St. George, or from a mound 4 miles west, on Santa Clara River; last two numbers from Kanab); Nos. 21,142–50 (Santa Clara River); Nos. 21,290, 21,679–21,704, 21,706, 22,-044–50 (southern Utah); 24,145–24,238 (Mohave Indians, Colorado River). Catalog Nos. 54,965–55,482, also include materials from Utah.

[28] Frederic Ward Putnam (1839–1915). A student of Agassiz who played one of the foremost parts in the development of anthropology in the United States. Director of Peabody Academy of Science, 1869–73. Curator of Peabody Museum of American Archaeology and Ethnology, 1874–1915. One of the founders of the *American Naturalist;* later a curator of the American Museum of Natural History. See *Dictionary of American Biography* (1937), XV, 276–78.

Nos. 700–55. Specimens collected from the Mohave Indians in March, 1876, (Catalog in files of Peabody Museum, another in Smithsonian Accession 5,070).

Soon after the beginning of the year 1876, Palmer started on a campaign of travel that carried him from St. George to San Diego, back to Arizona, then twice more across California before the end of the summer. He wanted particularly to collect material of articles used by the Arizona Indians along the Gila and Colorado rivers, and he carried out a part of this plan, combining it with active plant collecting in western Arizona. He went by coach to Ehrenberg, Arizona, and took a river-steamer up to the Mohave Reservation, where he stayed eight days, shipping his ethnological material by boat from Ehrenberg upon his return there.[29] He then went overland to Wickenburg and Prescott, collecting plants as he went, and back to the Colorado again and over the toll road to Hardyville. From here he took the stage into California by the Mojave River route across the desert to San Bernardino, where he arrived about the end of May. At Crafton, he was welcomed by Dr. C. C. Parry and J. G. Lemmon,[30] who were exploring the flora of the Mojave Desert. A party was formed for a trip to San Bernardino Mountain, but on the return trip Palmer was thrown from his horse and injured so severely that he decided to give up for the rest of the season the heavy work of digging and packing archaeological specimens, and go to San Luis Obispo to collect plants.[31] Actually it seems he had collected little archaeological material since March.

About the end of June, he reached San Luis Obispo and spent six weeks in short collecting trips out from there, concluding his work with a trip north to San Francisco through Monterey County and the

[29] Records of the Division of Ethnology, United States National Museum; see footnote 27, above.

[30] Palmer's acquaintance with Parry dated back at least to 1870, when Parry was botanist of the Department of Agriculture, but the two men had not previously worked together in the field. Parry had come to Utah in the summer of 1875, and as early as September of that year had suggested to Palmer the possibility of a joint botanical expedition. See Rodgers, *American Botany*, 64–65.

John Gill Lemmon (1832–1908). Amateur botanist, writer, collector, later influential in the forestry movement in California. In 1866, with health broken by the Civil War, Lemmon emigrated to Sierra Valley, California. See *Dictionary of American Biography* (1937), XI, 162–63.

[31] Letter to Putnam, June 15, 1876.

redwoods of the Santa Lucia Mountains. Finally he took his plants to Parry's home in Davenport, Iowa, to enlist help in getting them arranged into sets.

The plant collections of 1876 are listed in the Gray Herbarium.[32] The list is accompanied by an enumeration of localities and dates of collection, beginning at Ehrenberg, Arizona, on March 4, and ending at Camp Halleck, Nevada, on August 26. Most of the known facts relative to his plant collections of 1876 are contained in this manuscript, but the dates given therein are not always correct. The plants included 660 numbers, distributed by C. C. Parry. The bulk of the collection, comprising numbers 1–560, was arranged systematically before numbering and was apparently named by Asa Gray. A supplementary series comprising Nos. 561–649, and eleven unnumbered collections, was listed separately by Gray; the first set of these was sent for determination to George Engelmann. Palmer wrote Engelmann about these:

A package of plants is forwarded to you. Dr. Parry may have written to you regarding them. Each specimen is numbered and a letter attached which designates the locality after you have identified them forward Dr. Parry a list of the names and numbers so he can name his—the plants you retain. They was collected at the following localities. Colorado River Valley Arizona March (are marked A) Hass-ay-ampa valley central Arizona on a beginning of April (B). Prescott Arizona mountain district central Arizona latter part of April (C), 25 miles north east of San Luis Obispo California July (E).[33]

As discussed in an earlier paper, some 272 plants, or about two-fifths of the entire collection, originated in Arizona.[34] With the exception of about 50 numbers collected in Nevada in August, the rest were from California. The largest series, about 130 numbers, was collected on the Mojave Desert, either at Rock Springs or along the Mojave River; another considerable series was obtained in the vicinity of San Luis Obispo and on the trip northward through the redwoods. About 50 collections are not assigned any recognizable source in the Gray Herbarium manuscript. I have never seen any estimate of the number of sets of plant specimens collected in 1876,

[32] *Miscellaneous Plant Lists,* Vol. 3 (MS).
[33] On December 13, 1876.
[34] See References and Sources No. 41.

but it was probably at least ten. A cursory check through lists of exsiccatae cited in recent systematic papers shows that at least six or seven sets were distributed to American herbaria alone.

The archaeological collections are discussed briefly above. It may be that they included no more than the materials obtained at the Mohave Agency in March.

In December, 1876, Palmer was engaged by the Peabody Museum to excavate Indian mounds in southern Utah. He reached St. George about the end of the year and made his headquarters there until the following June. He worked in mounds in Washington and Kane counties, and made five trips, each of about a week, for botanical collecting. These took him to St. Thomas, Nevada, to Mt. Trumbull, Arizona, to Mokiak Pass, Arizona (twice), and to the site of the Mountain Meadow massacre north of St. George. Late in June, he moved his base to Paragonah (then Red Creek), Utah, where he collected plants and insects, and also investigated some near-by mounds. He moved on north to Beaver, Utah, where in addition to his archaeological work he made several trips for botanical collecting in the high mountains to the eastward. He examined mounds for about two weeks near Spring Lake Villa, then took all his collections of the summer to Salt Lake City for shipping. The terminus of the Utah Southern Railroad was seven miles from Spring Lake, but south of this point he had had to carry all his collections by wagon.

The archaeological collections of 1877 were large ones; Palmer noted the shipment of nine boxes and four bales from Salt Lake City.[35] The catalog of this collection, in the files of the Peabody Museum, includes 186 individual items. His butterflies of this year were made the subject of a special paper, and he made some other entomological collections.[36]

The plant collections were sent to Davenport, and there, with Parry's help, arranged systematically before numbering. There were 502 numbered collections (or 532, including 30 which were assigned fractional numbers, e.g.: 142½, 302½). A list of the collection, with localities for most of the numbers, is in the Gray Herbarium.[37] Only the following localities are mentioned: St. Thomas, Nevada; Beaver Dam, Mokiak Pass and Mt. Trumbull, Arizona; St. George, Mountain

[35] Telegram to F. W. Putnam, August 14, 1877.

[36] *United States Geological and Geographical Survey of the Territories, Bulletin No. 4* (1878), 253–58.

[37] *Miscellaneous Plant Lists,* Vol. 3 (MS).

Meadows, "Beaver City," Red Creek, and "Beaver Valley near Red Creek," Utah. About one-third of the entire collection came from St. George; about 125 numbers, as discussed elsewhere, originated in Arizona;[38] approximately 80 numbers came from the vicinity of Beaver and about the same number probably came from Red Creek and vicinity; the rest of the collections (except those of unknown source) came either from the vicinity of St. Thomas, Nevada, (about 28 numbers) or from Mountain Meadows (14 numbers).

The number of sets of plants collected in 1877 was apparently at least eighteen. In the Gray Herbarium is the following note:[39]

Palmer, S. Utah Arizona	—	1877	—	Set 6	— 314 sp.
				Set 11	484 sp.
				Set 12	439 sp.
				Set 14	388 sp.
				Set 18	255 sp.
				Set 13	432 sp.

The following table sets forth what is known, or surmised, of the size and disposition of the entire collection:

Set Number[40]	*Number of Specimens*	*Taken by*	*Modern Location*	*Price*
1	532?	Gray Herbarium	Gray Herbarium	
2		Canby	N. Y. Botanical Garden	
3		Crooke[41]	N. Y. Botanical Garden	
4		Vasey	U. S. National Herbarium	

[38] See References and Sources No. 41.

[39] *Miscellaneous Plant Lists,* Vol. 3, (MS), 56.

[40] Data on sets 2 to 4 in letter, Parry to Palmer, Nov. 7, 1877; data on set 5 in letter, Parry to Palmer, Nov. 17, 1877 (Parry notes also that Martindale and Engelmann are to get sets); data on sets 17 and 18 from a note by Watson, on a letter from Parry to Gray, Nov. 9, 1877; set 16 is erroneously called set 6 in the note mentioned in footnote 39.

[41] John J. Crooke (1824–1911), of New York City, a member of the Torrey Botanical Club and a patron of botany, through whose generosity the Meissner Herbarium and other collections were acquired for the Torrey Herbarium of Columbia College. These now form a part of the holdings of the New York Botanical Garden. See *Bulletin of the Torrey Botanical Club,* Vol. VI (1876), 128.

5		Redfield	Mo. Botanical Garden	$28
6				
7				
8				
9				
10				
11	484			
12	439			
13	432			
14	388			
15				
16	314			
17	298			14
18	255			15

X TO SAN LUIS POTOSÍ WITH PARRY, 1878

FROM SALT LAKE CITY, Palmer shipped his Utah plants to Parry about the first of September. Palmer himself followed close behind, to help make the plants "into sets so they can be sold at once as Parry and myself are talking of going to Mexico this coming winter."[1] This was the first intimation of what subsequently developed into one of the most important collecting trips ever made to northern Mexico.

Parry and Palmer conceived the scheme of raising $1,000 from several contributors, this to be repaid in sets of the plants they hoped to collect. By November 9, the project had begun to take shape; Parry wrote to Gray: "The Mexican scheme seems to be working favorably. Canby will subscribe $200. Martindale & Redfield probably $200.00 more—Engel[mann] $100.—." Two weeks later C. S. Sargent had promised $100,[2] and a part of Palmer's expenses were paid by the Peabody Museum, which engaged him to make investigations in mounds and Indian villages.

The partners began their expedition in Mexico City early in January, 1878, and left two weeks later on their four-day stage trip to San Luis Potosí. Parry and Palmer had agreed that Parry would "manage the botanical division" of the expedition, and therefore Palmer was free to make plans to investigate a series of mounds and

[1] Letter to Engelmann, from Davenport, Iowa, Sept. 2, 1877.

[2] Letter, Parry to Palmer, Nov. 24, 1877. This is Charles Sprague Sargent (1841–1927). Director of the Arnold Arboretum, 1873–1927. Author of *Silva of North America* and many other works on trees. See *Dictionary of American Biography* (1937), XVI, 354–55.

other remains in the vicinity of San Luis Potosí. Palmer was assisted in his investigation by a resident of San Luis Potosí, a Dr. Barroeta, and in less than a month had accumulated enough material to fill "three large boxes and two bales." He was also collecting birds; by the end of March he had more than 150 ("stuffed and in good condition"). In mid-February he left on a trip of five or six weeks' duration to the eastern part of the state of San Luis Potosí, and this was followed by a three weeks' trip to Zacatecas. He was disappointed in the "ruins" near Zacatecas, which had been so "mutilated that I found but little." Early in May, he went to Mexico City for a period of more than two months, devoted almost entirely to archaeological work. The last week in July he returned to San Luis Potosí to devote himself to plant collecting for the rest of the year.

Parry in the meantime had remained at San Luis Potosí, collecting plants as opportunity offered. He noted once that he had been "on a short trip to an Hacienda at foot of mts. & picked up a few nice things."[3] After more than three months at San Luis Potosí he sounded less optimistic: "I am still stuck here in the dry-land waiting for rains; only the higher mts offer any fruitful botanizing. . . . I have been studying & sketching Cacti & Agaves for Engel[mann]. . . . E. writes often and sends encouraging letters, which is quite a treat in this thirsty land."[4]

All in all, Parry seems to have had a rather unhappy time at San Luis Potosí. For one thing, he was not entirely pleased with Palmer as a co-worker: "I would gladly turn over the job [of plant collecting] to Palmer but I am not satisfied with his way of doing work. He is persistent and industrious, but not enterprising. Likes to be waited on."[5]

Parry's own enterprise, however, was not phenomenally great. He collected only about 220 numbers, in sets of ten, between the first recorded collection about the first of April and the last on July 22.[6] He left for his home in Iowa about the first of August, soon after Palmer's return from Mexico City. The third day out, traveling by "Mexican cart train" on the old road north to Saltillo, he developed an inflammation of the eyes which kept him nearly blind most of the

[3] Letter to Engelmann, March 11, 1878.
[4] Letter to Gray, May 7, 1878.
[5] Letter to Engelmann, April 18, 1878.
[6] Parry's field notebook, in the library of Iowa State College.

way to Saltillo and caused him to stop over there for ten days to recuperate.[7]

After Parry's departure, Palmer spent more than three months collecting plants, probably wholly in the one state of San Luis Potosí. Few details of his activities are known, but he visited several of the higher mountain ranges south and southeast of the city, some of them fifty to sixty kilometers distant. He visited Álvarez several times and collected extensively in the rich oak forests there. In the midst of his botanical activity he found time to collect some hundreds of archaeological specimens.

His original plan had included a trip to Tampico as soon as he returned from Mexico City in the summer, but he found that yellow fever was raging in the lowlands, and it was not until mid-November that it was considered safe for him to leave for Tula and Tampico.[8] After a circuitous and somewhat interrupted trip by cart, on muleback, and by river steamer, he reached Tampico early in February with an important collection of plants.[9]

Palmer's own collections of 1878 included insects, birds, plants, and archaeological specimens. The large archaeological collection of more than 1,200 specimens was accessioned by the Peabody Museum,[10] the birds form a part of the collections of the Harvard Museum of Comparative Zoology;[11] and many of the insects are in the Museum of Comparative Zoology also, having been acquired from the personal collection of Samuel Scudder.[12]

Parry had taken his own plant collections directly to his home in Davenport, and all those made by Palmer before leaving San Luis Potosí were sent to Davenport also. There Parry arranged the "joint" collection systematically and then assigned the numbers (1–1010) under which the specimens were afterward distributed. This took some months; late in February he noted: "Just finishing sorting up to the end of Compositae numbering up to 555 . . . will finish sorting

[7] Letter to Gray, September 13, 1878.

[8] Letter to Putnam, November 13, 1878.

[9] His route is known in considerable detail, and is set forth in the geographical catalog of this work, under the heading *San Luis Potosí* (*Estado*).

[10] Accession 79–14.

[11] Catalog Nos. 25,931–26,039, 26,567–26,677, 26,679–82.

[12] Samuel Hubbard Scudder (1837–1911). A student of Agassiz. Native and long-time resident of Boston, and an acknowledged expert on various groups of insects, especially Orthoptera. See *Dictionary of American Biography* (1937), XVI, 525–26.

this week; then to distribute, will make up at least 1000 sp. Polypetalae gone to Kew."[13]

This last statement refers to the fact that Parry, upon his own responsibility, was sending a complete set to W. B. Hemsley,[14] with the understanding that the specimens were to be cited in his forthcoming account of the plants of Mexico and Central America.[15] Palmer was not pleased with this arrangement; he considered that Parry, by sending a "Complete set to Kew for nothing" and by setting aside the less complete sets as Palmer's share of the joint venture, had made him a financial loser in the whole affair.

The joint collection was distributed with a printed label lacking any reference to day or month of collection or to exact localities; apparently no exact locality data appear on any of the duplicate sets, or even on Parry's own set of the collection. Definite localities are known only for certain specimens which were sent to Gray for determination,[16] and for a few others.[17] It may be inferred, however, that both Parry and Palmer collected extensively for distribution at the following localities near San Luis Potosí: Escalerilla, Morales, San Rafael, and Sierra de San Miguelito.[18] From the known richness of the flora near Álvarez, and the fact that Palmer made several trips there after Parry's departure, it is also probable that numerous specimens came from there. Doubtless other specimens came from the desert plain which extends eastward from the city of San Luis Potosí.

A list of Nos. 1–1,010 is preserved at the Gray Herbarium[19] and, as noted above, most of the numbers were cited by Hemsley in the *Biologia Centrali-Americana.*

It may be emphasized that this Parry and Palmer collection, although distributed under the names of the two men, was not worked

[13] Letter to Gray, February 23, 1879.

[14] William Botting Hemsley (1843–1924). Botanist at Kew, 1865–67, 1883–1908. Author of and contributor to many published floras. See Britten and Boulger, *Biographical Index of Deceased British and Irish Botanists* (2nd. ed.), 144.

[15] *Biologia Centrali-Americana,* I (1888), iv.

[16] See *Proceedings of the American Academy of Arts and Sciences,* Vol. XV (1879), 25–41.

[17] See *Memoirs of the Gray Herbarium,* Vol. I (1917), 82; also D. S. Correll in *United States Department of Agriculture, Agriculture Monograph No. 11* (1952), 99.

[18] From a series of pencilled notes in Palmer's hand, in the National Herbarium Collection.

[19] *Miscellaneous Plant Lists,* Vol. I (MS).

at jointly to any extent. Parry was in San Luis Potosí from about January 23 to August 3; during this same time Palmer was also in the city for the following periods only: January 23–February 16, March 25–April 5, April 26–May 7, July 26–August 3. Palmer was occupied chiefly with his archaeological work during these times and collected but few plants, but it appears that approximately 700 numbers were collected by Palmer alone between the first of August and the middle of November.

In addition, Palmer collected 130 numbers of plants on his trip from San Luis Potosí to Tampico. These are listed in manuscript at the Gray Herbarium,[20] and most of them were cited by Hemsley in the *Biologia.* The series was arranged systematically, apparently by Gray to whom the plants were turned over for determination, and then assigned numbers 1,030–1,159, inclusive. The number of sets was at least seven. Palmer wrote of this collection: "I have some plants collected by myself in the inter-tropical region between San Luis Potosi and Tampico. These are not incorporated in the sets—as they are my private property—one set has been taken out of them for Gray—another for Sir John Hooker.[21] The balence quite a pile which I will sell to your Herbarium for fifty dollars."[22]

Vasey seems to have accepted this offer, for at least a partial set is now in the National Herbarium. Certain collections are represented in the British Museum (Natural History), at Kew, in the herbarium of John Donnell Smith (now a part of the National Herbarium), at the Academy of Natural Sciences of Philadelphia, and at the Missouri Botanical Garden.

Apparently at least ten sets of the Parry and Palmer collection (Nos. 1–1,010) were distributed. In addition to those for which Canby, Engelmann, Martindale, Redfield, and Sargent had contracted in advance, one set was retained by Parry, one was sent by him to Kew, and one was bought by Ernest Cosson and is now in Paris. The Gray Herbarium and the United States National Herbarium also possess sets, and there were almost certainly various small series in addition to the principal ones.

20 *Ibid.*

21 Evidently Palmer meant Joseph Dalton Hooker.

22 Letter to Vasey, May 5, 1879.

XI TEXAS AND NORTHERN MEXICO, 1879–80

PALMER RETURNED TO CAMBRIDGE, but in two months' time he had made arrangements for another trip to Mexico. This time he was to conduct archaeological investigations in Texas and northern Mexico for the Peabody Museum, and to collect plants for sale by himself.[1] He went directly to San Antonio, Texas, and from this base made a number of trips into different parts of eastern Texas. He traveled by rail as much as possible, for, as a representative of an accredited scientific institution, he was able to secure passes on most of the roads. His archaeological work, which was the primary purpose of his visit to Texas, kept him fully occupied, even though he found few ancient remains at many of the localities from which he had reports. His most satisfactory sites were at Longview, which he worked in July, and near Georgetown, in October.

Most of the information about his travels is derived from a printed itinerary of his plant collections. Since this was made up as an exact copy of Palmer's handwritten notes, which were lacking in accuracy concerning dates, distances, directions, and spelling, some care is necessary in interpreting it.[2]

After trips to Uvalde and Laredo to collect plants, and hurried trips to the northeastern and central counties in October, he spent most of November in the vicinity of Houston, and some time working

[1] Letter from F. W. Putnam, June 24, 1879. See References and Sources No. 123a.

[2] The original, or an early copy of it, in Palmer's hand, is in the National Herbarium.

out from Corpus Christi in December, before returning to San Antonio to pack and ship his collections.

The second, and in some ways more rewarding, phase of his trip began with the new year. He took passage in a coach to Monterrey; this was a considerable venture. There was no regular coach line, but Palmer arranged with other travelers to hire a "private conveyance" for the trip, which they expected to last fifteen to eighteen days. The party reached Monterrey about the middle of February, and Palmer spent nearly a month there and at Guajuco enjoying the sun and collecting plants. He was also much interested in a subject that in later years occupied a great deal of his attention, namely the native uses of plants. He never failed to investigate the city markets in the Mexican towns he visited, and he invariably found interesting native plants and plant products offered for sale.

He finished his botanizing at Monterrey and went up to Saltillo to take advantage of the spring to botanize in the mountains there. He lost no time: "I arrived in this place yesturday and at once arranged to visit a mountain section containing pine and oak start in two days will be absent 8 days then visit another mountain locality for plants and trees finishing up my work at this place by spending some days among the Magueys and Cactus."[3]

The "mountain section containing pine and oak" is accessible at several places east and southeast of Saltillo, and even today supports a rich mountain flora. He secured large collections there, including species which have not been reported again from Coahuila. Then after about a month of working out from Saltillo, he took up his archaeological work again and set out on a trip of two months' duration—a trip which took him to Parras, San Lorenzo de Laguna, and Acatita, and back to Saltillo at the end of June.

His primary objective in this trip to the "Laguna" district of western Coahuila was the exploration of a series of prehistoric burial caves, some of which had been known for half a century. The results of the cave explorations have been summarized by Cordelia A. Studley,[4] but almost nothing is known of Palmer's itineraries or methods of travel in the sparsely populated areas between Parras and Acatita, or in the areas near Coyote and San Lorenzo. The Merwin Catalogue includes several items which apparently have to do with the details

[3] Letter to Engelmann, March 21, 1880.

[4] *Report of the Peabody Museum of American Archaeology and Ethnology*, Vol. III (1884), 233–59.

of this trip and others in Coahuila.[5] The items in question are Nos. 79, 81, 175, and 184; unfortunately the whereabouts of all four are unknown.

Upon returning to Saltillo, Palmer again plunged into his botanical work. He collected in various mountain ranges near Saltillo, and also as far east as Lirios and the high mountains which he had visited first in the spring. About the middle of August, he moved north to Monclova and passed more than a month there investigating burial caves and the flora of several near-by points. Late in September, he returned to Texas by way of Eagle Pass, and two weeks later he returned to San Antonio to conclude his affairs and get back to Cambridge.

Here it may be noted incidentally that to Palmer belongs the distinction of having been the first to call the attention of scientists to the depredations of the boll weevil. He found this insect, which had previously been known to science only through a few museum specimens, so destructive in the cotton-growing areas of Coahuila that the growers were being forced to give up the crop. The incident is interestingly recounted by L. O. Howard.[6]

The collections of 1879–80 are of primary importance. The archaeological materials, especially those from Coahuila, remain among the most important series ever to have come from this area. A total of 1,446 specimens was collected in 1879,[7] and the collections of 1880 included 259 specimens from Coahuila (localities given are San Lorenzo Cave, Monclova Cave, Acatita Cave, and Coyote Cave) and 295 specimens from Texas.[8] In addition to this imposing series of 2,000 specimens, Palmer collected approximately 17,000 specimens of plants, comprising Nos. 1–1,441 and a supplementary series comprising Nos. 2,001–2,147.

The entire collection of plants was reported upon by Sereno Watson.[9] The numbers under which the plants were reported and distributed were arbitrarily assigned after the arrangement of the

[5] See References and Sources No. 45.

[6] See *Smithsonian Miscellaneous Collections,* Vol. LXXXIV (1930), 124–25. See also Palmer's original letter to the Commissioner of Agriculture, published in *Bureau of Entomology Bulletin No. 114,* 62 Cong., 2 sess., *Sen. Doc. 305* (1912), 15.

[7] Peabody Museum Accession 79–87.

[8] Peabody Museum Accession 80–28.

[9] *Proceedings of the American Academy of Arts and Sciences,* Vol. XVII (1882), 316–61; Vol. XVIII (1883), 96–191.

collection in systematic order. The supplementary series, Nos. 2,001–2,147, was handled in the same way, but without relation to the larger collection. These were received, apparently after the sorting of the main series, "in a separate supplementary bundle."

Palmer's method of labeling his plants was to pack all the specimens from a single locality into one bundle, marking this with a reference letter. When forwarding the plants to Harvard he accompanied the shipment by a handwritten key to the reference letters; this key, as mentioned above, was printed for distribution with the plants and is the basis for most of what is known today about his travels in 1879 and 1880. There are thirty-two items identified in the key, designated by the letters of the alphabet with the addition of C½, M½, N½, O½, R½, and AA. Palmer noted that the "letters with half numbers refur to later date of same locality." The key was printed exactly as Palmer wrote it, which explains such egregious errors as the use of "Juraz" for Juárez, "Lerios" for Lirios, and the impossible location given for San Lorenzo de Laguna.

In the Gray Herbarium, accompanying manuscript lists of plants of the collection of 1879–80, is a note indicating the disposition of the several sets, with the numbers of specimens in each, the price, and the date each was sent out. The first ten sets were distributed in May, 1881, but the remainder were not disposed of until later. In the fall of 1882, Palmer advertised for sale the next three sets:

> TEXAN AND MEXICAN PLANTS
>
> FOR SALE, Sets 11, 12 and 13, of my collections in Southwestern Texas and Northern Mexico in 1879–80. They contain about 770, 725 and 680 species respectively—named or soon to be named—besides about 150 duplicate numbers, mostly from different localities. Price $80, $75 and $70 each.
>
> Apply to SERENO WATSON, Cambridge, Mass., who will deliver the sets, and to whom payment may be made.[10]

Following is a complete list of the sets of 1879–80:

[10] *American Naturalist*, Vol. XVI (October, 1882), inner front cover page; Vol. XVI (November, 1882), inner front cover page.

Set Number	*Recipient*	*Date Sent*	*Price*	*Number of Specimens*
1	Harvard Herbarium			1,441
2	W. M. Canby	May 28, 1881	$139	1,441
3	I. C. Martindale	May 28, 1881	139	1,441
4	Kew	May 30, 1881	138	1,433
5	C. J. Maximowicz	May 17	130	1,362
6	Dr. G. Vasey	May 14	124	1,288
7	Addison Brown[11]	May 14	118	1,225
8	E. Boissier	May 17	111	1,153
9	E. Cosson[12]	May 17	105	1,089
10	J. H. Redfield	May 28	98	1,018
11	Donnell Smith[13]	November, 1882	80	952
12	C. G. Pringle[14]	December, 1882	75	888
13	University of Vienna	May, 1884	70	819
14	D. C. Eaton	May 14	74	768
15	C. C. Parry[15]			378
16	C. S. Sargent	May 13	10	77

[11] Addison Brown (1830–1913). Jurist, admiralty lawyer, a founder of the New York Botanical Garden, and co-author with N. L. Britton of the *Illustrated Flora*, 1896–98. See *Dictionary of American Biography* (1937), III, 99–100.

[12] Ernest Saint Charles Cosson (1819–89). French botanist, known for his encouragement of botanical exploration and his work on the botany of French North Africa. His very large private herbarium is now in the Museum National d'Histoire Naturelle, Paris. See *Bulletin de la Société Botanique de France*, Vol. XXXVII (1890), *LXV–LXXXI*.

[13] Captain John Donnell Smith (1829–1928). A graduate of Yale University, officer in the Confederate Army during the Civil War, long-time resident of Baltimore, and for many years active in studies of the flora of Central America. His large botanical library, and herbarium said to contain more than 100,000 specimens were presented to the Smithsonian Institution. See *Annual Report of the United States National Museum*, 1929 (1929), 39–40.

[14] Cyrus Guernsey Pringle (1838–1911). The most famous of professional plant collectors in nineteenth-century America, specialized, from about 1885 on, in Mexican plants. He collected not only herbarium materials, but bulbs and other living plants for nurserymen. His own herbarium is now at the University of Vermont.

[15] Parry's own herbarium was bought for Iowa State College, at Ames, shortly after his death in 1890.

XII WORK FOR THE BUREAU OF ETHNOLOGY, 1881–84

THE SEVEN-YEAR PERIOD ending in 1880 was one of the most active and productive periods of Palmer's life. In it he established himself as a botanical collector of the first rank, each year gathering an important collection from some botanically little-known area. His archaeological collections of 1877 in Utah, of 1878 in San Luis Potosí and elsewhere, and of 1879–80 in Texas and Coahuila were likewise very important in this field and doubtless led to his being considered for the post which he was to hold for the next three years, 1881–84—the post of field worker in the newly established Bureau of Ethnology of the Smithsonian Institution, under the direction of J. W. Powell.[1]

Having finished his work in Texas late in October, 1880, Palmer returned to Cambridge, where he had spent the intervals between trips since 1873. During the winter, Professor Baird was instrumental in securing for him the appointment in the Bureau of Ethnology, and in mid-June, 1881, Palmer came to Washington for instructions. He was appointed for a year, at a monthly salary of $125, the work to consist principally of excavation in the aboriginal mounds of Tennessee and Arkansas. He was allowed to collect woods for Professor Sargent while in the field (presumably as a personal venture), but I

[1] John Wesley Powell (1834–1902). Fought in Civil War, and lost an arm. Taught geology after the war. In 1869, with aid from Congress and the Smithsonian Institution, led expedition down the Colorado River. Director, U.S. Geological and Geographical Survey of the Territories, 1875. Director, U.S. Geological Survey, 1880–94. Director, Bureau of Ethnology Smithsonian Institution, 1879. See *Dictionary of American Biography* (1937), XV, 146–48.

can find no record that he actually carried on such work in addition to his regular duties. Apart from a few plants collected in western North Carolina and sent to Sereno Watson in July, 1881, Palmer seems to have confined himself strictly to his ethnological work.

The years that Palmer spent as a field assistant for the Bureau of Ethnology were not his most productive or most successful ones. His work was for the most part that of a preliminary or exploratory investigator; during much of the time he was in the field he was traveling from one mound area to another, often investigating the authenticity of reported occurrences of relics. He had neither the strength for excavation nor the patience and technical skill required for the meticulous dismemberment of the mounds according to the most approved practices, and so most of the mounds and other aboriginal sites which he visited briefly were subsequently studied in detail by other workers. As far as actual specimens were concerned, he seems to have sent to Washington during his work for the Bureau approximately 2,000 individual collections taken from mounds and other remains.[2] Many of these were of considerable interest, but were for the most part the results of haphazard collecting and so did not always represent complete series of data from individual sites. Palmer's work is occasionally referred to (it seems to me without much warmth) in the comprehensive reports on the mound explorations of the Bureau of Ethnology, published in 1891 and 1894 by Professor Cyrus Thomas, who had been in charge of the work since its inception in 1881. From comparison of Palmer's notes with the published accounts of certain sites mentioned by Thomas, it is evident that the field work was done by Palmer although in most cases no credit is given him.[3]

From the biographer's standpoint, the years 1881–84 are among the most disappointing of Palmer's life. During the entire three-year period of his work for the Bureau of Ethnology, for example, he wrote no more than fifty-four letters that I have been able to trace —this is approximately one letter every three weeks—and with the exception of a few newsy letters to Sereno Watson, most of them

[2] The most important series, as recorded in the Division of Ethnology, U. S. National Museum, are Catalog Nos. 62,751–63,200 (Tennessee and Arkansas, 1881–82), and 75,002–11, 75,018–23, 91,451–91,601, 91,826–96, 92,001–92,033, 90,485–90,508 (all from Georgia, Alabama, and South Carolina, 1884).

[3] Safford quotes Palmer at some length on the "unfair" treatment he received from the workers of the Bureau of Ethnology.

are brief and matter-of-fact reports accompanying shipments of specimens to Cyrus Thomas, to Powell, or to Baird. During the ten months of the field season of 1877, Palmer wrote, in contrast, at least 38 letters that have been preserved, or almost one a week, and many of these were informative summaries of his travels written to Vasey, to Engelmann, or to D. C. Eaton. As a direct consequence we know where he was almost every day during 1877, and it is possible to follow his routes with considerable confidence, while from 1881 to 1884 we can present nothing more than a skeleton account pieced together from these relatively few letters, from Palmer's monthly reports (which sometimes failed to appear monthly) to the director of the Bureau, and from some published data.

We may surmise that Palmer's failure, during these years, to write many letters stemmed from the fact that he was not engaged in botanical collecting, and most of the men he knew were botanists—Parry, Eaton, Vasey, Engelmann, and Watson to name the most prominent. In a sense, as I have pointed out above, these men were his patrons, not really his friends, and it may be that the peculiar indifference which made him more or less self-sufficient during his life manifested itself at this time in this way—if he was not writing about botanical concerns with which these men might aid him, then he simply did not bother to write to them.

Some information about Palmer's work for the first three months of his appointment, in 1881, is to be found in his first monthly reports even though there is a disappointing lack of coherent detail in them. We know that he visited the Cherokee Indians at Yellow Hill, North Carolina, and secured a number of examples of their handiwork. Later in July, he moved over into Tennessee and began the investigation of prehistoric mounds.[4] One of his most important collections of this season was in the McMahan mound near Sevierville, Tennessee; W. H. Holmes lists about seventy articles taken from the excavations here.[5]

About the middle of October, Palmer moved his headquarters to Arkansas, where he spent more than three months working in mounds, chiefly in the bayou country just west of the Mississippi River. In Arkansas it is possible to follow his movements in some detail, thanks to the Arkansas Historical Association, which has published all his

[4] His movements in this state are summarized, under the heading *Tennessee,* in the geographical catalog of the present work.

[5] *Annual Report of the Bureau of Ethnology* (1884), III, 433–89.

notes and manuscripts pertaining to that state.[6] Most of the Arkansas localities which Palmer visited or mentioned are also discussed in the reports published by Cyrus Thomas, and many are illustrated by Thomas.[7]

The part of Arkansas which was intensively explored included, in the words of Thomas, "the lands bordering the Mississippi and lower Arkansas and the area drained by the White and St. Francis rivers." Palmer's work during this first season in the field was centered in Mississippi, Arkansas, Monroe, Phillips and St. Francis counties. Soon after the beginning of the new year, 1882, he found himself unable to continue because of continued rains and consequent floods, and in February he returned to Washington.

As soon as weather permitted, he began work again in the states east of the Mississippi. He was in eastern Tennessee most of the spring, with a few days out to visit Charleston, Missouri, to investigate reports of the making of spurious "mound pottery" for sale to tourists and museums.

Palmer's work for the first fiscal year of his employment with the Bureau of Ethnology seems to have been but moderately successful. The number of specimens which he amassed was large,[8] but Thomas either mentions briefly or passes over entirely many of the localities at which Palmer excavated.[9]

In late summer of 1882, Palmer began active excavations in Indiana, mostly within a radius of fifteen miles from Vincennes.[10] By mid-October, however, he was back in Arkansas, where he continued his excavations until February. This year he concentrated his efforts in an area southeast of Little Rock, in the lowlands along the Arkansas River. Later he visited in quick succession a series of mounds and other remains in Louisiana, Mississippi, Alabama, and Tennessee, before returning to Washington.

[6] This is Item No. 30 of the Merwin Catalogue (see References and Sources No. 45), apparently published verbatim and in its entirety. See also References and Sources No. 88.

[7] *Bureau of Ethnology Bulletin No. 12* (1891); *Annual Report of the Bureau of Ethnology* (1894), XII.

[8] Holmes, *Annual Report of the Bureau of Ethnology* (1884), III, 433–89, cites 365 collections made by Palmer up to about mid-December, 1881. Presumably this number was much increased by the end of the year.

[9] See References and Sources Nos. 117–19.

[10] For details see his report in the archives of the Bureau of American Ethnology (Catalog No. 2,400). By September 24 he had collected 309 ethnological specimens.

The autumn of 1883 was spent mostly in central Arkansas—in Saline, Hot Springs, and Lonoke counties. During the early winter of 1884, Palmer collected in southwestern Alabama, from Mobile north to about Tuscaloosa. He left Mobile late in March and spent several weeks working in a group of mounds near Blakely, Georgia. His work in this area is not mentioned by Thomas, but from the six weeks which he spent there it may be supposed that Palmer collected extensively. Following this he went to northern Georgia, where he visited mounds in White County and the gold mines at Dahlonega. He inspected some mounds in South Carolina on his way to Washington. He rounded out the fiscal year, and his work for the Bureau of Ethnology, with a trip to take measurements on the Knapp mounds near Little Rock. He wrote Watson[11] that he planned to go on to Natchez to measure other mounds there, and then he expected to leave for the Gulf Coast to collect for the New Orleans Exposition.[12]

Congressional appropriations for the New Orleans Exposition were made on July 7, which left the Smithsonian officials with little more than four months in which to prepare their exhibits. Various collectors were at once put in the field. Palmer was asked to go to the Gulf Coast of Florida.[13] The official report on his work says:

The collection of Dr. Palmer was made for the purpose of representing at the World's Fair, in New Orleans, the varied animal resources of the coral reef and sponge regions of Southern and Western Florida. It consisted for the most part of finely prepared specimens of commercial and other sponges, ornamental corals, and the larger species of Crustaceans and Mollusks used as food, and required 65 large shipping cases to transport it to Washington.[14]

Palmer was in the field before the middle of July, leaving Cedar

[11] Letter of June 30 [1884] in Gray Herbarium.

[12] This was properly the "World's Industrial and Cotton Centennial Exposition" which opened December 16, 1884, and closed June 30, 1885. Exhibits showing various aspects of commerce, industry, and natural history were contributed by the United States Government; a special appropriation of $300,000 was made for this purpose, of which $75,000 was set aside for the use of the Smithsonian Institution. See *Annual Report of the Smithsonian Institution*, 1884 (1885), 63–65. The Smithsonian sent numerous exhibits, the total weight of which was 176,000 pounds!

[13] Baird's letter to Secretary of the Treasury, June 2, 1884.

[14] *Annual Report of the Smithsonian Institution*, 1884 (1885), 60.

Keys, Florida, by boat for Key West. He visited the Dry Tortugas and some of the Florida keys and spent most of August working the coastal waters near Key West. Early in September, he collected in Biscayne Bay near Miami, and later the same month he was back in Key West packing and shipping his collections. He completed his work early in October and returned at once to Washington.

In December, 1884, Palmer returned to the southwestern United States. He came by rail from Washington to Yuma, Arizona, and soon set out down the Colorado with a party of travelers to visit the "Grass Camp" of the Cocopa Indians, not far from the old shipyard at Puerta Isabel, Sonora. He wanted particularly to secure material of the grass used by these Indians for food, but was unsuccessful. (He made another, and this time successful, attempt in 1889; the grass proved to be an undescribed species and was named for him, *Uniola palmeri.*) A full account of this 1884 trip may be found in the geographical catalogue of this book, under the heading "Colonia Lerdo."

During the months of January and February, 1885, he was conducting ethnological investigations among the Indians of southern Arizona. His first base of operations was at Mesa, and from there, after nearly a month, he transferred to the Pima Agency at Sacaton. His collecting activities were eminently successful; he shipped a large accumulation of Indian material to the Smithsonian soon after the first of March.[15] After finishing at the Pima Agency he intended to visit the Apaches in southeastern Arizona, but his health would not permit it and he abruptly changed his plans and returned to Washington.

[15] Division of Ethnology, U.S. National Museum. Catalog Nos. 75,989–76,179, from the Pima, Yuma, and Cocopa Indians, Nos. 114,730–55, from Phoenix, Pima Agency, and Mesa, and Nos. 129,840–65 collected in 1884 from the Yaquis.

XIII THREE TRIPS TO MEXICO, 1885–87

THE YEAR 1885 marked Palmer's return to botanical collecting. In mid-July he left for Mexico, having in view not only a botanical collection but also, under the auspices of the Smithsonian Institution, an ethnological study of the Tarahumare Indians of southwestern Chihuahua. Baird had enlisted, to aid Palmer's study, the support of A. R. Shepherd,[1] a former governor of the District of Columbia who was now part owner and general manager of silver mines at Batopilas, in the Tarahumare country, and in an area which had hardly been touched botanically.

The railroads had crept into Mexico since Palmer's visit in 1880, so that he was able to go by rail from El Paso, Texas, as far south as Jiménez, Chihuahua, whence he took a stage for the short journey to Parral, on the edge of the silver-mining country. Here Shepherd had arranged to have him met, and he completed the journey by mule train, six days over the mountains to Batopilas.[2]

[1] Alexander Robey Shepherd (1835–1902). Prominent in government affairs of the District of Columbia, 1861–74, and largely responsible for civic improvements in that period. Unwise handling of finances said to have led to his retirement from politics. He moved to Batopilas in 1880 and converted the mines there into a valuable property. See *Dictionary of American Biography* (1937), XVII, 77–78. For less objective accounts of Shepherd, see *Records of the Columbia Historical Society,* Vol. XIV (1911), 49–66; for a portrait, see the same publication, volume XXIV: facing 192 (pl. VI). 1922. For a first-hand account of the Shepherd family, the silver mine at Batopilas, and life there, see Grant Shepherd, *The Silver Magnet* (New York, 1938).

[2] For discussion of the route followed, see in the geographical catalog of this work, under the heading *Chihuahua* (*Estado*).

The work of the first part of the summer seems to have been principally botanical in nature. Palmer spent August and September collecting in the vicinity of Batopilas, with one or more short trips to near-by points along the Río Batopilas. Then, early in October, he moved to the Indian village of Norogachic, where he stayed for almost two months more, concentrating upon his ethnological collections.[3] Leaving Norogachic, he returned over the same route to Parral, and was back in El Paso by the middle of December with six hundred pounds of specimens.

The plant collections of 1885 were among the first, and remain among the most important, to have come from southwestern Chihuahua. The specimens included approximately 522 numbers, including duplicate and supplementary ones. A printed list of the whole series was prepared at the Gray Herbarium, and reports on the collection were published by Watson[4] and Gray.[5]

For the first time in Palmer's collecting career, the published numbers assigned to his collections were more or less chronological instead of following an arbitrary systematic arrangement. He originally numbered the plants consecutively, in six lots corresponding to locality: San Miguel (Nos. 1–23), San José (24–79), San Miguel (80–250), Frailes (251–297), Yerbabuena (298–313), Cumbre (314–368), and Norogachic (369–455). He added to these the series A to Z and AA to VV, collected at San Miguel and Norogachic respectively, and consisting of economic or useful plants from the two localities. Finally, as was often his custom in other years, he kept separate some or all of the grasses and grasslike plants, so that these had to be given duplicate and supplementary numbers after the rest of the collection had been numbered.

Inconsistencies in the principal series, Nos. 1–455, stem chiefly from Palmer's custom, also followed in later years, of assigning vacant numbers to any plant needing a number. Nos. 322, 330, 332, and 364, for example, are from Norogachic, although the rest of the series from 314 to 368 are from Cumbre. Apparently Palmer had omitted to use these four numbers in his first cataloging of the collections or had lost or discarded the specimens to which they originally pertained, and simply used the numbers again for specimens from a different locality.

[3] In the records of the Division of Ethnology, U. S. National Museum, these include Catalog Nos. 115,776–115,801, and perhaps also 115,802–13.

[4] *Proceedings of the American Academy of Arts and Sciences*, Vol. XXI (1886), 414–45.

[5] *Ibid.*, 378–409.

The number of sets collected in 1885 was probably twelve; Palmer wrote:

I don't think my plants will allow of more than twelve sets—as Pringle sets his at eight dollars per hundred mine will have to sell for the same, though they cost more to collect the locality from which obtained was so far from the Rail Road had not Governor Shepherd rendered me assistance the plants would not realize what they cost to get.[6]

The first set of the collections went to the Gray Herbarium. A set of 434 specimens went to Kew, and one of 430 to St. Petersburgh.[7] Other definite records pertaining to the distribution of the sets seem not to have been kept, but some specimens are known to be at Philadelphia (Academy of Natural Sciences), British Museum (Natural History), Iowa State College, New York Botanical Garden, and United States National Herbarium.

Of the original field notes for 1885, only those for the grasses are known to be extant. These, comprising seventy-four numbers from Batopilas, Cumbre, and Norogachic, are preserved at the National Herbarium.

In 1886, Palmer gave some thought to the selection of his next field of activity. The area finally selected, after consultation with Watson, was the neighborhood of Guadalajara, Jalisco. No naturalist had made extensive collections in Jalisco since the voyages of the *Blossom* and the *Sulphur* half a century before, and the flora of this part of southwestern Mexico was virtually unknown. The railroad did not reach Guadalajara until 1888,[8] so the last two hundred kilometers of Palmer's journey was by stagecoach.

He made his headquarters in Guadalajara from June until mid-November, when he returned to Washington. He spent the entire summer collecting plants at and near the city, which at that time numbered some 70,000 inhabitants. Because of the unique geographical situation of Guadalajara—on the plain at the very brim of the wild and precipitous barranca of the Río Grande de Santiago—he was able to make large collections of the nearly undisturbed native flora without ever traveling more than fifteen kilometers from the city. He made

[6] Letter to Sereno Watson, February 1886.

[7] Letter, Palmer to Watson, April 10, 1886.

[8] See F. W. Powell, *The Railroads of Mexico* (Boston, 1921).

five trips of a few days each to the cotton mill at Río Blanco, which lies at the head of one of the branches of the barranca. He spent a week at a hacienda at river level in the Barranca de Ibarra, some six hundred meters in elevation below Guadalajara, and he made short trips to Tequila and to Chapala. For knowledge of his itinerary and his collections we are almost wholly dependent upon the report published the next year by Watson[9] and upon a manuscript itinerary compiled and annotated by Watson.[10]

The plant collection from Jalisco comprised approximately 770 numbers. There were fourteen major sets, and five "less than half the size of the others."[11] The first set went to the Gray Herbarium; the others were sold at $10 a hundred. Apparently no list of the recipients was kept. The British Museum ordered a set, and a set of 666 specimens was sent to Kew in March, 1887.[12] D. C. Eaton took a set numbering 565 specimens.[13] The collection of this year is represented also by sets in Paris (from the herbarium of Glaziou) and in Geneva (from the Barbey-Boissier herbarium).

In addition to botanical collections in 1886, Palmer took time to assemble representative series of ethnological materials, especially the pottery for which the area around San Pedro and Tonalá is noted. These he presented to the National Museum, a total of about ninety specimens of his own gathering and also a large series collected by an acquaintance who was a resident of Guadalajara.[14]

After a long winter and spring in Washington, Palmer spent the summer and fall of 1887 at Guaymas, Sonora, as a botanical collector for the Division of Botany, United States Department of Agriculture, at a salary of $100 a month.[15] His Jalisco junket had cost him over $700, and his plant specimens probably brought him in a total of a little over $200 more than this. He reached Guaymas at the end of

[9] *Proceedings of the American Academy of Arts and Sciences,* Vol. XXII (1887), 396–465.

[10] Palmer collection, PEI.

[11] Palmer letter to Watson, March 15 [1887].

[12] Palmer letter to Watson, March 15 [1887].

[13] Letter from Palmer to Eaton, April 6 [1887].

[14] See records of the Divsion of Ethnology, U.S.N.M. Nos. 127,959–79, and 132,356–132,426 are Palmer's collections. Nos. 115,792–115,821, and 126,-564–126,693 are attributed in part to Palmer and in part to Rev. D. F. Watkins. If actually *catalogued* by the National Museum in April 1886, as stated in the records, these earlier series cannot have been collected by Palmer.

[15] Letter in PEI files.

May, and after a short trip across the Gulf to Mulegé he settled down to collect plants near Guaymas until late in October.

After a trip by Gulf steamer to the island of San Pedro Mártir, where he stayed nearly two weeks, Palmer spent a few days in Guaymas before crossing again to Baja California to spend a month at Los Angeles Bay. He finally returned to Washington by rail soon after the first of January, 1888, with a collection of some six hundred species of plants. The cost of this year's trip, as he noted, was $814.15 in Mexican currency.

Back in Washington, Palmer himself sorted his plants into sets and sent the principal set to Sereno Watson for determination. Watson prepared a manuscript list of specimens and localities,[16] and also published a report on the entire collection.[17] The highest number in the series is 696, but Nos. 352–99, 420, 425–99, and 607–20 are wanting. There are accordingly about 560 collections in the largest set, including several duplicate and supplementary numbers.

The number of sets was fourteen.[18] Apparently no list of the recipients was kept, though it is known that Set No. 10, 380 specimens, was purchased by D. C. Eaton.[19]

[16] Palmer collection, PEI.

[17] *Proceedings of the American Academy of Arts and Sciences,* Vol. XXIV (1889), 36–82.

[18] Letter, Palmer to Watson, April 11, 1888.

[19] Letter, Palmer to Eaton, May 8, [1888].

XIV COLLECTING FOR THE DEPARTMENT OF AGRICULTURE, 1888–93

GEORGE VASEY, the botanist of the United States Department of Agriculture, became in his later years increasingly impressed with the importance of maintaining a strong national herbarium as a reference collection. To further this end, he encouraged the Department to send collectors and explorers into little-known parts of the United States, primarily to survey the areas for grasses and other plants of possible economic importance but also to make general floristic studies. Therefore, when Palmer returned to Washington in the spring of 1888, looking for a new field of investigation, he was sent at Vasey's behest to California, with instructions to obtain not only herbarium specimens but also photographs of certain characteristic features of the Californian vegetation. One of his objectives was Mt. Whitney, the highest mountain in the United States and, botanically, little explored.

Palmer made his way to California once again, but before actually attempting to reach the base of Mt. Whitney, he went to San Bernardino and discussed the trip with W. G. Wright,[1] an entomologist whom Palmer had met in California twelve years before. Wright decided to join Palmer on the expedition, and together they went

[1] William Greenwood Wright (?1830–1912). Moved to California from New Jersey after the Civil War. He moved to San Bernardino in 1873 and ran a planing mill there until 1897. Palmer had met him in 1876 and knew him as a "collector of insects." His special interest was in Lepidoptera, and he became an authority in his field. His principal published work was *The Butterflies of the West Coast of the United States* (San Francisco, 1905). See Essig, *A History of Entomology,* 802–804.

by rail as far as Caliente, then had to take the stage the last forty miles to Kernville—a town of which Palmer did not approve: "Kernville is an abandoned mining town. . . . It is a whisky-blighted place; saloons occupy the two principal corners in this little hamlet, and on Sundays the streets are carpeted with playing cards and filled with gamblers."

Unfortunately Palmer and Wright found that they had come too early and that snow still remained in the high mountains, making access to Mt. Whitney impossible. They were forced to postpone their expedition, but did take time to collect near Kernville and the near-by Greenhorn Mountains before returning to San Bernardino. Early in July, Palmer made another trip to Kernville, and from there set out into the mountains with pack train and guide. Perhaps the guide was one of the whiskey-blighted individuals whom Palmer had seen on his first visit; at any rate he proved to be incompetent and totally unfamiliar with the country into which they were going, and on the third day he refused to go farther. The party perforce turned back, as Palmer said, "to our first camp in the mountains[.] hear [*sic*] was a long wet meadow."[2] After this second failure, the plan to reach Mt. Whitney was abandoned, and Palmer moved to San Diego, where he spent the rest of the year in indifferent health, but able to collect a few plants, including lichens, near the city and on the islands off the coast of California.

With a re-appointment in 1889 as botanical collector for the Division of Botany,[3] Palmer went by boat to San Quintín on the Pacific coast of Baja California, about one-fourth of the way down the peninsula. His collecting there however was indifferent:

> I collected every day; I did not go very far from the harbor, as it was very hard to walk in the loose sand. . . . I crossed the harbor . . . climbing two of the volcanic peaks. . . . I soon exhausted the field . . . and had no means of reaching the interior. . . . A steamer from the south coming into the harbour I took passage on board of her and went to San Diego.[4]

[2] Letter to Vasey, July 29, 1888. This is presumably the "Long Meadow" cited in the published account of this trip.

[3] At a stipend of $100 a month, plus traveling expenses not to exceed $50 a month.

[4] Typescript in PEI collection.

By the first of March, he was back in San Diego, engaging passage on a schooner for an extended trip halfway down the peninsula of Baja California to the islands of Cedros, San Benito, and Guadalupe. He spent seven days on Guadalupe, noting that some introduced weeds had become more abundant there since his first visit in 1875 and that a few native species were becoming much less abundant than formerly.[5] His most arduous trip was by mule wagon to the mines of Calmallí, inland from Lagoon Head. He returned to San Diego in April, this time ready to leave for the Colorado River as soon as he could arrange to get off.

Years before, perhaps on his first trips to Puerta Isabel in 1869 and 1870, Palmer had been interested in a plant which formed one of the principal foods of the Cocopa Indians—a grass which covered large areas in the tidal lowlands of the lower Colorado River. He had made a special trip from Yuma in December, 1884, to secure material of this grass, but had found that it was completely out of flower and so of no value for specimens. He had made another attempt in November, 1888, but had been unable to obtain satisfactory transportation. Now at last he was successful; he reached Yuma the third week in April, and met there A. B. Alexander and C. H. Gilbert[6] of the United States Fish Commission, who were detailed to make explorations in the lower Colorado and the Gila River for the purpose of ascertaining the existence of shad in those streams.[7] Palmer joined Alexander and Gilbert, and the three men shared expenses of the trip by wagon to Lerdo and thence by boat to the "Grass Camp" of the Cocopas, an area estimated to occupy 40,000 to 50,000 acres. The harvest was in progress upon their arrival, and Palmer was finally able to get good information about the crop and to obtain satisfactory specimens. An account of the trip, and of the locality, was written by Vasey.[8]

In spite of the success of this trip to the Colorado River, the remainder of the spring, and of the year 1889, was an unpleasant interlude in Palmer's life. Early in June, he was kept by a severe respira-

[5] An account of Guadalupe Island by Hemsley in *Gardener's Chronicle*, New Series, Vol. XXIV (1885), 632–33, compares the conditions found by Palmer in 1875 with those noted by E. L. Greene in 1885.

[6] Charles Henry Gilbert (1859–1928). Student of David Starr Jordan; ichthyologist, who taught at the universities of Cincinnati, Indiana, and Stanford. From 1880, affiliated with the United States Fish Commission. See *Dictionary of American Biography* (1937), VII, 267.

[7] *Report of the Commissioner of Fish and Fisheries*, 1888 (1891), 444.

[8] *Report of the Secretary of Agriculture*, 1889 (1890), 393–94.

tory infection from a projected trip to the interior of Baja California. Later the same month he was severely stricken by "enlargement of the liver," and was hospitalized in San Diego. His health continued poor throughout the fall. In mid-November, he underwent an operation to correct a rectal defect, but in December he improved rapidly. His appointment with the Department of Agriculture was renewed, and at the end of the year he left for Guaymas on a new collecting trip.

The plants which Palmer had collected up to this time—in 1888 and 1889—probably included about 725 numbers. (Collections were numbered from 1 to 958, but Nos. 311–599 were not used.) The vascular plants were enumerated in an annotated series of published catalogs, together with abridged versions of the collector's field notes, by Vasey and J. N. Rose.[9] Two of these catalogs comprised the first of the *Contributions from the U.S. National Herbarium,* a series begun at Vasey's instigation.

The Californian collections of 1888 (Nos. 18–247, except 31, 107, and 151) were listed in the first part of the first contribution.[10] Nos. 248–310 were used for lichens and other things collected at San Diego and on the islands off the coast, in the fall of 1888. Some of these were reported in a list published by J. W. Eckfeldt.[11] Field notes of 1888 are preserved in the National Herbarium as follows: Nos. 1–277 (Nos. 248–277 were originally numbered separately by Palmer, 1–30). Nos. 1–11, 11a, and 12–17, not mentioned by Vasey and Rose in their report, were grasses and sedges from the Greenhorn Mountains; Nos. 31 and 151, from the same locality, represented a moss or lichen, and a fungus, respectively. No. 107, from the north fork of the Kern River, appears to have been a shrub.

The collection from San Quintín was reported by Vasey and Rose in a separate contribution, actually the first to appear in print.[12] This

[9] Joseph Nelson Rose (1862–1928). Associated, as a student, with J. M. Coulter. Assistant botanist, United States Department of Agriculture, from 1888, and assistant curator, United States National Museum, from 1896. Known especially for his work on Mexican plants, and responsible for most of the identifications of Palmer's later Mexican collections. See *Dictionary of American Biography* (1937), XVI, 159–61.

[10] *Contributions from the United States National Herbarium* (1890), I, 1–8.

[11] *Contributions from the United States National Herbarium* (1893), I, 291–92.

[12] *Proceedings of the United States National Museum,* Vol. XI (1889), 527–36. A few specimens from Lagoon Head were also reported.

series comprised Nos. 600–741. There are several missing numbers in the series as reported, possibly because Palmer's original field catalog was lost. It was sent to Washington with the plants, but was thought to have been overlooked when the shipment was unpacked. Palmer made up a second catalog from memory, so inconsistencies or apparent errors in this series of numbers are probably chargeable to this loss. The number of sets collected at San Quintín was at least seven. Palmer noted: "I think you will find several sets it occurred to me that you wished sufficient for your exchanges."[13] Vasey's reply notes that "Mr. Rose makes something over 1000 specimens beside the lichens," and that the Department of Agriculture is buying the whole collection, a total of 1,200 specimens.[14] Vasey also notes that sets of "your plants" (year not specified, but presumably California collections of 1888, or San Quintín collections, or both), were sent to Berlin and Paris, and to N. L. Britton,[15] J. D. Smith, E. L. Greene,[16] and (a partial set) to the California Academy of Sciences.

The second collection of 1889, that from Lagoon Head, from the islands off Baja California, and from Lerdo, comprised Nos. 651–958 (Nos. 651–741 duplicated the earlier series from San Quintín), all of which were fully reported by Vasey and Rose.[17] The number of sets collected is unknown. Field notes for Nos. 651–958 (651–741 pertaining to the coastal islands only, not San Quintín), are preserved in the National Herbarium.

For the two years beginning in January of 1890, Palmer was almost continuously in the field, collecting in five Mexican states on

[13] Letter to Vasey, March 1, 1889.

[14] Letter to Palmer, PEI files, May 29, 1889.

[15] Nathaniel Lord Britton (1859–1934). American botanist, active in organization of New York Botanical Garden and its first director, 1896–1927. Author of the *Illustrated Flora of Northern United States and Canada* and many other works. In 1889, he was an instructor at Columbia University. His own herbarium is now at the New York Botanical Garden. See *Torreya*, Vol. XXXIV (1934), 84.

[16] Edward Lee Greene (1843–1915). American botanist, clergyman, moved to Colorado in 1870. Was ordained in Episcopal church in 1873 and preached for some years. Had wide field knowledge of West American plants, and strong independent ideas about systematic botany and nomenclature. Became Roman Catholic in 1885. Taught botany at University of California, 1885–95; Catholic University, 1895–1904. Associate of Smithsonian Institution, 1904–14. His herbarium was left to Notre Dame University. See *Dictionary of American Biography* (1937), VII, 564–65.

[17] *Contributions from the United States National Herbarium* (1890), I, 9–28.

the Pacific coast, and in Arizona. An account of his work is hardly more than a travelogue.

He reached Guaymas, Sonora, by steamer, early in January, made a two-week trip to the tip of Baja California, visited the islands of Raza and San Pedro Mártir, collected at Santa Águeda and Santa Rosalía on the Baja California side of the Gulf, returned to Guaymas, and left at once for two weeks at Álamos, Sonora. He packed all this traveling into three months' time.

In mid-April, he went by rail to Fort Huachuca in southeastern Arizona; there he collected for nearly a month before going on to Fort Apache in the White Mountains. As an aside, indicating the difficulties of travel in the Apache country even as late as 1890, it may be noticed that in order to get from a point about 125 miles *south* of Fort Apache he had to go by rail to Albuquerque, New Mexico, thence by rail to Holbrook (more than 100 miles *north* of Fort Apache), and finally, the last two days, by stage. On the way south from Holbrook, he stopped by chance at the ranch of a former acquaintance, and was persuaded by friendship and good collecting to stop over for ten days; this was at Willow Springs. Early in July, he terminated the work in Arizona and went to San Francisco to wait for word of the beginning of the autumn rains in Sonora and Baja California.

Late in August, he went again to Guaymas, and from there on trips to Agiabampo, Álamos, and Carmen Island. In October, he began preparations for a longer trip, this time to Colima, a territory unfamiliar to him and little worked by naturalists. The first part of this journey was accomplished by steamer to Manzanillo, the great port of western Mexico, where Palmer spent nearly six weeks. He collected in the vicinity of Manzanillo Bay until early in January, 1891, then spent a few weeks inland at the city of Colima and a short time at Armería. Finishing his Colima collecting, he returned to Manzanillo, went north to Guaymas, and from there set out on a long trip home to Washington.

Mexico, however, remained a fertile field for Palmer, and after a three months' stay in Washington he went to Guaymas about the first of August, in continuation of his work for the Division of Botany, to prepare for a trip to Sinaloa. Two weeks later he was in Culiacán. He visited Imala in late August, and again, while enroute to Lodiego, in September. After another short stay at Culiacán, he returned to Guaymas.

The period between mid-December, 1891, and April, 1892, was taken up by a trip to Tepic. He disembarked at San Blas, and spent the first two months of the year collecting in the vicinity of the city of Tepic, in the localities known for the classic collections of the botanists of the *Blossom.* Palmer's collecting in this area came to a halt, when he was disabled for some weeks with a rheumatic infection and was forced to return to California to recuperate, about the first of May.

He spent the summer of 1892 in California, still in the employ of the Division of Botany, staying about two weeks at Chico, collecting for a time in the vicinity of San Francisco (chiefly in Marin County), making a trip to Placer and Eldorado counties and even one trip to Mt. Shasta. On this Mt. Shasta excursion he spent nearly three weeks, chiefly in the vicinity of Sisson. Then he returned to San Francisco and finished the work of the year by a trip to Tulare and Visalia, from which he returned about September 10.

The plant collections made during the three-year period ending in 1892 were numbered consecutively from 1 to about 2,780, the longest series of Palmer's career. They were studied and distributed in several lots, and more than half of them were reported upon in detail by Vasey and Rose, or by Rose alone, in a series of five papers.[18] The published reports cover Nos. 1–1,410 (a few numbers missing), and 1,810–12. No reports were published on the 1891–92 collections from Sinaloa and Nayarit, or on the California collections of 1892. A set of field notes covering this same period is preserved. Nos. 1–144, 148–61, 177–210, and 265–72 are at the National Herbarium, and Nos. 145–47, 162–76, 211–64, 273–1,410, 1,413–1,809, 1,813–2,099, and 2,300–2,780, are in the manuscript collection of the Division of Plant Exploration and Introduction. Nos. 450–59 are repeated, 2,100–2,299 were not used, and 2,031–40 apply to a series from Chico, California, but also seem to have been used for a series from Tepic, for which no notes are preserved.

Palmer's field notes beginning about with this period were in some cases very detailed, although sometimes difficult to interpret because of his unorthodox composition and orthography. He usually included mention of the size and general aspect of the plant itself, as well as characters of the flowers and fruit, the uses if any, and the habitat. As his notes were but rarely, and never consistently, copied onto the

[18] *Contributions from the United States National Herbarium* (1890–95), I, 63–90, 91–116, 117–27, 129–34, 293–392.

printed labels which were distributed with the sets of plants, these original field catalogs on newspaper stock constitute the only sources of information about his collections beyond the bare localities given on the labels and the abridged notes which were included in the published papers by Rose and Vasey.

The collections numbered 1–2,780 seem to have been distributed in at least four (probably more) different lots. Records of some of the distributions have been preserved at the National Herbarium. No records are available for the early numbers (probably Nos. 1–885), and partial records only for Nos. 1,413–2,040 (see below). There are complete records, however, for the California collections of 1892 (presumably Nos. 2,031–2,768), and for a series of about 500 numbers collected in 1890–91 (perhaps the series including Nos. 886–1,410, from the state of Colima). This last series will be considered first:

Set Number	*Recipient*	*Number of Specimens*
1	U. S. National Herbarium	525 (est.)
2	Royal Botanic Gardens, Kew	476
3	Gray Herbarium	464
4	New York	435
5	John Donnell Smith	394
6	California Academy of Sciences	354
7	British Museum, Natural History	299
8	Berlin	259
9	De Candolle Herbarium, Geneva	217
10	T. S. Brandegee[19]	163
11	St. Petersburgh	141
12	Missouri Botanical Garden	104

The "California" collections of 1892, presumably Nos. 2,031–2,768, were distributed as follows:

Set Number	*Recipient*	*Number of Specimens*[20]
1	U. S. National Herbarium	538
2	C. E. Bessey[21]	[564] (est.)
3	C. E. Bessey	[400] (est.)

[19] Townshend Stith Brandegee (1843–1925). A civil engineer who turned later in life to botany. He began the study of Californian and Lower Californian floras a few years before this time. The Brandegee Herbarium was donated to the University of California, at Berkeley. See *University of California Publications in Botany,* Vol. XIII (1926), 155–78.

[20] Nos. 2,100–2,299 were omitted by the collector from his numbered series.

4	Biltmore Herbarium[22]	327
5	W. M. Canby	265
6	Calcutta	188
7	Berlin	135
8	M. E. Jones[23]	96
9	New York	62
10	L. H. Pammel[24]	38
11	W. S. Moffatt, Chicago[25]	24
12	A. S. Hitchcock, Manhattan, Kansas[26]	18

[21] Charles Edwin Bessey (1845–1915). Botanist and administrator, best remembered for his publications toward a natural system of classification of vascular plants. He became professor of botany at the University of Nebraska in 1884, and was connected with that institution until his death. For a sketch of his life see *American Journal of Botany,* Vol. II (1915), 505–18, or *Dictionary of American Biography,* II (1937), 229. In the list at the National Herbarium the numbers of specimens in Bessey's sets are not recorded.

[22] The Biltmore Herbarium was established at Biltmore, North Carolina, by George W. Vanderbilt. It grew to contain approximately 100,000 specimens, but was inundated and damaged by floods of July 15 and 16, 1916. Active effort by Chauncey Delos Beadle, the curator of the herbarium at the time of the flood, resulted in the salvage of most of the types and other especially valuable specimens. The undamaged remainder, including about 25,000 specimens, was presented to the United States National Museum in 1917 by Mrs. Vanderbilt, the widow of the founder. I am indebted to Conrad V. Morton for most of the above information.

[23] Marcus Eugene Jones (1852–1934). Botanist and botanical explorer, particularly of the Great Basin. His herbarium became the property of Pomona College, Claremont, California. For an interesting sketch of Jones, with reference to many biographical sources, see Joseph Ewan, *Rocky Mountain Naturalists* (Denver, 1950), 79–88.

[24] Louis Hermann Pammel (1862–1931). Botanist and conservationist, worked as a young man under Farlow and Trelease. Head of department of botany at Iowa State College, Ames, Iowa, from 1889. See *Dictionary of American Biography* (1937), XIV, 197–98.

[25] Will Sayer Moffatt (1847–1941). M. D., Hahnemann Medical College, Chicago, 1868. Lived and practiced medicine in the vicinity of Chicago. Was an enthusiastic amateur botanist and the author of several papers, the best known of which was "The Higher Fungi of the Chicago Region," *Natural History Survey* [of the Chicago Academy of Sciences] *Bulletin No. 7.* Part I (1909), "The Hymenomycetes" (pp. 1–156, 24 plates); Part II (1923), "The Gastromycetes [*sic*] (pp. 1–24, 26 plates). His herbarium ultimately passed into the custody of the University of Illinois. See George D. Fuller, "Will Sayer Moffatt," *Transactions of the Illinois Academy of Science,* Vol. XXXVII (1944), 132.

[26] Albert Spear Hitchcock (1865–1935). Known in later life as an agrostologist. From 1892 to 1901 he was professor of botany at Kansas State College, Manhattan, Kansas, and was active in building up the herbarium there.

The number of sets collected was probably large throughout this three-year period, but Palmer made no consistent effort to build up uniform sets. A complete record of Nos. 1,413–2,040 shows that there were as many as thirty-eight duplicate sets of some numbers, but the last sixteen sets included fewer than 10 numbers each, whereas the first ten sets included 585, 508, 444, 370, 308, 254, 203, 175, 139, and 107 numbers. Since the series from 1,413 to 2,040 comprises 628 numbers, the sets were probably numbered after the removal of the original series for the National Herbarium, so the set containing 585 numbers was actually the largest duplicate set.

The field season of 1893, Palmer's last as a field agent of the Division of Botany of the Department of Agriculture, was spent in a botanical survey of the Snake River Plains of southern Idaho, under the supervision of F. V. Coville, the new botanist of the Department of Agriculture, who had succeeded to the post after the death of Vasey on March 4, 1893.[27] The principal center of the Department's operations in Idaho was at Pocatello, which Palmer reached on May 6, before the spring was well under way. He traveled by train as much as possible, but found it necessary to visit many areas by stage. He visited successively Market Lake, Shoshone, and Blue Lakes; Blackfoot, Arco, and Big Butte; Idaho Falls and Dubois; Blackfoot and Big Butte; Shoshone and Blue Lakes. He left for Washington, D. C., early in September. Detailed accounts of his travels will be found in the geographical catalog of his work under the entries headed *Idaho, Blackfoot,* and *Pocatello*. His journal and his book of field notes are preserved in the National Herbarium, making it possible to follow his activities in detail.

The plants collected in 1893 were distributed under Nos. 1–603. The principal series comprises Nos. 1–550, arranged more or less chronologically, as follows: Early numbers collected in May and June were cataloged in groups according to locality, but not arranged chronologically within the groups (Nos. 2–58, Pocatello; 59–87, Blue

[27] Frederick Vernon Coville (1867–1937). Botanist of the U. S. Department of Agriculture, and curator of the National Herbarium. He succeeded George Vasey at the latter's death. Under Coville's leadership the National Herbarium was returned to the official custody of the Smithsonian Institution and its functions were much expanded. He was known widely for his pioneer work in cultivation of desirable strains of the wild blueberry. See *Journal of the Washington Academy of Sciences,* Vol. XXVII (1937), 83–84.

Lake; 88–121, Shoshone Falls; 122–159, Shoshone). Later collections, up to and including 550, are strictly chronological in arrangement.

A second series, Nos. 551–602, consists of miscellaneous specimens, mostly from Big Butte Station or Blackfoot, arranged systematically before numbering, and entered in the catalog by some person other than Palmer. This second series presumably includes specimens overlooked by Palmer in his first cataloging, or those which he mixed with collections of other species.

A list of the duplicate sets of each number is preserved at the National Herbarium. The number of duplicate sets was twenty-one; the first ten included 458, 390, 335, 273, 219, 177, 132, 106, 79, and 58 numbers, respectively. In addition to the original set at the National Herbarium, others are located at the Gray Herbarium, the Chicago Natural History Museum, the Missouri Botanical Garden, the New York Botanical Garden, the University of Wyoming, the California Academy of Sciences, and the University of California at Berkeley.

XV THE LAST YEARS, 1894–1911

AFTER THE CONCLUSION of his work for the Department of Agriculture in 1893, Palmer made his home for most of the time in Washington. He did make eleven trips to Mexico and one short excursion to Cuba during the remaining sixteen years of his life, but his adventures in these later years make less interesting telling than do those of the early days. After 1890, the railroads had reached the important Mexican cities and even into the timber country in western Durango, and this increasing ease of transportation to the urban areas, and his advancing years, combined to make it easiest for him to limit his collecting to the vicinity of the larger cities. As a result many of his specimens of the period between 1894 and 1910 are from Acapulco, Durango, Chihuahua, Saltillo, San Luis Potosí, Victoria, or Tampico. He also paid more and more attention to the city markets in which plants were sold and to the many purposes for which plants were used, and some of his most valuable contributions were made by his notes on economic plants.[1]

In spite of his years, however, he did manage to get into some places that have not been visited by other collectors before or since his time. When he was seventy-five years old he undertook a strenuous trip into northwestern Durango, including eight days on horseback to collect at San Ramón. Even on his last trip, a year before his death

[1] His ethnological collections in these later years were almost all turned over to the National Museum as gifts from the collector, and number approximately 300. They are enumerated in the records of the Division of Ethnology, United States National Museum.

at the age of eighty, he felt strong enough to go on a three-day excursion by a coastwise schooner to the island of Juana Ramírez in the hot lowlands of Veracruz.

Beginning in 1899, and continuing until the end of his life, Palmer was for long periods on the rolls of the Department of Agriculture as a "laborer" or as an "expert." This was an arrangement made by Coville to enable Palmer to work with the botanists of the Division (principally Rose, and L. H. Dewey[2]), in the arranging and labeling of his collections and notes on economic plants of Mexico. Palmer put the matter in his own way: "Mr. Coville has prevailed upon me to stay hear this summer to aid him in working up much of the Economic material collected by me."[3]

This was a valuable project, but the work had been put off almost too long. Palmer was asked to supply, from memory or from incomplete notes, data pertaining to specimens some of which dated back many years. Much of value was saved, however, in spite of the difficulty of the task, and many subsequent publications dealing with Mexican plants owe a debt to the data supplied with Palmer's specimens. He worked at this during the periods, usually in the winter months, when he was in Washington. His appointments were terminated on occasions when he went off to collect in Mexico, and renewed upon his return. Perhaps it was Coville's way of providing him with a means of support, however inadequate, during the times when his current collections were not bringing in any revenues.

As far as I have been able to learn, Palmer's later trips to Mexico were financed (with one or two exceptions) with little or no outside aid, merely by the sales of sets of his plants. Few records of these transactions have been preserved, however, among his papers.

During the winter of 1894–95 Palmer spent about five and one-half months collecting at Acapulco, Guerrero, which at that time was a small coastal town most easily accessible (as he reached it) by steamer from San Francisco. The collection was made "for several scientific institutions, among them Harvard University."[4] A part of

[2] Lyster Hoxie Dewey (1865–1944). Botanist, U. S. Department of Agriculture, from 1890 until his retirement in 1935. His early work was in agrostology and the study of noxious weeds; later he became widely known as a specialist on plant fibers other than cotton. See *Science*, Vol. CI (1945), 11–12.

[3] Letter to Trelease, April 22, 1899.

[4] Letter from B. L. Robinson, September 8, 1894.

the collection was the subject of a published report by M. L. Fernald,[5] and Frank Lamson-Scribner[6] reported upon the grasses. Probably the largest set (out of twelve) went to the Gray Herbarium in return for determinations. The sets apparently varied considerably in size; the largest included 635 numbers. Notes by Palmer among the Rose correspondence in the National Herbarium indicate that while Set 5 was priced at $45.50 (that is, presumably 455 specimens at $0.10 each), Set 10 was valued at $28.00, and Set 11 at $25.50.

A complete set of the field notes for 1894–95 (except Nos. 249 and 635) is in the collection of the Division of Plant Exploration and Introduction.

The numbers assigned to the plant collections of this season have little meaning, although they are roughly chronological in arrangement. Palmer's method of "cataloguing" as in other years, was to wait until a number of collections had accumulated, then to assemble the sets and assign numbers to the collections according to locality and date. Presumably he worked from memory, but there is no evidence for or against this except that in many instances during his career he furnished locality and other data from memory (a notable instance was in 1889 when a part of his notes was lost), and it may be supposed that it was his usual custom to depend upon memory. While working out from Acapulco, he seems to have kept no specific locality records, being content to let the one general locality do for all his collections, but he made some attempt to date the specimens. He collected until the end of December before beginning to "catalogue"; according to his numbers which he then assigned, he had accumulated by this time about 325 collections of about 12 specimens each. Presumably most of the month of January was spent in the cataloging, for he collected fewer than 50 additional numbers during the month. By March 5, he had "catalogued" 420 numbers out of 600 collected, and by March 23 he had reached number 570. The cataloging seems to have been finished on or before the first of April.

Apparently he finished all actual collecting about March 10, and left for San Francisco the first of April.

One of the very few personal accounts of Palmer that I have been able to obtain was given me some years ago by the late Major Edward

[5] *Proceedings of the American Academy of Arts and Sciences,* Vol. XXXIII (1897), 86–94.

[6] *United States Department of Agriculture, Division of Agrostology Bulletin No. 4* (1897), 7–11.

A. Goldman,[7] who was collecting mammals about Acapulco the winter of 1894–95; the two men were guests at the same hotel, and on occasion rode together on short collecting trips into the near-by hills. Palmer's collecting during this season was limited by the extent of these one- or two-day trips on horseback. Major Goldman remembered Palmer as an old man (he was in his early sixties), not strong but active, and continuously at work, pressing and changing blotters during long hours, joking and talking with the other guests at the hotel.

Palmer spent the summer of 1896 collecting in the state of Durango. He left Washington early in March and made his headquarters at the city of Durango until mid-November. He reached Durango early enough to visit Santiago Papasquiaro and Mina Tres Reyes in order to collect the spring flora following the melting of the snow in the mountains (mid-April). Later he visited Nombre de Dios; still later he returned to Santiago Papasquiaro, visited Dos Cajetes, and collected rather extensively about Durango itself. He returned to Washington by way of San Pedro, Coahuila, and Eagle Pass.

The collection of this year comprised 974 numbers, in about ten sets; the fullest set is presumably at the Gray Herbarium, where the determinations were made.[8] Sets are known to be at Berlin, Chicago Natural History Museum, Gray Herbarium, Missouri Botanical Garden, New York Botanical Garden, and the National Herbarium. Set 9 comprised 628 specimens. Nearly complete sets of the field notes are in the Gray Herbarium and in the Division of Plant Exploration and Introduction.

In May of 1897, Palmer was authorized by the Department of Agriculture to furnish a "report on the timber trees of Mexico, the wood of which is now commercially imported into this country, and on the trees growing successfully in the arid regions of Mexico." I cannot find that this somewhat grandiose project was ever completed,

[7] Edward Alphonso Goldman (1873–1946). Mammalogist and field biologist, associated from 1892 to 1906 with Edward William Nelson in biological exploration of Mexico. A summary of their work was published after Goldman's death. See Edward Alphonso Goldman, "Biological Investigations in Mexico," *Smithsonian Miscellaneous Collections*, Vol. CXV (1951); also *Journal of the Washington Academy of Sciences*, Vol. XXXVII (1947), 35–36.

[8] Note by Palmer in the National Herbarium collection.

but Palmer did undertake it, choosing the western states of Mexico for his summer's work, and leaving Washington late in May for Colima. J. N. Rose traveled with him, by way of El Paso and probably Nogales and Guaymas, as far as Mazatlán. Palmer then went on alone to Manzanillo and Colima, which he reached before July 1. He stayed in and near Colima until sometime in August, collecting 176 numbers of plants, then transferred himself to Guaymas where he stayed until late in October, visiting and collecting in the meantime at Topolobampo, Sinaloa, and several spots near Guaymas. His plant collections for the year comprised probably 279 (or 283) numbers; a nearly complete set of field notes is in the Division of Plant Exploration and Introduction. The number of sets collected is unknown.

The relatively small number of plants collected by Palmer in 1897 seems to be in part the result of his work on the timber trees of Mexico, a task which necessitated the making of wood samples, and other activities aside from general plant collecting. He seems to have been weakened, also, by serious attacks of fever, first at Colima and later at Guaymas.

In 1898, Palmer chose to visit Saltillo, which he reached about mid-April; apparently he made his headquarters in this city until after the middle of July, when he went on to San Luis Potosí. While at Saltillo on this first stay, he collected 277 numbers. He employed his usual method of letting his collections accumulate before numbering them, for he noted that when he had collected about 200 "species," he had "catalogued" but 135.[9] At the National Herbarium is a nearly complete set of field notes which includes Nos. 9–277 and numerous supplementary numbers (60½, 63½, etc.); another nearly complete set is at the Gray Herbarium.

Leaving Saltillo in July, Palmer visited San Luis Potosí, where he collected chiefly the "economical" plants on sale in the city market. The collection numbers are approximately 588–742, inclusive; an incomplete set of notes for these is at the Gray Herbarium. He then traveled through the state of Guanajuato, primarily to obtain pictures and notes relative to the economic uses of plants. Returning to Saltillo (probably early in September), he collected about 150 additional numbers of plants. His intention was to return to Washington at once, but being unable to go by way of New Orleans as he had intended, because of the prevalence of yellow fever there, he spent

[9] Letter to Rose, June 5, 1898.

Hacienda of Peotillos, San Luis Potosí, as it looks today.
This is the gate to the stables.

The Market Place at Monterrey, Nuevo León, in Palmer's time;
Cerro de la Silla in the distance.

From a photograph in the Palmer Collection
Division of Plant Exploration and Introduction

Courtesy Smithsonian Institution

Edward Palmer
From a photograph thought to have been made soon after the Civil War.

the month of October in a trip to the cities of Parras and Torreón in Coahuila, to Mapimí, in Durango, and to the city of Zacatecas. Many of his collections at these places were from the city markets. At Zacatecas he was stricken with what he later reported as pneumonia, and was forced to return to Saltillo as soon as he could move; about the middle of November he left for Washington.

The collections of 1898 included at least 814 numbers, but no complete set of field notes is known to be extant. The set at the National Herbarium includes Nos. 9–375, 377–552, 555–87, 704, 786–803, 806–13. The series 588–785 was apparently used for collections from San Luis Potosí (588–742) and from Zacatecas (743–85), as indicated by a manuscript list in the Division of Plant Exploration and Introduction. Nos. 553, 804, and 805 are listed among those received by the Missouri Botanical Garden. The entire series, as far as known, is listed below:

Specimen Numbers	*Place Collected*	*Date*
1–277	Saltillo	April 15–June 30
278–375	Saltillo	September
376–422	Saltillo	September
423–54	Parras	October 6–11
455–516	Torreón	October 13–20
516½–53	Mapimí	October 21–23
554	(missing)	
555–56	Mapimí	October 21–23
557–85	Saltillo	November 2–5
586–87	Mapimí	October 21–23
588–742	San Luis Potosí	July 20–August ?10
743–85	Zacatecas	October 24–November 2
786–88	Torreón	October 13–20
789	Parras	October 6–11
790–803	Saltillo	September
804–805	Parras	October 6–11
806–14	?Saltillo	September

The number of sets collected in 1898 was probably about ten; partial sets are known to be at Washington, Chicago, Gray Herbarium, Missouri Botanical Garden, New York Botanical Garden, University of California, and Geneva.

Palmer's only botanical trip of 1899 (and his only trip between 1898 and 1902) was a short visit in May to Mammoth Cave, Kentucky. Nothing is known of this trip except that he collected a few plants; he presented 215 specimens to the Smithsonian Institution, and approximately one-fourth this number was accessioned by the National Herbarium. Presumably he made a collection of 50 or 60 numbers and gave the original set and all duplicates to the National Herbarium; occasionally one of these specimens turns up elsewhere (e.g. at New York).

From July, 1899, when he began to work over his economic collections for the Department of Agriculture, until the termination of his appointment in January, 1902, he seems to have been in Washington nearly continuously. In 1902, he joined C. L. Pollard[10] and William Palmer[11] on a trip to eastern Cuba. His companions were sponsored by the Smithsonian Institution, while he apparently went independently. The trip resulted in "an interesting collection of plants, birds, bats, insects, and marine invertebrates."[12] The party reached Baracoa, near the eastern tip of the island, after a trip of five days by steamer from Havana, and promptly sought permission to extend their stay. Pollard wrote:

> This section of the island is of a far more tropical cast than Western Cuba, and the results of two days' collecting are so good that I take this opportunity of suggesting that we be permitted to remain on the island until March 1. This will give us six weeks clear in Cuba.[13]

This permission was granted, and the party did not return to Havana until about the end of February. What is known of the itinerary on the island is set forth in the geographical catalog of this work,

[10] Charles Louis Pollard (1872–1945). Botanist; assistant curator, United States Department of Agriculture, 1894–95; Division of Plants, United States National Museum, 1895–1903; editor, *Plant World*, 1899–1907. See *American Men of Science* (1938), 1,125.

[11] William Palmer (1856–1921). Taxidermist, naturalist, and zoological collector. Born in England (no relation to Edward Palmer), the son of Joseph Palmer, who came to the United States in 1873 and became a taxidermist and modeler at the United States National Museum. William soon followed in his father's work and continued to work for the Museum until his death. See *Auk*, Vol. XXXIX (1922), 305–21.

[12] *Annual Report of the Smithsonian Institution*, 1902 (1903), 35.

[13] Letter to Coville, in PEI files, January 26, 1902.

under the entry *Cuba.* Plant collections included about 400 numbers, distributed under the names of all three collectors, of Pollard and William Palmer, or of Edward Palmer alone. Probably the number of sets was small, and apparently no list of specimens and no field notes were preserved. The principal set of specimens is in the National Herbarium.

In August of the same year, after a few months in Washington, Edward Palmer began operations again in San Luis Potosí. He made two trips out of the city to the mountains at Álvarez—by rail where in 1878 he had gone on horseback—and a trip to Las Canoas in the eastern lowlands, but most of his time in San Luis Potosí he spent in an attempt to develop methods of canning "Tuna Juice, Pulque and Agua Miel."[14] He wrote that he had spent $100 and a month's time, on abortive attempts at canning, but was discouraged because of the continued bursting of the sealed cans and was being forced to admit his failure.[15]

After leaving San Luis Potosí early in November, he spent a few weeks in Saltillo before returning to Washington.

The Mexican collections of 1902 included Nos. 1–454, and perhaps also 455–75. An incomplete series of the field notes for Nos. 27–475 is filed at the Gray Herbarium, and a second partial set is in the files of the Division of Plant Exploration and Introduction. The number of sets collected was probably at least ten; partial sets are known to be at Washington, Chicago, Gray Herbarium, New York Botanical Garden, Missouri Botanical Garden, University of California, California Academy of Sciences, and Copenhagen. The numbered series of collections was approximately as follows:

Specimen Numbers	*Place Collected*	*Date*
1–25		
26–44	San Luis Potosí market	August 18–20
45–86	Álvarez	September 5–10
87–100	San Luis Potosí market	September 12–16
101–40	Álvarez	September 5–10

[14] The *tuna* is the fruit of any one of several species of *Opuntia; agua miel* is the sweet liquid extracted from the base of the inflorescence of certain species of *Agave,* and *pulque* is a fermented drink made from this liquid. San Luis Potosí is located in an area where Opuntias are extremely abundant, and the fruits form an important article of commerce. Pulque is a cheap and popular beverage in many areas.

[15] Letter to Rose, September 23, 1902.

141–213	Álvarez	September 28–October 3
214–77	Las Canoas	October 15–21
278–370	Saltillo	November 10–20
371–441	Concepción del Oro	November 22
442–52	Álvarez	September 28–October 3
453–54	San Luis Potosí market	September 12–16
455–75		

After his return from San Luis Potosí in December, 1902, Palmer seems to have spent most of his time in Washington until May, 1904, when he went to the city of San Luis Potosí again. Almost nothing is known about his whereabouts during the year 1903, but if he made any trips out of Washington they were doubtless of short duration. From January to May, 1904, he was employed as an "expert" by the Bureau of Plant Industry, in Washington, to continue the work on his notes and specimens which he had begun in 1899 and had continued in 1900 and 1901.

From May through July, he collected in the state of San Luis Potosí, visiting Río Verde, San Dieguito, Santa María del Río, and Álvarez. During the months of August, September, and October he made his headquarters at Saltillo, making several trips out from that place; these are discussed under *Saltillo* in the geographical catalog of this book. Sometime in November he returned to Washington.

Palmer was troubled by ill health this summer, and for much of the time during September and October, especially, he devoted as much time and strength as he had to the collection of various living succulents for study by J. N. Rose rather than to the more strenuous general collecting. After about the first of September, he seems to have confined himself to the immediate vicinity of Saltillo.

The herbarium specimens collected in 1904 seem to have comprised 476 numbers, approximately as follows:

Specimen Numbers	*Place Collected*	*Date*
1–61	Río Verde	June 2–8
62–84	"Half Moon Lake," near Río Verde	June 2–8
84½–154	San Dieguito	June 13–16
154½–62	Santa María del Río	June 21–23
163	San Luis Potosí	July 10

164–251	Álvarez	July 13–23
252–326 (?325)	Concepción del Oro	August 11–14
326–30	General Cepeda	August 16–17
331	Saltillo	August 23
332–84	Chorro Grande	August 29–31
385–431	San Lorenzo Cañon	September 21–23

The sequence, origins, and dates of Nos. 432–76, inclusive, are not well established. As was Palmer's custom, he inserted into his number series, late in the season, several collections which had previously been overlooked or which had not yet dried when his previous cataloging was in process. These include Nos. 449, from Concepción del Oro; 450–52, from Chorro Grande; 454, from General Cepeda; 463–65, from Río Verde; 466–67, from Concepción del Oro; 468–71, from San Lorenzo Cañon; and 472 from Álvarez. I have not checked these numbers against any specimens; the numbers are taken from a typed list among the Palmer manuscripts. The remaining numbers (432–48, 453, 455–62, 473–76) are unaccounted for, or seem to have been collected either in Saltillo itself or at the Cerro del Pueblo just west of that city.

A tolerably complete set of field notes for the collections of 1904 is in the Gray Herbarium. The number of sets collected is unknown to me.

After a few months in Washington, Palmer returned to Saltillo in 1905 to continue the work of the previous summer. He collected in and near that city during the month of April; he spent most of the months of May and June in the state of San Luis Potosí; and he returned then to Saltillo to spend July and the first third of August. He was back in Washington before September 1, when he again took up his work as "expert" for the Bureau of Plant Industry.

The specimens collected in Mexico in 1905 comprise Nos. 500–769, inclusive, continuing the numbered series begun in 1904, Nos. 477–99 omitted. The number of sets of plants collected is unknown to me. The collections may be enumerated approximately as follows:

Specimen Numbers	*Place Collected*	*Date*
500–27	Saltillo	April 9–11
528–33		
?534–?57	San Lorenzo Cañon	April 16

558-62	Agua Nueva	April 18
563	Saltillo	April 21
564-66	Saltillo	April 11
567-72	Zapatillo	May 1-3
573-74	Río Verde	May 11-13
575-607	Álvarez	May 19-22
608-609	Peotillos	May 25-27
610-17	San Luis Potosí	May 24
618-46	San Dieguito	June 7-10
647-49	San Luis Potosí	May 24 (?June 20)
650-85	Rascón	June 19-22
686	?Saltillo	June 28
687		
688	Saltillo	July 25
689		
690	Saltillo	July 28
691-92		
693-700	San Lorenzo Cañon	July 9
701-703		
704-13	Saltillo	July 28
714-25	Chorro Grande	July 16-19
726-27		
728-38	Saltillo	July 25
739-40		
741-51	San Lorenzo Cañon	July 9
752-64	Saltillo	August 10
765	Chorro Grande	July 16-19
766	Rascón	June 21
767-69	Saltillo	August 11

The numbers from 686 to 769, inclusive, are rather doubtfully enumerated above. By no means all have been checked, and sequences given are based partially upon inference from known data. For example, Nos. 741, 744-48, and 751, are definitely known or stated to have been collected on July 9 at San Lorenzo Cañon; it is inferred that the remaining numbers in the series between 741 and 751 are from the same locality.

A nearly complete set of the field notes for this year is at the Gray Herbarium, and the set at the Division of Plant Exploration and Introduction includes (in addition to two field books having to do with tunas from the market of San Luis Potosí) the following numbers: later copies of Nos. 501, 502, 507, 510, 516, 548, and original copies of Nos. 558–62, 567–685, 766.

Palmer's appointment in the Bureau of Plant Industry was terminated at the end of January, 1906, and on March 5 he left Washington for the city of Durango. He collected in the state of Durango until mid-September, and sometime thereafter returned to Washington. His collections and travels in Durango were remarkable ones for a man seventy-five years old; the former in fact have not been surpassed in interest by any other collections from that part of Mexico. As soon as he reached the city of Durango he made plans to go to Tepehuanes, at the end of the railroad about 150 kilometers northwest of Durango, "to see what is there." From Tepehuanes he made a strenuous trip to the mine called San Ramón, a project which entailed a four-day ride on horseback each way. On his return he was enthusiastic, and ready for another excursion: "I returned two days ago from Paradise (San Ramone mine) . . . the only way to get to that place is on horse back four long days ride each way . . . am going by team to morrow to a box cannon 9 miles."[16]

San Ramón today is even less accessible than it was in Palmer's time, because most of the railroad to Tepehuanes has been abandoned with the depletion of the timber supplies in that region. Palmer's collection from San Ramón remains one of the very few ever made in that remote northwestern corner of Durango.

Because of an injury sustained on a collecting trip, Palmer returned to Durango city and rested until mid-July, when he made a trip on horseback or by stage to Otinapa, in the high pine-covered hills northwest of the city. After nearly two weeks there he returned and set out again for the country near the end of the railroad line to Tepehuanes. This completed an active collecting season which netted him some 569 numbers.

The collections were distributed as follows:

Specimen Numbers	*Place Collected*	*Date*
1–8	Durango	March 12–15
9–47	Tepehuanes	March 25–April 16
48–50	Tovar	May 28–31

[16] Letter to Rose, May 26, 1906.

51–210	San Ramón	April 21–May 18
211–27	Quebrada Honda	May 20–21
228–57	Tovar	
258–331	Tepehuanes	June 4–25
332–465	Otinapa	July 25–August 5
466–530	Tejamen	August 21–27
531	San Ramón	
532	Tepehuanes	June 4–25
533	Tovar	
534–35	San Ramón	
536–45	Tejamen	
546–55	Otinapa	
556–58	Durango	September 15
559–60	Otinapa	
561–63	Tepehuanes	June 4–25
564–69	Tejamen	

A set of the field notes for 1906 is in the files of the Division of Plant Exploration and Introduction.

The next trip out of Washington was to Ciudad Victoria, the capital of Tamaulipas, in January, 1907. Palmer collected in Tamaulipas, chiefly in the vicinity of Ciudad Victoria, until mid-June when he returned to Washington. His longest trip out from Ciudad Victoria was by rail to Arguelles, thence by stage to Xicoténcatl and wagon to Gómez Farías.

The collections of 1907 comprise 584 numbers, of which Nos. 268–359, 562, and 582–83 were collected at Gómez Farías and the rest in or near Ciudad Victoria. The Division of Plant Exploration and Introduction has on file the original field books including data for all the Nos. 1–584; the Division has also a typewritten copy of Palmer's diary from February 4 to June 18. The number of sets of plants collected in Tamaulipas was probably more than five.

The summer of 1907 was spent in Washington. On October 30, Palmer again undertook his appointment as "expert" with the Bureau of Plant Industry, continuing work on his Mexican notes and collections. The appointment continued until the end of January, 1908. Late in March of the same year he left for the city of Chihuahua, where his activities were to center until nearly the end of June. His field books and pocket diary are in the files of the Division of Plant Exploration and Introduction. The plants collected comprise Nos. 1–457, mostly taken in or near the city of Chihuahua. Relatively few came from other, near-by points, and some 85 numbers were taken on a longer trip to Madera, 125 miles northwest of Chihuahua. The collections may be enumerated approximately as follows:

Specimen Numbers	*Place Collected*	*Date*
1–125	Chihuahua	April 8–27
126–39	Santa Eulalia	April 28–29
140–223	Chihuahua	May 1–21
224–33	(missing)	
234–59	Aldama	May 13–16
260–330	Madera	May 27–June 2
331–80	Chihuahua	June 5–10
381	Aldama	
382–88	Santa Rosalía	June 13–15
389–437	Chihuahua market	April 1–June 26
438–49	Madera	
450–51	Chihuahua	April 8–27
452–53	Chihuahua	May 1–21
454–55	Madera	
456–57	Santa Eulalia	

The diary indicates that Nos. 1–125 and 450–51, distributed as from the city of Chihuahua, were collected at various points about the city: The city water dam on the Chuviscar River (April 8–9), Quinta Carolina (April 10), La Junta (April 13), Hacienda Robinson (April 14), along the river near the city and actually in the city (April 15, 17, 18, 27), the city market (April 20–23), Cerro de Santa Rosa (April 24), and "hills east of the city," reached by coach (April 25). The remainder of the time between April 8 and 27 was spent in drying specimens and changing blotters.

Nos. 140–223 and 452–53, according to the information in Palmer's diary, were taken chiefly at Rancheta Fresno (May 4), along the river near the city (May 7, 12), about ponds and in wheat fields near the city (May 21), and at Cerro de Santa Rosa (May 18).

The field books referred to above, as well as the set of Palmer's field notes in the Gray Herbarium, give the dates of the collection at

Aldama as May 15–17. The diary states definitely, however, that Palmer left Chihuahua for Aldama at 8:00 A.M. on the thirteenth, leaving Aldama on the return trip at 5:00 P.M. on the sixteenth.

Nos. 389–437, taken in the city market at Chihuahua, comprise for the most part seeds and fruits (various varieties of corn, beans, peppers, and other vegetables) and include also such things as orange blossoms (for tea) and native drugs. Most of these numbers (perhaps all of them) are not represented by conventional herbarium specimens, and I do not know what disposition was made of them upon Palmer's return to Washington.

The specimens taken in the city market, as well as some of the other specimens, were accompanied by full notes on uses, qualities, prices, and common or vernacular names, these notes almost all written in Spanish by Palmer's companion or assistant, Rafael Venegas.

The number of sets of herbarium material collected in 1908 was probably about ten.

Dr. Palmer returned from Chihuahua directly to Washington about the end of June, 1908, and doubtless was in Washington during most of the year 1909. Sometime in December, 1909, he left on what was to be his last collecting trip, to Tampico, Tamaulipas. He reached Tampico shortly before the first of January, 1910, and made the city his headquarters for about six months, collecting in that time about 600 numbers of plants. The manuscript collection of the Division of Plant Exploration and Introduction contains a typed copy of his journal written during his stay in Tampico, and also his field books for the entire period. The journal and the field books are not always in agreement, doubtless as a result of Palmer's faulty system of numbering his collections and perhaps owing also to his failing memory in his eightieth year. The collections may be enumerated approximately as follows:

Specimen Numbers	*Place Collected*	*Date*
1–181	Tampico	January 1–31
182–250	Tampico	March 10–April 19
251–304	La Barra	February 1–8
305–40	Tampico	April 27–30
341–75	Pánuco	April 20–25
351–99	Pueblo Viejo	February 10–25
400–50	Pueblo Viejo	May 23–31

451–71	Juana Ramírez	March 8–9
472–95	Tampico	May 1–22
496–510	Tampico	June 3–6
511–30	(missing)	
531–60	Pueblo Viejo	June 1–2
561–62	La Barra	
563–76	Tampico	June 3–6
575–80	Tampico	March 10–April 19, and April 27–30 (all fungi, 575–76 duplicates)
581	La Barra	
582–87	Tampico	January 1–31
588–89	Tampico	April 27–30
590–91	La Barra	

The above enumeration is that of the entries in the field books. The diary shows that except for one- or two-day trips to the island of Juana Ramírez (March 8–9, or 8–11), and Laguna de la Puerta (March 23–24), and a five-day trip (April 20–25) to Pánuco, Dr. Palmer spent his nights in his hotel in Tampico, making daily excursions to near-by points to collect plants. Specimens distributed as from Pueblo Viejo and La Barra were evidently not collected during any protracted visits to these localities, but from day to day, Palmer completing the sets of each number by repeated visits. During the period February 10–25, for example, when the field books show that Nos. 351–99 were collected at Pueblo Viejo, the diary indicates that Palmer visited what he called "Old Town" only on the twelfth, twenty-third, and twenty-fourth; most of the time he spent in Tampico, and he made at least one botanizing trip to La Barra during this same period. Thus not too much trust should be placed in the dates of the collections made in 1910 as those dates appear in the field notes and on the printed labels distributed with the specimens. It is evident that Palmer made no attempt to designate specific dates and localities for individual collections, but rather grouped them into general divisions for the sake of convenience. In some cases the diary and the field books are wholly at variance, as in June: according to the field books, Nos. 531–60 were collected at Pueblo Viejo, June 1–2. The diary, however, says that the first two days of June were spent in "Botanical Housework," presumably in Tampico.

It may be noted incidentally that Nos. 351–75, inclusive, and 575–76, are duplicated.

The number of sets of specimens collected in 1910 was nine; most of these were distributed by the National Herbarium after Palmer's death. The bulk of the three largest sets was distributed by Dr. Palmer himself, the collections going to the National Herbarium, the Gray Herbarium, and the New York Botanical Garden, in the order named. The remaining sets were distributed as follows:

Recipient	*Number of specimens*
Missouri Botanical Garden	512
Kew	495
British Museum	471
Geneva	439
California Academy of Sciences	397
Field Museum	394

Palmer returned to Washington from Tampico, via New Orleans, about the middle of June, 1910. In his last months (and indeed in the last decade of his life) he wrote relatively few letters, so we know almost nothing of him and his doings in the closing months of 1910. The occasion of his eightieth birthday was celebrated January 10, 1911, at a meeting in his honor of the Botanical Society of Washington, and Safford has recorded for posterity the biographical sketch read at this gathering, which was attended by a considerable number of botanists. Three months later, April 10, 1911, Palmer died in the city of Washington.

As Safford has well said, "Scarcely a monograph of a family or genus appears, including representatives in Mexico and the southwestern United States, but among the species described are new ones based upon types collected by Edward Palmer." In 1911, Safford counted 1,162 species of flowering plants made known to science from Palmer's collections and in the more than forty years since Palmer's death the number may well have reached 2,000 or more. As a collector of plants during six active decades he added no small amount to the total of scientific knowledge, and we may hope that he was sufficiently repaid for the decision made in his youth, to "spend his life in the prosecution of science" in the ways for which he was best fitted.

GEOGRAPHICAL INDEX

I *Introduction*

THIS INDEXED ACCOUNT of Edward Palmer's travels is intended primarily for the use of those who need information to supplement published data, information about specimens which are inadequately documented, or information about localities which the collector may have visited. The actual details of Palmer's travels or whereabouts in any given year may be found in the preceding biographical study.

The primary list of localities occurring in this index is given in a strictly alphabetical manner, without reference to geography or chronology. Under each individual locality, however, the arrangement is chronological; the work of each year, or each visit when visits do not coincide with the calendar years, is discussed separately, and a brief account is given of Palmer's activities at each locality. The dates of his arrivals and departures, when known, are given, and references are made to his previous and subsequent travels, to enable the user of the index to follow his itineraries with a minimum of difficulty. Numbers in italics in parentheses following individual items in the geographical list, refer to correspondingly numbered items listed in References and Sources.

The index also contains summarized accounts under the names of the several states and territories, of the United States and Mexico. These summaries have been cross-indexed against the individual localities. Other general geographical entries include the few foreign countries (other than Mexico) which Palmer visited, and certain counties in the United States.

Every locality in the United States is referred to its proper state and county if possible. In certain cases, usually in the larger counties in the Western states, the position is given more precisely. County boundaries given are those in force in 1950, not necessarily those of Palmer's time. With the exception of well-known urban centers like New York and Philadelphia, every locality is referred, if possible, to one or more maps on which its position is shown.

Most of the states in which Palmer worked have been mapped by the General Land Office of the United States Department of the Interior, and these maps have proved to be more generally useful than any other series in listing his localities. Many of the earlier editions were current at the time of his travels. Because of the large scale on which the Land Office maps are drawn, and the various types of information included on them, they provide a convenient (often the only) means of locating ranches, springs, and other minor or ephemeral features of the territory. Although these maps are not available in every library, there are files of them in major library centers, and no other series covering the period from 1865 to 1900 can compare with them for completeness, accuracy, and detail.

When a locality in the index is listed on one of the maps of the General Land Office, this is indicated as follows:

Beaver Dam, Arizona (Mohave County) GLO, 1921

The name of the state mapped is not given in this abbreviated citation, because the GLO maps are of individual states except in the few cases discussed individually in the index. When the same locality is listed in the same geographic position on several editions of the GLO maps for that state, the most recent edition is usually cited, on the assumption that the more recent editions will be more generally available.

Certain states in which Palmer made important collections have not been mapped by the General Land Office. These include Texas (which controls its own public land) and Tennessee. The localities at which he worked in these states are nearly all well-known places, listed on most ordinary maps, and are located sufficiently, with the few exceptions treated in the text, by designation of the county.

Localities in the Indian Territory, which Palmer visited in 1863 and again in 1868, are discussed in some detail in the text. General discussion of his itineraries there will be found under the heading *Indian Territory,* but individual localities appear in the list under

Oklahoma, and are located with reference to modern boundaries of that state, thus:

Blue River, [Oklahoma] (Johnston County) GLO, 1876

At the time of Palmer's travels in the Indian Territory the boundaries of the several Indian nations were subject to change, and many settlements, military posts, and reference points were either newly established or temporary. Contemporary maps were few, and those which survive are of limited usefulness because the country was changing so rapidly.

In a few cases, when Palmer's localities have not been found on the GLO maps or other general maps of states or territories, reference has been made to the topographic maps of the United States Geological Survey. These are cited as USGS, with the abbreviation followed by the name of the sheet or quadrangle.

Localities along the Florida Keys, and some on the New England coast, are well covered by charts published by the U.S. Coast and Geodetic Survey. These charts are serially numbered (the same number retained through different editions), and are referred to thus:

Eastern Dry Rocks, Florida (Monroe County) CGS, 1251

Places in Hispanic America (Mexico, West Indies, Central and South America) are located primarily by reference to the *Map of Hispanic America at 1: 1,000,000,* published by the American Geographical Society of New York. The Millionth Map, as it is sometimes known, comprises 107 sheets designated by name and number, e.g. Guadalajara, N.F–13. Sheets south of the equator are designated by the letter S, e.g. Asunción, S.G–21. The index to this map was published in twelve parts in 1943–44, by the United States Government Printing Office. When one of Palmer's localities is listed on the Millionth Map, it is cited thus:

Imala, Sinaloa 24°52′N., 107°15′W. N.G–13

The co-ordinates of latitude and longitude are taken directly from the map, in lieu of citation of county or other minor political division. Minor civil divisions in Mexico, where Palmer did most of his botanical work between 1878 and 1910, have frequently changed boundaries and are not readily located on ordinary maps. Major civil divisions in Mexico (states and territories) are named without additional citation of the name of the country (e.g. Armería, Colima, not

Armería, Colima, México). For localities in Latin American countries other than Mexico, the name of the country is cited in each case, and the names of major civil divisions are given in parentheses.

Localities in Mexico which are not found on the Millionth Map are for the most part listed on the *Atlas Geográfico de los Estados Unidos Mexicanos, construido y editado en la Dirección de Geografía Meteorología e Hidrología,* published in Mexico in 1943, at a scale of 1 : 500,000. This atlas, an official publication, comprises fifty-one named and numbered sheets. When one of Palmer's localities is listed therein, and reference is made to this, the citation follows this form:

Lirios, Los, Coahuila 25°23′N., 100°38′W. Atlas, 27

This refers to sheet (*hoja*) No. 27, of the *Atlas,* the sheet designated as "Hoja Monterrey (25°–100°30′)."

Localities in Hispanic America which are not found on these general maps are discussed and located individually in the text. The few localities in Canada, Great Britain, and northeastern United States are treated individually in a similar fashion.

II *List of Maps Used as General References*

I PRIMARILY FOR THE UNITED STATES

CGS (United States Coast and Geodetic Survey).

1. For the New England coast. Charts 801 (edition of 1919), 1,201 (1921), 1,204 (1917), 1,210 (1921).

2. For southern Florida, Florida Keys, and Bahama Islands. Charts 1,002 (edition of 1917), 1,248 (1921), 1,249 (1921), 1,251 (third edition, 1940), and 1,351 (third edition, 1952).

GLO (Maps of individual states, published by the General Land Office, U.S. Department of the Interior. Scale varies from ten to twenty miles to the inch; most often one inch equals about twelve miles.)

1. State of Alabama (1882, 1889, 1915).

2. Territory of Arizona (1876, 1879, 1883, 1887, 1897); State of Arizona (1912, 1921, 1933).

3. State of Arkansas (1886, 1914).

4. State of California (1876, 1879, 1900, 1907, 1928).

5. State of Colorado (1897, 1910, 1934).
6. State of Florida (1866, 1876, 1911, 1926).
7. State of Idaho (1899, 1939).
8. State of Illinois (1885).
9. Indian Territory (1876, 1879, 1883, 1885); see also Oklahoma Territory.
10. State of Indiana (1886).
11. State of Iowa (1885).
12. State of Kansas (1884, 1891, 1912, 1925).
13. State of Louisiana (1887, 1930).
14. State of Mississippi (1885, 1915).
15. State of Missouri (1878, 1891).
16. State of Nebraska (1890, 1922).
17. State of Nevada (1876, 1894, 1930, 1941).
18. Territory of New Mexico (1866, 1886; State of New Mexico (1912, 1936).
19. Oklahoma Territory (1894, 1898); see also Indian Territory.
20. Territory of Utah (1876, 1893); State of Utah, (1902, 1908, 1937).

USGS (Large-scale topographic maps published by the United States Geological Survey, or by the War Department, Corps of Engineers, scale 1/62,500 or 1/125,000.)

1. Arkansas, Holly Grove Quadrangle, Grid Zone "C," 1/62,500 (edition of 1940).
2. Arkansas, Little Rock Sheet, 1/125,000 (edition of 1893).
3. Arkansas, Noble Lake Quadrangle, Grid Zone "C," 1/62,500 (edition of 1935).
4. Arkansas, Varner Quadrangle, Grid Zone "C" 1/62,500 (edition of 1935).
5. Arkansas–Mississippi, Lamont Quadrangle, Grid Zone "C," 1/62,500 (edition of 1939).
6. California (San Diego County), Cuyamaca Quadrangle, 1/125,000 (edition of 1903); surveyed in 1891, and 1901–1902.
7. California, San Jacinto Quadrangle, 1/125,000 (edition of 1901, reprinted 1905).
8. California, Tamalpais Sheet, 1/62,500 (edition of 1897, reprinted 1907).
9. Indian Territory–Oklahoma, Chickasha Quadrangle, 1/125,000 (edition of 1904).

10. Indian Territory–Oklahoma, Stonewall Quadrangle, 1/125,-000 (edition of 1901).

11. Indian Territory (Chickasaw Nation), Tishomingo Quadrangle, 1/125,000 (edition of 1901).

12. Maine (Cumberland County), Casco Bay Quadrangle, 1/62,-500 (edition of 1916).

13. Nevada–Arizona, St. Thomas Sheet (edition of 1886, reprinted 1929).

Miscellaneous source maps.

1. California. Map of the state of California compiled expressly for the Immigration Association of California [1885?] [ca. 31 miles to 1 inch].

2. California. U.S. Geological Survey maps at scale of 1/1,000,-000, published uniformly with the projected International Map of World: North I 10, Point Conception, 32°–36° N., 120°–126°W.

3. Kansas and Nebraska. Map showing the progress of the public surveys in Kansas and Nebraska, 1865. Surveyors Gen[ls] Office, Leavenworth, Kansas, August 25, 1865. [One inch equals about 18 miles. Shows roads and proposed railroads to the west.]

4. New England. U.S.G.S. maps at scale of 1/1,000,000, published uniformly with the projected International map of the World: North K 19, Boston, 40°–44°N., 66–72°W. (1912).

5. Utah. Map of Utah Territory. U.S. Geol. & Geog. Survey, Geology of High Plateaus of Utah, Capt. E. E. Dutton, Atlas Sheet No. 8. Scale 1 inch equals 10 miles. (No date.) Data from various surveys, including King, Wheeler, and Hayden.

II PRIMARILY FOR LATIN AMERICA

AMS (U.S. Army Map Service. Scale 1/250,000. A series of thirteen sheets, useful for the highlands of eastern Mexico, west to longitude 100°. No more published.)

1. E–14–N–II, Mexico City (1947). [19°–20°N., 98°–100°W.]
2. F–14–N–V, Tula (1947). [22°–23°N., 98°–100°W.]

Atlas (*Atlas geográfico de la República Mexicana,* escala 1/500,000, México, D. F. Dirección de Geografía Meteorología e Hidrología, 1943. [Title varies: on cover *Atlas geográfico de los Estados Unidos Mexicanos.*] Consists of fifty-one named and numbered sheets ["hojas"], which are also identified by the co-ordinates in latitude and longitude of their central points. The sheets listed here, all of which are cited by number elsewhere in the Geographical Index of this work, have been found particularly useful in tracing Palmer's itineraries.)

1. Altar, 31°–112°30′	(Sonora)
11. Chilpancingo, 17°–100°30′	(Guerrero)
18. Jiménez, 27°–103°30′	(Coahuila)
26. México, 19°–100°30′	(Distrito Federal)
27. Monterrey, 25°–100°30′	(Coahuila, Nuevo León)
31. Parral, 27°–106°30′	(Chihuahua)
36. Puebla, 19°–97°30′	(Puebla, Veracruz)
42. S. Luis Potosí, 23°–100°30′	(San Luis Potosí)

N.C–16 to N.H–13 and S.E–21 to S.I–21 (American Geographical Society, Map of Hispanic America, 1/1,000,000. The plan of the map conforms in general to the projected International Map of the World at the same scale; see above under miscellaneous source maps, United States, for N.I–10, N.K–19. The sheets listed below are those actually consulted in the compilation of the Geographical Index to this work; in some cases individual sheets have been superseded by later editions.)

N.C–16. Lago de Nicaragua (Provisional edition, 1937). [8°–12°N., 84°–90°W.].

N.C–17. Panamá (Provisional edition, 1928). [7°–12°N., 78°–84°W.].

N.D–15. Ciudad de Guatemala (Provisional edition, 1935). [12°–16° N., 90°–96°W.].

N.D–16. Tegucigalpa (Provisional edition, 1937). [12°–16°N., 83° 20′–90°W.].

N.E.–13. Colima (Provisional edition, 1933). [16°–20°N., 102°–108°W.].

N.E–14. Ciudad de México (Provisional edition, 1938). [15°40′–20° N., 96°–102°W.].

N.E–15. Istmo de Tehuantepec (Provisional edition, 1938). [16°–20° N., 90°–96°W.].

N.E–20. Lesser Antilles–North (Provisional edition, 1927). [16°–20°N., 60°–66°W.].

N.F–13. Guadalajara (Provisional edition, 1940). [20°–24°N., 102°–108°W.].

N.F.–14. San Luis Potosí (Provisional edition, 1932). [20°–24°N., 96°–102°W.].

N.F-16. Yucatán (Provisional edition, 1927). [20°-24°N., 84°-90°30′W.].
N.F-18. Santiago de Cuba (Provisional edition, 1940). [19°45′-24°N., 72°-78°W.].
N.G-12. Baja California-Sur (Provisional edition, 1924). [22°50′-28°N., 108°-115°W.].
N.G-13. Culiacán (Provisional Edition, 1935). [24°-28°N., 102°-108°W.].
N.G-14. Monterrey (Provisional edition, 1937). [24°-28°N., 96°-102°W.].
[N.H-11]. Baja California-Norte (Provisional Edition, 1928). [28°-33°N., 112°-118°25′W.].
N.H-12. Sonora (Provisional edition, 1937). [28°-32°20′N., 108°-114°W.].
N.H.-13. Chihuahua (Provisional edition, 1934). [28°-32°N., 102°-108°W.].
S.E-21. Corumbá (Provisional edition, 1931). [16°-20°S., 54°-60°W.].
S.F-21. Río Apa (Provisional edition, 1940). [20°-24°S., 54°-60°W.].
S.G-21. Asunción. Carte Internationale du Monde au 1 000 000e (Edicão Provisoria, Sept. 7, 1922). [24°-28°S., 54°-60°W.].
S.H-21. Uruguayana (Provisional edition, 1940). [28°-32°S., 54°-60°W.].
S.I-21. Buenos Aires-Montevideo (Provisional edition, 1940). [32°-36°S., 54°-60°W.].

Localities are usually listed in the index exactly as they appear on the maps which are used as references. Isla de Cedros and Río Paraná, for example, are listed as given above and not as Cedros, Isla de, and Paraná, Río. In these cases and numerous others, however, appropriate cross references have been inserted. When Palmer misspelled a name, as he frequently did, and the erroneous spelling has been perpetuated by publication or otherwise, it is indexed with reference to the name as usually spelled. When his spelling or wording varied, the variants are explained in the text, except for a relatively few localities in which the differences seemed too trivial to explain, or in which correct usage was not clear; when a part of the name of a locality is put between parentheses, the usual implication is that the name has been used both with and without the part thus indicated. Thus Hacienda Peotillo(s), Hell('s) Canyon, Holl(e)y Wood,

Sierra (de) San Miguelito, Talley's (Ranch), Tecate (Valley Station).

Distances in the United States are given in miles, as Palmer himself expressed them. For localities in Hispanic America, metric equivalents are given as needed.

A word about the numbers on Palmer's specimens may not be amiss. Most of his plant collections bear a serial number, whereas such numbers are often, or usually lacking from zoological and other collections. It has obviously not been possible to work out tables showing the date and place of every botanical collection, but inclusive series of numbered collections from many individual localities are cited on the following pages. From these series as cited, when the year and general region of collection is known, it is usually possible to work out approximate date and locality for any given collection.

The serial numbers on Palmer's plant specimens in herbaria are usually of little value except as means of comparison with corresponding specimens in other herbaria, and even such comparison must be made with caution.

Palmer's collections before 1885 were usually numbered by him in the field, in more or less chronological sequence. Later they were sorted by those to whom they were sent for determination, the original numbers suppressed, and the individual species renumbered arbitrarily, after their rearrangement in some systematic order. The same (arbitrary) number was often given to all plants that seemed to belong to the same species regardless of their place of origin. Standard collecting practice was to gather all available material of any desired species whenever opportunity offered, and subsequently to complete the suite of the (supposed) same species at a later time, often at a locality remote from the first. Thus one of Palmer's field numbers might on occasion include more than one species, and material from more than one locality. Two or more such field numbers were sometimes combined during the process of identification, and the whole distributed under a new, arbitrarily assigned number which was thought to pertain to one species only. All chronological and geographical sequence of the collections was thus destroyed, making it impossible for later workers to associate the specimens from any given locality except by indirect means.

In 1885, and thereafter, Palmer's own field numbers were permanently assigned to the specimens and distributed with them. A new series was begun at the beginning of almost every field season, so that in citing a number it is usually necessary to cite the year of collection also.

Even in later years, however, there is little continuity expressed by the serial numbers of the specimens, even though they may be approximately chronological in order. This is primarily because of Palmer's method of "cataloguing," that is, of numbering his collections and writing up his notes upon them. His notes were usually rather complete, but were often written up from memory some time after the actual specimens were dried. His practice was to collect a number of specimens at a locality, keeping these in the order of drying, or in no particular order, then to write up the "catalogue" for these before collecting more. For a specific example of this, see page 108.

As may readily be surmised, it has proved impossible to avoid the excessive repetition of Palmer's name and of the personal pronouns "he" and "his" through hundreds of essentially similar paragraphs of unembellished statistical information. Use of the telegraphic style ("Arrived . . ." rather than "He arrived . . .") has seemed to provide a welcome variation, but no attempt has been, or could be, made to employ this style throughout. The reader may suppose that when a verb is used without a subject in the following pages, the implied subject is Dr. Palmer. Many times I have been tempted to refer to him, in the literary tradition, as "our hero."

III *Annotated List of Localities*

Acapulco, Guerrero 16°51′N., 99°56′W. N.E–14

1862. Arrived February 18 on steamer *Sonora,* having left San Francisco, California, February 11. Collected shells. Continued by steamer to Panama, and went on overland the same day (February 25) to Aspinwall (now Colón, C.Z.), where he took the S. S. *Northern Light* to New York, arriving March 6 (*114b; 123a; 125g*).

1870. February. Touched here enroute from San Francisco, California, *q.v.,* to Panama (*45,* item 53).

1894–95. Arrived October 17, 1894, from San Francisco, probably after a stop at Mazatlán; lodged at the Hotel del Pacífico and collected about 635 numbers in about twelve sets. Began to collect about October 20; collected Nos. 1–43 (October 25–31), 44–158 and 620 (November), 159–323, 622 (in part), 623, 624, and 631 (December). Visited El Marqués January 9, 1895, returning January 14; collected

Nos. 324–362, 615, 616, 621 in part, 625, 626, 628, 632, 633 (January), 363–547, 603, 604 in part, 612, 617, 618, 627, 634, 635 (February), 548–602 (March 1–10), 604 in part, 605–11, 613, 614, 621 in part, 622 in part, 630 (March), 629 (undated). Probably no collecting was done after about March 10. Probably Palmer left Acapulco about April 1, 1895, stopping over at Manzanillo (April 7) and collecting No. 619. A note among the Palmer manuscripts says that he left April 10, on the *City of Sydney*, but this does not agree with the date of his visit to Manzanillo as noted by him in his field notes and in a letter (April 23) to J. N. Rose (*114i; 123a; 123c*).

Acatita, Coahuila 26°30′N., 103°06′W. Atlas, 18

1880. Collected Indian remains from caves here (May 31). In Palmer's field notes (*34d*) the locality is referred to as a "mining camp 25 or 6 leagues N. of San Pedro"; see San Pedro. Cordelia A. Studley (*116*) gives the spelling "Acateta" and the location as "26 leagues east of Parras." Little is known about Palmer's itineraries on this trip from Saltillo and Parras; it is probable that additional valuable information pertinent to it is contained in the items numbered 79, 81, 175, and 184, of the Merwin Catalogue (*45*). All these items pertain to travels in Coahuila in 1880, but none has been located.

Achiabampo, Sonora

1890. See Agiabampo.

Acoma Indians [of New Mexico] (Eastern Valencia County)

1869. About May 5. Safford states that Palmer visited the pueblos of Acoma Chiquito and Acoma Grande. Item No. 1 of the Merwin Catalogue (*45*) is entitled "Acama [*sic*] Indians of New Mexico. (Manuscript). Observations made in 1869, while among them, by Dr. Palmer . . ." I have not seen this manuscript, and I know nothing further about Palmer's visits to the Acoma pueblo. Possibly his "Acoma Grande" is the principal pueblo, long established on the Acoma mesa, and his "Acoma Chiquito" may be another name for Acomita, which in his time was a small village of temporary dwellings, primarily for the use of agricultural workers who descended from the principal settlement on the mesa. Acoma Pueblo and Acomita are listed on the GLO map of 1886. See Fort Wingate (*123b*).

Adair Bay, Sonora

1870. See Bahía de Adair.

Adams County, Mississippi

1883. Palmer reported mounds at White Apple village, according to Thomas (*118*). See also Washington, Mississippi.

Adams' Mound, Arkansas

1883. Near Heckatoo, *q.v.*

Agency

1870. See Colorado River Agency.

Agiabampo, Sonora 26°23'N., 109°09'W. N.G–12

1890. On the Gulf coast, just north of the Sinaloan boundary. Palmer left Guaymas (September 10) on the steamer *Romero Rubio*, reaching Agiabampo September 12; he left September 13 for Álamos, returning October 3; after this he was ill for some time with intermittent fever, according to his own published note (*84*), in which he used the spelling Achiabampo and gave the date as October, 1870. He left for Guaymas on the *Romero Rubio* (October 29). He collected Nos. 752–815 (except 812); the field notes give the dates of collection as October 3–15 (*114i; 123a; 123c*).

Agua Caliente, California (Riverside County)

1870. September (?). A stage station on the Ehrenberg–San Bernardino route, shown on Bergland's (*126*) map in latitude 33°49'N., longitude 116°35'W. See Los Angeles.

Agua Caliente, California (San Diego County)

1867. August (?). Same as Warner Springs. After leaving Vallecito, *q.v.*, by stage, Palmer reached the Agua Caliente valley after entering a "crooked mountain pass into an arid desert region . . . , ascending a divide into a region of live oaks," then dropping into the valley near Warner's Ranch, *q.v.* See also Los Angeles.

1875. A few collections were made here (July 24). Also called Hot Springs by Palmer; see Julian.

Agua Nueva, Coahuila 25°12'N., 101°06'W. N.G–14

1905. On the railroad to Concepción del Oro, about 25 km. a little west of south from Saltillo; a small village on the arid plain at the foot of Carneros Pass. Palmer came by rail from Saltillo (April 18); collected Nos. 558–62 (*123c*).

Aguascalientes, Aguascalientes 21°53'N., 102°17'W. N.F–13

1878. Probably visited the city on return trip from Zacatecas to San Luis Potosí (in April). Probably collected no plants (*34d*). The locality is cited in other connections (*34c*).

Akron, Arkansas (Independence County) GLO, 1886

?1883. ?October. Palmer's published notes refer to excavations in mounds here, in T 12 N, R 4 E, 9 miles northwest [i.e. ?west] of Jacksonport, on the Big Bottom of the White River. Cyrus Thomas (*119*) mentions these mounds and says they are "near Akron" (*88*).

Alabama GLO, 1882, 1889

1883. It is not possible to give a connected account of Palmer's activities in this state. He worked here for the Bureau of Ethnology for parts of this and the following year, principally in the southern half of the state, in the drainage basins of the Alabama and Tombigbee rivers. He was in Blountsville, *q.v.*, on May 15; perhaps at this same time he visited shell heaps at Huntsville and mounds near Florence before leaving for Tennessee, *q.v.* At some time this year, according to Thomas (*118*), Palmer visited a prehistoric village site in Lowndes County.

1884. Tuscaloosa, January 13 (year uncertain; Palmer wrote "the past ten days has been very cold nearly to zero") on this date he had just been to Greensboro and planned to start the next day down the Tombigbee River enroute to Mobile. On March 12 he was at Montgomery, having collected near Paces Landing on the Tombigbee River 9 miles from Demopolis; from here he went to Mobile and left there for Georgia about March 20 (*34a, 114b*).

Thomas (*118*) mentions a number of mounds and other localities "reported," "described," or "explored" by Palmer, but gives no dates for these. The localities in question are in Elmore, Hale, Sumter, and Talladega counties; the more probable date seems to be 1884, when Palmer is known to have been in this same general area for some days.

Additional information about Palmer's activities in this state in 1883 and 1884 may doubtless be found in Item No. 3 of the Merwin Catalogue (*45*), which I have not been able to locate. This is entitled "ALABAMA. (Manuscript) Descriptions of Towns, Indian Mounds, Forts, etc. Notes by Dr. Palmer in 1883–84. Tuscaloosa, Gunthersville [*sic*], Mounds near Blakely, Montgomery, etc. 47 MSS. pages. 8vo."

The records of the Division of Ethnology, U.S. National Museum, Catalog Nos. 91,451–91,601, and 90,485–90,508, include specimens from the following counties: Elmore, Lowndes, Barbour (Eufaula), Mobile, Clarke (French's Landing), Sumter, Lauderdale (Florence).

Álamo de Parras, Coahuila

1880. See Viesca; by Palmer called "Almo de Parras."

Álamos, Sonora 27°01′N., 108°58′W. N.G–12

1890. Arrived (March 22 or 23) by stage from Guaymas. Collected Nos. 276–415. Left (April 8) for Guaymas, by stage via Batomoral, Coraca, Cocorit, and Torin. Nos. 276–80, 294, 295, 299, 302–308, 310, 311, 313–19, 322–27, 329–31, 335, 355, 367, 375–83, 389–99, 401–404, and 411, are from the vicinity of Álamos; Nos. 414 and 415 were purchased at Álamos, the former supposed to have come from near the mouth of the Yaqui River; the rest of Palmer's collections are from the "Álamos Sierra," said to be 6 miles south of the town and 5,877 feet high (*123a; 123c*).

1890. Arrived (about September 15) by stage from Agiabampo; collected Nos. 627–751 and 812; left for Agiabampo by stage (October 2). The dates of collections are given in the field notes as September 16–30 (*97; 123a; 123c*).

Albany, Georgia (Dougherty County)

1884. A few ethnological specimens collected here; see Blakely.

Albuquerque, Brazil (Mato Grosso) 19°23′S., 57°28′W. S.E–21

1853. See Río Paraná; the village is about 6 km. northwest of Porto Albuquerque on the Río Paraguay. Specimens were collected here and daguerreotypes made, December 4–7 (*52; 123a; 125c*).

Albuquerque, New Mexico (Bernalillo County) GLO, 1936

1869. Arrived by coach (April 13) from Santa Fé; left by army ambulance for Fort Wingate, *q.v.* (presumably April 13 or 14), the trip said to be just 137 miles (*114g*).

1890. May or June, enroute from Fort Huachuca to Holbrook. See Arizona.

Aldama, Chihuahua 28°50′N., 105°54′W. N.H–13

1908. Arrived May 13, from Chihuahua. Collected Nos. 234–59, and 381. Left for Chihuahua May 16. Aldama lies northeast of the city of Chihuahua, although said by Palmer to be 6 leagues east (*123a; 123c*).

Almo de Parras, Coahuila

1880. See Viesca.

Alpattie Flats, Florida (St. Lucie and Martin counties)

1874. February; see Fort Bassinger. Said to be 10 miles west, then 24 miles north of west, from St. Lucie. This is evidently the area called "Hal-pa-ti-o-kee," or "Alpatiokee Swamp," on early Florida maps, and "Hapatiokee Swamp" on the GLO map, 1911. The spelling "Alpattie" was used by Frederick A. Ober in his letter reporting the Okeechobee Expedition (*10*), but on his earlier trip to Florida in 1872 he had called it "Alpatiokee," and explained that the word was Seminole for Alligator Creek.[1]

Altamira, Tamaulipas 22°24′N., 97°55′W. N.F–14

1910. Visited May 10, according to Palmer's journal. This locality lies on the railroad to Ciudad Victoria, about 27 km. north-northwest of Tampico (*123a*).

Altar, Sonora 30°43′N., 111°44′W. N.H–12

1869. November 4, enroute from Tucson to Guaymas, *q.v.*

Altata, Sinaloa 24°38′N., 107°56′W. N.G–13

1891. August, enroute from Guaymas to Culiacán, *q.v.* Also spelled "Altatta" by Palmer (*123a*).

Álvarez, San Luis Potosí 22°03′N., 100°37′W. N.F–14

1878. Visited August 21 and perhaps again in September; also in October or early November. The site of Álvarez (now practically abandoned) was in the oak forests on the eastern summit slopes of the mountains about 40 km. southeast of the city of San Luis Potosí, at an elevation of about 2,400 m. At the time of Palmer's first visit it was accessible to pack trains and foot traffic only; he himself went there first on horseback. Before his second visit, in 1902, a railroad had been built from San Luis Potosí to a point somewhat beyond Álvarez. The railroad route is shown on most modern maps, but the rails were taken up about 1950 and parts of the roadbed are used by truck traffic. See Pila, and San Luis Potosí (*31; 90*).

[1] *Forest & Stream,* Vol. I (November 6, 1873), 193.

1902. Arrived about September 5, traveling by freight car. Collected Nos. 45–86 and 101–40. Returned to San Luis Potosí on a handcar, September 11. Made a second trip to Álvarez (September 28 to October 3), collecting Nos. 141–213 and 442–52 (*114i; 123a; 123c*).

1904. July 13–23. Collected Nos. 164–251, and 472; most of his collecting seems to have been done in the first days of the visit, as on July 25 he wrote from San Luis Potosí; "Had 3½ days good collecting weather, but for 5 days the rain fell in torrents, so I was obliged to return here yesterday" (*34a; 123a*).

1905. May 19–22, on a trip from San Luis Potosí. Collected Nos. 575–607 (*123a; 123c*).

Anderson County, Texas

1879. See Palestine. Archaeological collections made here (*34d*).

Angostura, San Luis Potosí 22°14′N., 100°03′W. N.F–14

1878. Palmer made some archaeological excavations here, probably about February 23 to March 8; this is the Hacienda de Angostura, which was located according to Palmer's field notes at 22°13′ 44″N., 99°50′W. Gray (*31*) cited some plants from this locality, erroneously assuming they had been collected in March, 1879. See Río Verde (*34b; 34d*).

Animas, (?Las), Coahuila

1880. Not located; said to be 14 leagues east by northeast of Monclova, *q.v.* Palmer collected archaeological material from a cave here (*34d*).

Apache Agency, Arizona

1885. See Phoenix.

Apa (or Appa) River

1853. See Río Apa.

Arbol Grande, Tamaulipas

1910. Visited from Tampico on April 17, May 1, 13, 19, and 28. Not located, but evidently near Tampico (*123a*).

Arco, Idaho (Butte County) GLO, 1939

1893. Arrived from Blackfoot, *q.v.*, by stage (June 17). Collected June 18 and 19 (Nos. 163–99, 560, and 602), leaving June 19 in time to reach Big Butte Station early on the twentieth. Palmer's diary says: "My favourite collecting ground was some small wet meadows caused by the overflow of [Lost] River."

Argentine Republic

1853–55. See Paraguay.

Arguelles, Tamaulipas 23°02′N., 98°45′W. N.F–14

1907. A station on the Ciudad Victoria–Tampico railroad, visited April 12 enroute to Gómez Farías, and again on the return trip (April 22–23). Spelled "Argueyes" on some maps (*123a*).

Arivaipa Creek, Arizona (Pinal County) GLO, 1933

1866–67. See Camp Grant.

Arizona GLO, 1876, 1879, 1883, 1887, 1897, 1933

1865. See Fort Whipple, Camp Lincoln.

1866. See Camp Lincoln, Fort Whipple, Camp Grant.

1867. See Camp Grant, Tucson.

1869. See Fort Wingate, Fort Whipple, Yuma, Tucson. Visited Fort Defiance, Oraibi, Cañon de Chelly (all early June); leaving Fort Wingate, N. M. (June 22), reached Navajo Springs (about June 24), forded the Little Colorado River (June 30), climbed San Francisco Peak (July 4), proceeded to Fort Whipple (July 9), made a trip to Bill Williams Mountain, *q.v.* (July 20–30), left for Fort Mohave and Yuma on August 19.

1870. See St. Thomas, Hardyville, Yuma, Los Angeles.

1875. See St. George, Utah, and Muddy River, Nevada; Palmer doubtless passed through Arizona on a trip to the latter.

1876. Arrived in Ehrenberg (March 3), visited Williams Fork and Aubrey (March 11–12), the Colorado River Agency (March 14–22), returning to Ehrenberg; left for Wickenburg (April 8) and Prescott (April 20–22); left Prescott for Hardyville (about May 4) via Juniper Mountains, Cottonwood Creek (May 4), Cerbat Mountains (May 6), and Union Pass. Reached Hardyville (May 8); left for San Bernardino (May 13).

1877. See St. George, Utah.

1884–85. See Yuma, Mesa, Phoenix.

1889. See Yuma.

1890. Reached Fort Huachuca from Guaymas about April 20; collected there until May 29; visited Tombstone about April 27; left for Fort Apache (May 29) by rail to Holbrook via Albuquerque, New Mexico, thence by stage; reached Willow Springs June 9 and Fort Apache about June 21; returned to Willow Springs July 5 or 6; reached Holbrook July 9–11, thence went by rail to San Francisco (*34a; 114i; 123a*).

Arizona City, Arizona

1867–70. Same as Yuma, *q.v.* Both names were current at the time of Palmer's early visits.

Arkadelphia, Arkansas (Clark County) GLO, 1886

1883. February 2–10. Visited Russell Mounds ("4 miles northwest"), Carpenter's Mound ("6 miles south"), and the old Indian salt works on Saline Bayou ("2 miles southeast"). The latter is described by Thomas (*119*, p. 247). Possibly it was also at this time that Palmer explored the Hays Mound, and others, southwest of Okolona near the junction of the Little Missouri and Antoine rivers, as reported by Thomas (*118*, pp. 16–17). See Arkansas (*88*).

1883. September 16–19. Possibly part of the work at the above stations was done at this time. See Arkansas (*88*).

Arkansas GLO, 1886, 1914

1863. See Fort Scott, Kansas.

1881–82. Palmer was engaged as a regular field assistant by the Bureau of Ethnology of the Smithsonian Institution, in connection with the work of the Bureau on mounds and other ancient works in the eastern United States. A summary of the organization of this work, together with descriptions and discussions of the individual localities, by Cyrus Thomas, may be found in the *Twelfth Annual Report of the Bureau of Ethnology* (*119*). Much supplementary information on localities is contained in the "Catalogue of Prehistoric Works east of the Rocky Mountains," by the same author (*118*). Palmer's work at this time in Arkansas was in Mississippi and Arkansas counties, *q.v.* (late October to December, 1881), Monroe County, *q.v.* (December), Phillips County (about January 1 to January 11, 1882), Lee and St. Francis counties (January). He returned to Washington, D. C., February 2. For documentation of Palmer's work in Arkansas, 1881–84, see the following items in References and Sources: *34a, 34b, 34d, 88, 114a, 114b, 114c.*

1882–83. After a brief visit to Mississippi County (about July 4 and 5), Palmer returned to Arkansas (probably from Indiana) before mid-October, 1882, and investigated mounds in the northeastern counties (chiefly Mississippi, Poinsett, and St. Francis, but also Cross) from about October 13 to early November. He then moved his headquarters to the area about Little Rock and worked in Pulaski and Jefferson counties, *q.v.* He spent about a week beginning January 3 in Lincoln County, *q.v.*, then worked in succession in Desha County (mid-January), Pulaski County (about January 20), Saline County (late January), Clark County (about February 2–10). Returning to Memphis, Tennessee, he visited Oldham, Arkansas (February 16–17) but did no work there. He seems also to have revisited Arkansas City on February 27, perhaps enroute to some locality in Mississippi or Louisiana, *q.v.* It may have been during this field season that he visited mounds in Chicot and Woodruff counties, Arkansas, as reported by Thomas (*118*).

1883. Palmer was in St. Louis June 24 and planned at that time to start "in a day or two" for Mexico, "stopping at Little Rock." Nothing is known of his movements between this date and September 16. He spent at least several days in mid-September in Clark and Saline counties, *q.v.*, visited Hot Springs in an attempt to alleviate his rheumatism (late September), then worked in White and Lonoke counties, *q.v.* (October 1–27), visited Jackson and Independence counties briefly (October 28–31), returned to Little Rock and apparently thence to Helena, Arkansas, or a locality near there (early November). By December 4 he was in Washington, D. C.

1884. On his way to the Gulf of Mexico, Palmer stopped at Little Rock (June 30) and visited the Knapp Mounds (July 1).

Arkansas City, Arkansas (Desha County) GLO, 1914

1882. Arrived from Drew County about December 1 and worked several days in this vicinity; see Desha County.

1883. Arrived January 10 from Garretson's Landing, *q.v.* Perhaps also visited here on February 27.

Arkansas County, Arkansas

1881. See Arkansas. Leaving Osceola about mid-November, Palmer came by river boat from Pecan Point to his new headquarters at Arkansas Post. He collected at the Menard Mounds (about 8 miles to the southeast) and at Grand Prairie ("15 miles northwest"), then moved to Monroe County about December 5. The Menard Mounds, an important group, were the site of considerable work; they were located by Thomas (*119*) and sometimes by Palmer as "7 miles west of Arkansas Post." The map published by Thomas (*119*, p. 230), however, shows them nearly at Poynter P. O. and near a supposed former bed of the White River, but actually almost on the Arkansas River. Poynter is shown on the Land Office map of 1886 as east of Arkansas Post; as the White River is also in this direction, it seems that the mounds are actually here also.

1883. Palmer gives this as the date of his visit to the Menard Mounds, which he describes fully. He also refers to "much work" on the same mounds "last year." This would seem to establish the date of his second visit as 1882, not 1883, but I cannot find any definite record of a visit to these mounds after 1881 (88).

Thomas describes the work in Arkansas County, and refers to work done here by Palmer "previous to his connection with the Bureau of Ethnology." I do not find any evidence to substantiate this reference to a previous visit.

Arkansas Post, Arkansas (southern Arkansas County)
GLO, 1914

1881. See Arkansas County. This locality is about 25 miles south of DeWitt.

1883. See Arkansas County.

Arkansas River

1862–63. See Colorado.

Armería, Colima 18°55′N., 103°57′W. N.E–13

1891. Visited here from Colima and collected Nos. 1,274–1,293. The field notes bear the date February 15, but among the Palmer manuscripts (*123a*) is a note in Palmer's hand: "Armeria, February 6 to 15, 1891." After this visit he seems to have returned to Colima for about two weeks (*123a; 123c*).

Arroyo Atajo, Argentina (Chaco) 27°20′S., 58°40′W.

1854. Palmer was here with the *Water Witch,* and collected plants, (October 9–19). A small arroyo, actually an arm of the Río Paraguay and west of that river; Lt. T. J. Page (52) located it "on the main river, three miles above its confluence with the Parana." Also spelled "Attajo" by the members of the La Plata Expedition (*114i; 125c*).

Arroyo de Chiva, Coahuila 27°02′N., 101°07′W. N.G–14

1880. Visited September 5, probably on a trip from Monclova, *q.v.;* it is about 30 km. northeast of that place.

Palmers mexican Plants
1891–92

1731 Ipomoea scopulonem Brandg.
1872 Vernonia (?) Palmeri. Rose
1968 Eupatorium Bertholdii Sch. Bip
2010 " " "
1845 Piptothrix Palmeri Gray
1965 a. Hyptis Chapalensis Briq
1524 Heliotropium phyllostachyum Torr
1876 Heterotoma tenella Turcz
322 Adiantum Shepherdi Hook
1177 Heterotoma tenella Turcz
1430 Parthenica mollis Gray
1431 Zizyphus sonorensis Wats
1437 Pellaea Seemanni Hook
1445 a. Croton
1458 Priva echinata Juss
1464 Capparis Cynophallophora L.
1466 a Capparis
1471 Heliopsis microcephala Rose
1474 Eupatorium albicaule var
laxius Robinson n var
1476 Mimosa spirocarpa Rose n sp
1477 Mimosa polyantha Benth.
1478 " laxiflora Benth.
1481 Tragoceros mocinianum Gray
1482 Euphorbia pilulifera L
1487 Mimosa laxiflora Benth

Courtesy University of California

Palmer's own handwritten list distributed with a set of his specimens collected in the season 1891–92. The earliest known samples of Palmer's writing are remarkably like those from his later years.

Palmers Mexican Plants 1906

11 Brickellia vernicosa Robinson
17 Berlandiera lyrata Benth
19 Baileya nudicaulis Harv. & Gray
20 Anagallis arvensis L
23 Asclepias nummularia Torr
28 Cryptantha pusilla Greene
34 Erigeron divergens T. & Gr var cinereus Gray
35 Gaillardia comosa Gray
39 Salvia Greggii Gray
41 Aster ericaefolius Rothr
44 Dysodia chrysanthemoides Lag.
53 Brickellia Galeottii Gray
61 Wigandia urens Choisy.
62 Buddleia verticillata. H.B.K.
70 Bouplandia linearis Robinson
74 Eupatorium ramonense Robinson n sp
77 Adiantum tenerum Sw
77½ "
90 Eupatorium malacolepis Robinson n sp
96 Stevia subpubescens Lag
98 Acrostichum
100 Asclepias linaria Cav
108 Orobanche ludoviciana Nutt
116 Rapanea ferruginea Mez
139 Vernonia paniculata D.C.
140 " capreaefolia (Sch Bip) Gleason

An example of Palmer's handwriting, from a list distributed with a set of his specimens collected in 1906. Many museum specimens collected by Palmer are accompanied by fragmentary, unsigned MSS, and comparison of such MSS with samples may serve to identify the author.

Aspinwall, New Granada 9°22′N., 79°54′W.

1862, 1870. See San Francisco. This is the present city of Colón, C. Z., *q.v.* on map sheet N.C–17.

Asunción, Paraguay 25°17′S., 57°42′W. S.G–21

1853–54. Numerous collections made during the first visit of the *Water Witch* (October 1–November 7, 1853), both here and in the Paraguayan Chaco west of the Río Paraguay, opposite Asunción. On the return from Corumbá, *q.v.* (December 20, 1853) Palmer was here with the ship until January 30, 1854, when he left with her for Pilar (January 31), Guardia Vermejo (February 1), Corrientes (February 1), the vicinity of La Paz (February 3–5) and Montevideo (February 12–April 17). Leaving Montevideo with the ship on April 17, Palmer reached Asunción May 1, left again July 14 for Corrientes. See also Río Paraná (*52; 123a; 125c*).

Atajo (or Attajo)

1854. See Arroyo Atajo.

Aubrey City, Arizona (Mohave County) GLO, 1876

1876. March 12. A settlement at the mouth of Williams Fork, also spelled by Palmer "Aubry" and "Auberry." Appears as "Aubrey" on the GLO map, 1897. See Ehrenberg (*45*, items 24, 90).

Auburn, California (Placer County) GLO, 1928

1892. Visited June 24, while Palmer was traveling by stage from Placerville. Collected Nos. 2,402, 2,403, and 2,420. See California, and Coloma (*123a; 123c*).

Austin, Texas (Travis County)

1879. Probably early in October, enroute from San Antonio to visit some Indian mounds. See Texas.

Bacon Spring, New Mexico (McKinley County) GLO, 1886

1869. See Fort Wingate. In R 15 W, T 15 N, northeast of Fort Wingate, on the route from Albuquerque. For the route see U. S. Geological Survey map of northwestern New Mexico, 1/250,000, contour interval 200 feet (edition of 1881, 1882–83). For Bacon Spring see also Rand McNally map of New Mexico, *ca.* 1880, scale *ca.* 30 miles/inch.

Bahama Islands CGS, 1002

1874. See Nassau.

Bahía de Adair, Sonora 31°30′N., 113°55′W. N.H–12

1870. On August 9 of this year Palmer wrote S. F. Baird from the steamer *Cocopah:* "I am steaming down the Colorado River, yes am bound for Adair Bay." He reached Yuma August 13, and was at Puerta Isabel on September 4. Robert E. C. Stearns cites mollusks collected at Pinecate [*sic*] Bay, but gives no date for the collections; since the Pinacate Range is a prominent feature of the country immediately northeast of Bahía de Adair, it may be supposed that the name Bahía Pinacate is in local use for the same bay. There appears to be no other evidence bearing on this or any other visit made by Palmer to this area (*114a; 115*).

Bahía de los Angeles, Baja California 29°N., 113°30′W. N.H–11

1887. On the gulf coast. Palmer came here from Guaymas, on the steamer *Ometepec* (November 22); collected Nos. 500–606, 629–33, 657, 660, 675, and 676. Probably left for Guaymas (perhaps via Mulegé), about December 20. Called "Los Angeles Bay" by Palmer (*123a; 145*).

Bahía de San Quintín, Baja California 30°23′N., 115°56′W. N.H–11

1889. See San Quintín.

Bahía de Santa Rosalía, Baja California 28°30′N., 114°10′W. N.H–11

1889. On the Pacific coast; called "Rosalia Bay" by Palmer; see Lagoon Head.

Baja California N.H–11, N.H–12, N.G–12

1869. See Sonora, and Puerta Isabel.

1870. Carmen Island (January 1), enroute from Guaymas; La Paz (January 5) and Cabo San Lucas; left the latter January 9 for San Francisco, *q.v.;* Cabo San Lucas (February 7), enroute from San Francisco to Panama. For a possible later visit see Colorado River, mouth of (*123a*).

1875. See Isla de Guadalupe, and Tantillas Mountains.

1887. See Sonora, Mulegé, Isla San Pedro Mártir, and Bahía de los Angeles.

1889. Reached San Quintín about January 22, by steamer from San Diego; returned to San Diego about February 26; left about

March 1, reaching Lagoon Head before March 6; visited mines at Calmallí (March 11–12), and Rosalia Bay; left for Cedros Island March 15, arrived March 17, left March 22, arrived on "West San Benito Island" March 24, collected there March 25, collected on Guadalupe Island March 27 to April 3. On a second trip out from San Diego in early June spent a day and a night at Ensenada and was confined to bed for fifteen days at Colnett, returning to San Diego June 25 (*23; 114i; 123a; 123d; 132; 134*).

1890. Visited La Paz (January 6); revisited La Paz, from Guaymas (about January 19 to about February 6), making while there one trip to Rancho San José (January 24); visited Raza Island (February 12), and San Pedro Mártir Island (February 13); crossed from Guaymas to Santa Rosalía (February 23) and collected there until March 3, when he visited Santa Águeda, on horseback; returned to Santa Rosalía (March 6) and left March 16 for Mulegé and Guaymas. Visited Carmen Island from Guaymas, October to November (*114i; 123a; 134*).

Bakersville, North Carolina (Mitchell County)

1881. See Tennessee, and North Carolina.

Baldwin, Florida (Duval County) GLO, 1866–1926

1874. Visited in April, doubtless on the trip between Jacksonville and Cedar Keys; see Florida. A railroad junction called "Baldwin Junction" by Palmer, but appearing as "Baldwin" on maps (*114i*).

Ballena, California (San Diego County) GLO, 1900

1889. About 35 miles northeast of San Diego. See California.

Baracoa, Cuba (Oriente) 20°22′N., 74°29′W. N.F–18

1902. See Cuba.

Barra, Tamaulipas

1910. See La Barra.

Barranca (or Baranca), La, Jalisco

1886. See Guadalajara, and La Barranca.

Batesville, Arkansas (Independence County)

GLO, 1886, 1914

1883. Arrived probably October 28 from Newport; probably went directly to Little Rock, October 31. See Independence County (*88*).

Batomoral, Sonora

1890. Not located, but W. E. Safford (*123b*) states that Palmer stopped here April 9 while enroute from Álamos, *q.v.*, to Guaymas, by stage.

Batopilas, Chihuahua 27°01′N., 107°40′W. N.G–13

1885. Arrived about August 1, by mule caravan from Parral. Safford (*123b*) says: "Journeying by stages from water to water, they reached Yerba Buena, on the eastern slope of the mountains, whence they ascended to the *cumbre* or summit, thence down a barranca by a winding road through Frailes to the Hacienda San Miguel, near Batopilas." Palmer seems to have made at least one trip down the Río Batopilas to Hacienda San José. Left Batopilas early in October for Norogachic. While at Batopilas (making his headquarters at Hacienda San Miguel), collected Nos. 1–23, 71, 80–162, 164–93, 197–244, 246–50, 270, A, C–O, Q–W, Y, Z^1, Z^2, AA, and duplicate or supplementary Nos. 1a, 1b, 1c, 2a, 3, 3a, 4, 4a, 5–9, 10a, 11, 13, 14, 16, 18, 21, 22, 110a, 110d, 110e, 110f, 115, 115a, 115b, 117, 117a, 161, 162, 215. The field notes pertaining to the grasses from this locality were preserved by George Vasey and are now at the National Herbarium, including Nos. 10a, 40, 48, 48A, 49, 49½ 49¾, 49A, 49B, 49C, 50, 50F, 51, 51A, 52, 63, 63½, 63A, 63B, 65, 66, 73, 76, 78, 110A, 110D, 110E, 110F, 115, 115A, 115B, 117, 117A, 118, 153, 158–62, 206, 207. Several of these numbers were reported by Sereno Watson (*143*) as from San José, *q.v.*, and it may well be that all the above numbers from 40 to 78, inclusive, were collected at San José and were first included by Palmer among plants from the inclusive locality "Batopilas." The collector states on the field notes that the plants were collected during the month of August.

This place, and the river of the same name, are spelled "Batopillas" on Sheet N.G–13 (Culiacán), published in 1935. In the index to this map—*Index to Map of Hispanic America* 1/1,000,000 Part II (1944), 24—and on all other maps I have seen, the word is listed as Batopilas. See Chihuahua (Estado) (*114b; 123a; 143*).

Baxter Springs, Kansas (Cherokee County) GLO, 1891

1868. See Indian Territory. Spelled "Backsteer's" by Palmer (*45*, item 297).

Bean's Spring, Arizona (Yavapai, or Coconino, County)

1869. Not located, and perhaps same as Bear Spring, *q.v.*, but supposed to have been visited July 21, two nights out from Fort Whipple on the way to Bill Williams Mountain (*123a*).

Bear Flat Station, California (San Bernardino County)

1876. Not definitely located; perhaps in or near Bear Valley, which appears on Bergland's (*126*) map just north of Holcomb Valley, in latitude 34°19′N., longitude 117°W. Visited June 11; see San Bernardino (*123b*).

Bear Spring, Arizona (Coconino County)

1869. Not located, but probably the spring of this name about 4 miles northeast of the present site of Flagstaff. Several collections were made here, including *Campanula parryi,* which in Arizona reaches its southern limit on or near the San Francisco Peaks. A "Bear Spring" also appears on atlas sheet 75 of the Wheeler surveys (1876), about 10 miles south of Bill Williams Mountain on the Prescott road (*114i*).

Bear Valley, Utah (northeastern Iron County) GLO, 1908

1877. The Gray Herbarium list of Palmer's collection of 1877 shows that he made about 40 collections of plants at "Beaver Valley near Red Creek, Utah." "Beaver" is probably an error for "Bear," since Bear Valley lies just northeast of Red Creek, off the west slope of Bear Valley Peak. Had "Beaver Valley" been intended, it would doubtless have been located from Beaver ("Beaver City") rather than from Red Creek. Samuel Scudder indicates that Palmer collected butterflies in Bear Valley, July 4. See Red Creek (*34a; 110*).

Beaver, Utah (Beaver County) GLO, 1937

1870. Visited in June, enroute from Salt Lake City to St. George, *q.v.* Called "Beaver City" by Palmer.

1877. Arrived from Paragonah (Red Creek) about July 12; collected about 80 numbers of plants; collected in the "Wasatch Mts. near Beaver" (July 12–18) and in the "Beaver Mts." (July 18–20). On July 20 Palmer wrote: "Just returned from my second trip to the high mountains near this place this finish my botanical collecting in Utah." See Copeland's Mill, and North Creek. Left about July 21 for Spring Lake Villa (*24; 34a; 34b; 34d; 110; 113*).

Beaver Creek, Arizona (Yavapai County) GLO, 1933

1866. Camp Lincoln, *q.v.*, was at the junction of Beaver Creek with Río Verde. Palmer visited the "celebrated caves" two miles upstream from Camp Lincoln; he also "collected several specimens" at Montezuma Well, "8 miles from original Camp Virde" (i.e. Camp Lincoln) and 100 yards back from Beaver Creek (*45*, items 16, 21).

Beaver Dam, Arizona (Mohave County) GLO, 1921

1877. About 26 numbers of plants collected here along the Virgin River, April 20–?23. According to Safford, Palmer also collected at Mesquite Flat, Arizona (i.e. probably Nevada), "12 miles from Beaver Dam." The modern name of Beaver Dam is Littlefield. See St. George, St. Thomas (*34a; 123a; 110*).

Beaver Dam Mountains, Utah (Washington County) GLO, 1937

1870. Visited in June, enroute from St. George, Utah, to St. Thomas, Nevada, *q.v.* The mountains are about 15 miles west of St. George.

Beaver Mountains, Utah

1877. Probably the mountains east of Beaver, *q.v.*

Beaver Springs, Arizona (Mohave County)

1870. A name used by Palmer for Beaver Dam Creek, which flows into the Virgin River at Littlefield, in northwestern Mohave County. See St. Thomas, Nevada, and the GLO map of Arizona (1933).

Beaver Valley, Utah

1877. See Bear Valley.

Bellavista, Nayarit 21°35′N., 104°53′W. N.F–13

1892. Visited by coach, from Tepic, February 11 (*45*, item 189).

Bell's Canyon, Arizona (Yavapai County)

1869. See Fort Whipple.

Benton, Arkansas (Saline County) GLO, 1886

1883. See Saline County.

Bent's Old Fort, Colorado

A name which when used by Palmer probably refers to Fort Lyon; for discussion see under Fort Lyon.

Big Blue River, Nebraska (Gage County) GLO, 1922

1858. See Doniphan County, Kansas.

Big Butte Station, Idaho (southeastern Butte County)
GLO, 1899

1893. A stage station said by Palmer to be 40 miles west of Blackfoot, *q.v.*, and to take its name from the largest of several near-by buttes. On this butte was a perennial spring from which came the water supply at the station; about this spring Palmer made most of his collections, June 20–24 and probably August 11–12. For specimens collected see Blackfoot.

Big Cañon (of the Tantillas Mountains), Baja California
1875. See Tantillas Mountains.

Big Canyon, Idaho (?Bannock County)

1893. Said to be 5 miles south of Pocatello, *q.v.* Palmer ascended the canyon 2½ miles to "see the extent of the desert plants" and collected Nos. 389–99 (July 22). He noted that "Gibson Jack Creek runs down the canon," and also that this creek furnished the water supply for Pocatello. Professor Ray J. Davis suggests that the canyon may be that of Mink Creek (*45*, item 128; *114i; 123a*).

Big Cypress Mound, Arkansas (?southern Monroe County)
1881. See Monroe County.

Big Lake, Arkansas (Mississippi County) GLO, 1886
1881. October 28; see Osceola.

Bill Williams Fork, Arizona (between Yuma and Mohave counties) GLO, 1876

1870. An early name for the stream now usually called Williams River, *q.v.*

Bill Williams Mountain, Arizona (Coconino County)
GLO, 1933

1869. Palmer made a trip here from Fort Whipple, which he left July 20. He camped the first night at Poston's or Preston's (i.e. Postle's or Postal's ?) Ranch, 22 miles from the fort. The second night's camp was at Bean's Spring. From Poston's Ranch the distances were: to Hell Canyon 12 miles, then to Turkey Creek 15 miles, "Quaker Aspens" 9 miles, and the mountain 8 miles. He reached Fort Whipple on the return on July 30, probably leaving the mountain July 28 (*114b; 114g; 123a*).

Bird Spring, Arizona

1869. See Fort Wingate. Not located, but said by Palmer to be but a few miles from Oraibi; possibly this was Palmer's corruption of Burro Spring.

Biscayne Bay, Florida (south of Miami, Dade County) GLO, 1926

1874. June 25–July 5, probably on a trip out from Key West; collected about 130 numbers of vascular plants and 21 of algae (*20; 22; 34a*).

1884. Perhaps visited in September of this year; see Florida (*123a*).

Bitter Spring, Nevada (Clark County)

1870. June 25, enroute from St. Thomas, Nevada, to Hardyville, *q.v.* The locality was about 18 miles southwest of the site of St. Thomas; called by Palmer "Bitter Springs." It is mapped on the St. Thomas sheet, USGS (1929) (*123a*).

Blackfoot, Idaho (Bingham County) GLO, 1939

1893. Arrived June 17, by rail from Pocatello; went the same day by stage to Arco and there collected Nos. 163–99, 560, and 602; returned to Big Butte Station (June 20) and collected Nos. 200–46 and a large supplementary series (see below), June 20–24; returned to Blackfoot (June 25) and collected Nos. 247–306 and a large supplementary series (see below); went to Dubois (Dry Creek) July 10 and collected Nos. 307–43, 564, 566, 571, 588, 599; returned to Idaho Falls (July 15) and collected Nos. 344–88; returned to Pocatello (July 20). On a second visit to Blackfoot arrived August 8, from Pocatello; collected Nos. 453–72 (August 9); went by stage (August 10) to Big Butte Station and collected Nos. 473–505 (August 11–12); some of the collections are labeled Big Butte Station and some merely Big Butte. Returned to Blackfoot (August 12) and to Pocatello, via Ross Fork (August 16). Collections from Blackfoot, in addition to the above, are Nos. 552, 554, 555, 557, 559, 567, 573, 580, 582, 584, 589, 591, 592, 597, and 601 (June 29–July 8); Nos. 553, 556, 558, 561, 563, 569, 570, 574, 577–79, 581, 583, 590, 593, 594, and 600 (June 20–24) are from the vicinity of Big Butte Station (*45*, item 128; *114i; 123a*).

Black River, Louisiana (Catahoula, or Concordia, Parish) GLO, 1930

1883. See Louisiana.

Blados, Mexico

1878. Same as Bledos, San Luis Potosí, *q.v.* (*34d*).

Blakely, Georgia (Early County)

1884. Arrived March 20, probably from Mobile, Alabama; stayed until about May 1, working at mounds about 7 miles north of Blakely and traveling there each day by wagon. The locality is also called "Bradley" in the records of the Division of Ethnology, which show that Catalog Nos. 92,001–33 were collected here (except 2 numbers from Albany, Georgia). See Georgia (*114c; 114f*).

Bledos, San Luis Potosí 21°51′N., 101°07′W. N.F–14

1878. This is probably the Hacienda Bledos which Palmer visited after Parry's departure from San Luis Potosí. The length of his stay is unknown, but he seems to have been here as early as September 25, and Scudder reports insects collected here October 1. He is known to have made a trip by burro to the Sierra de San Miguelito, a few kilometers to the north of Bledos, about this time, and he may have made but the one trip in this direction, including Bledos in his itinerary. Bledos lies in the foothills at an elevation of about 2,000 m., and at the present time is accessible only by a rather roundabout and difficult road by way of Pozos, Jesús María, and Villa de Reyes. Archaeological material was sent to the Peabody Museum from "Blados," which is doubtless Palmer's phonetic variant of the name. See Pila (*34d; 113*).

Blountsville, Alabama (Blount County) GLO, 1889

1883. Visited May 15; about this time Palmer seems also to have visited Crump Cave, said to be 15 miles southeast of Blountsville [15 miles south, according to Thomas (*119*), who calls it Camp's or Cramp's Cave] (*34a; 114b*).

Blue Lakes, Idaho (southwestern Jerome County) GLO, 1939

1893. A few miles north of Twin Falls, just north of the Snake River. Palmer made two visits here, driving a team from Shoshone. Arrived June 1; collected Nos. 59–87, 576; drove to Shoshone Falls June 3; returned to Shoshone, *q.v.*, on June 6, probably directly from Shoshone Falls. On the second visit arrived August 22; collected Nos. 519–31; returned to Shoshone August 24 by team (*123a*).

Blue River, [Oklahoma] (Johnston County) GLO, 1876

1868. See Boggy Depot. The road from Cherokee Town to Boggy Depot crossed Blue River east of Tishomingo. Palmer collected plants and birds here, probably near the stage road, but the dates as given in his field notes (June 20, 27, 29, and 30) appear to be no more than approximately correct (*114e; 120*).

Bluewater, New Mexico (Valencia County) GLO, 1886

1869. See Fort Wingate.

Bluffton, Texas (Burnet County)

1879. Palmer made about 22 collections here (October 10–15) and perhaps collected elsewhere in Burnet County. The dates conflict with those given for his visit to Georgetown, *q.v.* (*142*).

Blythe Colony, Sonora

1884–85. Same as Colonia Lerdo, *q.v.* This name not located on any map.

Boca de la Abra, Tamaulipas

1879. Not located on any map, but apparently the pass used by the modern highway, northeast of Antiguo Morelos, in latitude approximately 22°37′N., longitude 99°02′W. The mountain range through which the road passes is called variously the Sierra Tanchipa, Sierra del Abra de Tanchipa, or Sierra Boca del Abra. Palmer left Ciudad del Maíz, San Luis Potosí, on January 27, on horseback; he reached Boca de la Abra the third day and then, passing out of the mountains, camped the third night in the lowlands. His way seems subsequently to have led to Gavia, Las Norias, Naranjo and thence to Tantoyuquita, which he reached January 30th (*114i*).

Boca del Monte, Puebla 18°49′N., 97°19′W. Atlas, 36

1877. Palmer had breakfast here December 23, enroute by rail from Veracruz to Mexico City (*114i*).

Boggy Depot, [Oklahoma] (southwestern Atoka County) GLO, 1876

1868. In 1868 in the Choctaw Nation. Called "Boggey Depot" by Palmer, who apparently made a trip here over the road from Cherokee Town, *q.v.*, starting about June 20, and returning about July 3. The road went by way of present Mill Creek (Johnston County), crossed Pennington Creek about 1½ miles southeast of the present Reagan (Johnston County), and crossed Blue River east of Tishomingo, Johnston County.

Palmer's field notes covering the period from June 20 to July 2, inclusive (Nos. 295–441) are apparently confused, suggesting either that he made several quick trips along the above road or that he gave incorrect dates or localities for some collections. According to his notes he collected plants in the Choctaw Nation on June 24, 25, 26, 27, 28, 29, and 30, and July 1, and in the Chickasaw Nation on June 22, 23, 24, 25, 26, 27, and 28, and July 1 and 2. The western boundary of the Choctaw Nation was near Boggy Depot, running north and south almost in the center of R 8 E, but it does not seem likely that the collector traveled repeatedly back and forth, especially since some of the distances run to the order of 50 miles.

What seems to be a possible reconstruction of his trip to Boggy Depot is set forth below, with dates and localities as given by Palmer, with the localities enclosed in brackets if probably incorrect:

June 22, 23, 24. Chickasaw Nation (probably near Cherokee Town).

June 25. Boiling Spring, Chickasaw Nation; Pennington Creek; [Riley's Mills].

June 26. Pennington Creek; Boiling Spring; "Boiling Spring to Riley's Mills"; Riley's Mills, Choctaw Nation; Boggy Depot; Boggy River, Choctaw Nation.

June 27. [Blue River, Choctaw Nation]; [Riley's Mills]; [Pennington Creek]; "entrance to mts., Ft. Smith road, Choctaw Nation."

June 29. Boggy Depot; [Blue River].

June 30. Boggy Depot; [Blue River].

July 1. Boggy Depot; Blue River; Pennington Creek.

July 2. Pennington Creek; Boiling Spring; Flat Rock Creek; Mill Creek.

It seems likely that the trip to Boggy Depot took two days, with an overnight stop near Pennington Creek. Nothing is known of Palmer's mode of travel. The above localities are discussed under their own headings in the alphabetical index, except for "entrance to mts., Ft. Smith road, Choctaw Nation." From the dates given it may be surmised that this was near Boggy Depot, and Miss Muriel H. Wright suggests that it may have been in the rough canyon-like country just west and south of that place (*114e; 120*).

Boggy River, [Oklahoma] (Atoka County) GLO, 1894

1868. The road to Fort Smith crossed the river 1 mile east of Boggy Depot, *q.v.*[2]

Boiling Spring, [Oklahoma]

1868. Palmer collected plants here, in the Chickasaw Nation, probably June 25 and 26, and July 2; see Boggy Depot. Not located on any map, but most probably in the vicinity of the present village of Reagan, Johnston County, near the stage road crossing of Pennington Creek (*120*).

Bolinas Ridge, California (Marin County)

1892. Palmer located at the Summit Hotel and collected Nos. 2,041–48 and 2,096–2,354 (June 14–16). No. 2,333 is omitted, and Nos. 2,100–2,299, inclusive, are missing from the series, No. 2,300 following 2,099 in the field notes. The field notes indicate a second visit to Bolinas Ridge on June 25, when Nos. 2,405–2,418 were collected. The locality was mapped on the Tamalpais sheet, USGS (1907). See California (*123a; 123c*).

Boludo, San Luis Potosí or Tamaulipas

1878. Same as El Boludo, *q.v.*

Boston, Massachusetts

1873–81. See Cambridge.

Boundary Monument (near San Diego), California

1875. Visited September 16, probably while Palmer was returning from the Tantillas Mountains; he made several collections, and a single one at "Dry Creek near Boundary Monument," September 18 (*123a*). The monument in question is presumably one of those erected by W. H. Emory's party during the course of the United States and Mexican Boundary Survey more than twenty years before Palmer's visit. The monuments numbered 1 and 2, according to Emory's report, were located in longitudes 117°08′29.7″W., and 117°03′31.7″W., respectively.[3] It seems likely that Monument 2, which was not far from Tiajuana and consequently not far from the road over which he passed while on the way to Fort Yuma, was the one visited by Palmer.

[2] See *Chronicles of Oklahoma*, Vol. V (1927), 4–17.

[3] W. H. Emory, *Report on the United States and Mexican Boundary Survey* (1857), I, 242.

Bowling Green, Kentucky (Warren County)
1879. Palmer was here June 25, enroute to Texas. See Cambridge.

Bradley, Georgia
1884. Same as Blakely, *q.v.*

Bradley's Landing, Arkansas
?1881, 1883. Same as Oldham, *q.v.*

Brazil
1853. See Paraguay.

Bridal Veil Falls, California (San Bernardino County)
1876. May 29, in the ascent of San Bernardino Mountain; see San Bernardino.

Brookfield Mound, Arkansas
?1882. Near Harrisburgh, *q.v.*

Brown County, Kansas
1858. See Doniphan County.

Bryant Station, Arkansas (Saline County) GLO, 1886
1883. September 16. See Saline County. A station about 6 miles northeast of Benton, on the St. Louis, Iron Mt. & Southern Branch of the Missouri Pacific Railroad (*88*).

Buena Vista, San Luis Potosí 21°57′N., 99°05′W. N.F–14
1878–79. Visited about December 29 to January 1; see Ciudad del Maíz (*114i*).

Buenos Aires, Argentina 34°35′S., 58°24′W. S.I–21
1853. The *Water Witch* reached Montevideo in May, 1853, and lay at anchor there and at Buenos Aires until August 31, when she began the ascent of the Río Paraná. See Paraguay (*52; 123a; 125c*).

Buey, Tamaulipas 23°03′N., 99°57′W. N.F–14
1878. December ?4; see Sierra Naola (*114i*).

Burnet County, Texas
1878. See Bluffton.

Burnt Palm, California (?Riverside County)
1870. Palmer passed along the stage route from Ehrenberg, Ari-

zona, to San Bernardino; Burnt Palm was slightly northwest of the Salton Sea. See Los Angeles.

Byron Hot Springs, California (southeastern Contra Costa County) GLO, 1928

1892. Visited August 17–20, enroute from San Francisco to Tulare County; collected Nos. 2,672–82. See California (*123a; 123c*).

Cabin Creek, [Oklahoma] GLO, 1876

1863. See Fort Scott for Palmer's participation in the battle of Cabin Creek. Description of the battle is given in the *Chronicles of Oklahoma*.[4]

1868. January or early February, and October. See Indian Territory. Cabin Creek enters the Neosho River from the north in present Mayes County, Oklahoma, northeast of Pryor. The road from Fort Gibson to Fort Scott, in Palmer's time followed the course of the Neosho, 55 miles to Cabin Creek (*45*, item 297).

Cabo San Lucas, Baja California 22°52′N., 109°53′W. N.G–12

1870. The tip of the peninsula, visited January 9 and February 7; see San Francisco, and Baja California. Called "Cape San Lucas" by Palmer, who collected a number of shells and a few plants (*45*, item 53; *114e; 114h*).

Caesar Creek, Florida (Dade County) CGS, 1249

1884. Collections from here are cited by Rathbun (*94*), who calls it Caesar's Creek. It is a channel between Elliott Key and Old Rhodes Key, in latitude 25°23′N., longitude 80°14′W. See Florida.

Cajon, California

1875. See El Cajon.

Calamali, Baja California

1889. Same as Calmallí, *q.v.*, or see Lagoon Head.

Caliente, California (Kern County) GLO, 1928

1888. Arrived from San Bernardino by rail (June 2); stayed two days awaiting the stage to Kernville. Probably passed here again on the return from Kernville, and again on a second trip, in July (*114i*).

California GLO, 1876, 1907, 1928

1861–62. Arrived in Hangtown (Placerville) about August 24 or

[4] Vol. X (1932), 44–51.

25, and reached San Francisco August 26. Joined the Geological Survey of California, about October 10, working at San Diego as assistant to J. G. Cooper, collecting marine invertebrates. Left San Diego for San Francisco, January 26, 1862; left San Francisco for Acapulco, Guerrero, February 11. See San Francisco or Colorado (*114b; 114g; 123a*).

1867. See San Francisco.

1870. See Los Angeles, and San Francisco.

1875. After returning from Guadalupe Island, Palmer visited Soledad (June 23), Jamul Valley (June 25–26), returned to San Diego, made a trip to Tigh's Ranch (July 5–6), Talley's Ranch in the Cuyamaca Mountains (July 7–17), Julian (July 18–20). For other localities see Julian, whence he returned to San Diego, *q.v.*, and undertook a trip to the east, for which see Fort Yuma and Tantillas Mountains. Returning to San Diego again (September 16 or 18), he left for San Francisco (about October 7) and went on to St. George, Utah (about October 12).

1876. Came to San Bernardino after leaving Salt Lake City (about January 15); left for Arizona by coach (February 29). Leaving Hardyville, Arizona, by coach (about May 12 or 13), he passed Rock Springs, California (May 14), the sink of the Mojave River, Stoddards (May 19), and Crafton (May 23), arriving in San Bernardino May 25. He visited San Bernardino Mountain (May 29–31) and returned to Crafton; left on a trip to the Mojave River (June 8), reaching Stoddards (June 10), Holcomb's and Bear Flat Station (June 11), returning to Crafton (June 14). Went to San Luis Obispo, arriving June 26; visited Hollands Ranch and Clarks Creek (July 2–3), McGinnis Ranch (July 10), Cambria (July 17); left San Luis Obispo (July 21), reaching Pine Mountain and San Simeon Bay (July 22), Paso Robles Spring (July 28), Jolon (July 31), and the Santa Lucia Mountains (August 2). Reached San Francisco about mid-August and soon left for Nevada by train.

1888. Reached San Bernardino May 26; left with W. G. Wright, by rail, for Caliente (June 2), thence went by stage to Kernville; returned to San Bernardino (June 16); visited Los Angeles and San Diego; returned to San Bernardino (June 24); visited Victor (June 25–27); returned to Kernville, thence went to Long Meadow (mid-July) and returned to San Bernardino (late July); established headquarters at San Diego (August to December), visiting Catalina Island (August), the Coronados Islands (?August), and Yuma, Arizona (October). Left for San Quintín, Baja California, about January 20, 1889 (*23; 34a; 114i; 123a; 133*).

1889. Leaving San Diego (about May 15) for the Coahuila Valley and Warner's Ranch, Palmer traveled from El Cajon to Ballena by stage; he hired a team for the period May 18–22, but his movements are unknown. June 3 he wrote Vasey from San Diego: "Everything was dried up . . . so hastily returned." Apparently no plants were collected. See San Diego (*114i*).

1892. Reaching San Francisco from Nayarit, *q.v.* (probably early in May), Palmer went to Palm Springs to be cured of sciatic rheumatism. He returned to San Francisco (about May 19), went to Sacramento and Chico (about June 3–12), returned to San Francisco, visited Mt. Tamalpais (June 13), the Summit Hotel on Bolinas Ridge (June 14–16), Sausalito (June 20), Oakland (June 22), Coloma (June 23–24), Cool and Auburn (June 24); he is supposed to have made a second visit to Bolinas Ridge (June 25); he visited Petaluma (June 27) and Vallejo (July 6). He made a trip to Mt. Shasta and Sisson (July 13–27) and Edgewood (July 28–31), returning to San Francisco (about August 5) and making his headquarters at the California Academy of Sciences. He made a trip to Visalia and Tulare, via Byron Hot Springs (August 17–20), and Tracy (August 22–23), reaching "Tulare City" about August 25 and leaving there for Palm Springs, September 10. He probably left for Washington, D. C., about October 1 (*45*, item 61; *114i; 123a; 123c.*)

Callville, Nevada (Clark County)

1870. Spent the night of June 25–26 here; see Hardyville. On the Colorado River about 35 miles southwest of St. Thomas; the site is now submerged under the waters of Lake Mead. It was mapped on the St. Thomas Sheet, USGS (1929).

Calmallí, Baja California 28°05′N., 113°23′W. N.H–11

1889. See Lagoon Head. Collections said to have been made 40 or 45 miles inland from Lagoon Head are probably from this vicinity.

Cambria, California (northwestern San Luis Obispo County) GLO, 1928

1876. Palmer is said to have collected "a mile from the beach," July 17. About 15 numbers are listed by Gray. See California (*34a*).

Cambridge, Massachusetts (Middlesex County)

1873. Upon returning from Portland, Maine, in October, Palmer accepted a position with the Museum of Comparative Zoology. He gave this up in January, 1874, to go on a trip to Florida, *q.v.* (*20; 114i; 123a*).

1874. Returned from Florida (probably mid-September) and stayed until December, when he left by train for New Haven and San Francisco (*20; 34b; 123a*).

1876. See Davenport.

1877. Left Davenport, Iowa, for Cambridge, October 8; left Boston for New York, December 5 (*20; 24; 90; 114i*).

1879. Arrived from New York, *q.v.*, about March 20. Was engaged by the Peabody Museum to collect in Texas and Mexico. Left Boston, probably by boat for Norfolk, Virginia, about June 21, thence traveled by rail via Bowling Green, Kentucky (June 25), Nashville and Memphis, Tennessee (July 2), reaching Longview, Texas July 3 (*20; 34d; 114a; 114i; 123a*).

1880–81. Arrived from Texas about mid-November; left for Washington, D. C., about June 20, 1881.

Camp Apache, Arizona (southern Navajo County)
GLO, 1897

1890. Same as Fort Apache, *q.v.*

Camp Bowie, Arizona (northeastern Cochise County)
GLO, 1879

1869. Visited late in October, on a trip from Tucson; Palmer is said to have collected here the type of *Agave palmeri* Engelm., at this time. This locality appears on the GLO map, 1921, as Old Camp Bowie.

Camp Colorado, Arizona (Yuma County)

1870. Arrived from Murray's at the mouth of Williams Fork, probably about July 20; stayed "a day or two" and probably went by steamer to Yuma, *q.v.* Camp Colorado was an army post said by Palmer to be 25 miles below the mouth of Williams Fork; the post was 1 mile above the Colorado River agency of the Mohave Indians, and so about 47 miles above La Paz (*45*, item 15; *124a*).

Camp Date Creek, Arizona (southwestern Yavapai County) GLO, 1879

1869. Some collections were made here during a visit of several days or weeks; Palmer left for Ehrenberg September 16. This locality appears on the GLO map, 1921, as Old Camp Date Creek. See Yuma *(123a)*.

Campeche, Campeche 19°50′N., 90°32′W. N.E–15

1877. See Veracruz (Ciudad) (*114i*).

Camp Evans, Colorado (?Denver County)

1862. June 2. Not located on a map, but according to information furnished by Dr. L. R. Hafen, this was an army camp 2½ miles north of Denver, on the South Platte River. See Fort Leavenworth.

Camp Grant, Arizona (eastern Pinal County) GLO, 1879

1866–67. This locality appears on the GLO map, 1921, as Old Camp Grant. South of the Gila River at the junction of Arivaipa Creek and Río San Pedro, in R 16 E, T 7 S. Palmer arrived in December, 1866, from Camp Lincoln, *q.v.* He collected in the vicinity of the camp and on scouting trips with the troops. He went on one scout which left Camp Grant April 21, 1867, went up the Arivaipa 25 miles, then generally north an estimated 50 miles to the junction of the Gila and San Carlos ("St. Charles") rivers; on April 26, 8 miles west (i.e. down the Gila); on the twenty-seventh, south from the Gila and down the "San Romickeo" river, a tributary of the San Pedro, 20 miles; on the twenty-eighth, southwest down the "San Pedro hills" and along Willow Creek to Camp Grant. Because of recurrent malaria and perhaps other illness, Palmer on March 31 had requested the annulment of his contract as acting assistant surgeon, U.S.A., and he was relieved of his post by Army orders of May 29 and July 23, and his contract was annulled at San Francisco as of September 30. He left Camp Grant about August 1, for San Francisco, probably traveling via Davidson's Springs and Tucson and thence by the Southern Pacific Mail Stage line to Yuma, Los Angeles and his destination, *qq.v.*

At or near Camp Grant Palmer collected about 200 numbers of plants, which were sent to Engelmann for identification; a few duplicates are at the Gray Herbarium. He also collected about 100 birds, which were sent to the Smithsonian Institution, and an undetermined number of mammals. W. C. Barnes[5] (*7*) discusses the location of

Camp Grant, but is uncertain of its situation at the time of Palmer's stay there. From the latter's notes and remarks it is clear that in 1866–67 the post was on the Río San Pedro, at or near the mouth of Arivaipa Creek (*24; 45*, items 10, 20; *102; 114e; 123a; 125d; 125f*).

Camp Halleck, Nevada (Elko County) GLO, 1876

1876. Reached by train from San Francisco, *q.v.*, August 26. Palmer may have made a special trip here, since Camp Halleck lay several miles southeast from the line of the Central Pacific Railroad. Gray lists 28 collections from here (*34a*).

Camp Lincoln, Arizona (east-central Yavapai County) GLO, 1879

1865. Camp Lincoln (later called Camp or Fort Verde) was on the Río Verde about 55 or 60 miles by road east of Prescott, and about 7 miles below the mouth of Beaver Creek. In the early spring of 1866 the encampment was moved to the mouth of Beaver Creek.

After undertaking a contract as acting assistant surgeon, U.S.A., Palmer came here from Fort Whipple before November 1, 1865 (by order dated at Prescott, October 20), and was stationed here until about September 1, 1866, accompanying his unit on scouting trips and trips for supplies, visiting Fort Whipple and perhaps the San Francisco Mountains, and making an eight-day trip eastward "against the Apaches." From Camp Lincoln he went to Fort Whipple, where he was confined to the hospital for some time previous to November 1, 1866, before proceeding to Camp Grant, *q.v.* See Fort Whipple, and Grief Hill (*45*, item 22; *114b; 123a; 125d*).

1869. Palmer wrote on July 30, from Fort Whipple, that in two days he planned to leave for Camp Lincoln, a trip which he mentioned also in notes made in later years. A few specimens in the National Herbarium are labeled as from Camp Lincoln, with the date 1869 (*45*, item 22; *114b; 114i*).

Camp McDowell, Arizona (northeastern Maricopa County) GLO, 1879

1869. Listed on the GLO map of 1912, as "Old Ft. McDowell." See Yuma.

[5] Will C. Barnes, *Arizona Place Names*, University of Arizona *Bulletin No. 6* (1935). An extremely useful compendium of historical and geographical materials relating to Arizona.

Camp Mohave, Arizona

1869. Same as Fort Mohave, *q.v.*

Campo, California (San Diego County) GLO, 1928

1875. A few collections were made here August 17. The locality *(12)* is sometimes cited as "Milquatay." Safford says that Palmer's trip to the "Big Cañon of the Tantillas" was made by wagon from Campo; if that is true, Palmer doubtless left Campo September 5 or 6; see Fort Yuma (*34a; 123a*).

Camp Verde, Arizona GLO, 1933

1865–69. Same as Camp Lincoln, *q.v.*

Camp Wallen, Arizona (southwestern Cochise County) GLO, 1912

1867. Listed on the map as "Old Camp Wallin." See Wallen.

Camp Weld, Colorado Denver County

1862. Palmer arrived June 6, from Fort Leavenworth, *q.v.;* Camp Weld was then newly established 2 miles from Denver (within the present city limits). He was quartered here for about six months, collecting near Denver, and in the near-by high mountains, and also on trips to Fort Lyon, Colorado, Fort Larned, Kansas, and perhaps Fort Craig, New Mexico, *qq.v.* (*114b; 123a*).

Camp Willow Grove, Arizona (Mohave County) GLO, 1887

1876. Among Palmer's collections of this year is listed a single one from "Willow Grove"; it may be that this came from the site of Camp Willow Grove, which from 1866 to 1869 was an army camp on the Prescott–Camp Mohave road. See Arizona (*7, 34a*).

Canadian River, Indian Territory

1868. Palmer's field notes mention collections made near this river, July 19, presumably on a trip into the Seminole Nation, *q.v.*, from Cherokee Town, *q.v.*

Cano Quicksilver Mine, [San Luis Potosí]

1878. See El Carro.

Canoas, San Luis Potosí 21°57′N., 99°32′W. N.F–14

1902. Arrived from the city of San Luis Potosí, October 15; collected Nos. 214–77; returned to San Luis Potosí October 22. Canoas is a station on the railroad from San Luis Potosí to Tampico; it appears as "Las Canoas" on many Mexican maps. On the labels distributed from the National Herbarium with Palmer's collections, the name of the locality is spelled "Los Canos" (*114i; 123c*).

Cantillas Mountains, Baja California
1875. Same as Tantillas Mountains, *q.v.*

Cañon de Chelly, Arizona (northern Apache County)
GLO, 1933
1869. June 13. Palmer was here with a small party returning from Oraibi to Fort Defiance. A specimen of *Opuntia acanthocarpa* at the Missouri Botanical Garden bears this date and the notation "Canon De Chey." See Fort Wingate.

Cañon del Novillo, Tamaulipas
1907. The canyon of the Río San Marcos, southwest and west of Ciudad Victoria, *q.v.*

Cañon de Salamanca, Tamaulipas
1907. Near Ciudad Victoria, *q.v.;* same as Cañon Seco.

Cañon Seco, Tamaulipas
1907. Near Ciudad Victoria, *q.v.*

Canyon Spring, California (southern Riverside County)
1870. A stage station on the Ehrenberg–San Bernardino route, shown on Bergland's (*126*) map in latitude 33°32′N., longitude 115° 40′W. Called "Canyon Springs" by Palmer. See Los Angeles.

Cape Florida Reef, Florida (Dade County) GLO, 1926
1874. June 26–30, on a trip from Key West along the Keys toward Miami; collections were made here, and some are labeled simply "Cape Florida." Cape Florida is the southern tip of Key Biscayne, about 5 miles southeast of Miami. Cape Florida Reef is apparently the same as Cape Florida Shoal, a little offshore to the southeast (*20; 34a*).[6]

Cape San Lucas, Baja California
1870. See Cabo San Lucas.

[6] U. S. Coast and Geodetic Survey *Chart No. 1248* (1921).

Caracol Mountain or Mountains, Coahuila

1880. Palmer collected about 70 numbers of plants here, August 19–22. This range has not been located on any map, but it is said to be 21 (or 25) miles southeast of Monclova, and is apparently the same as the Sierra de la Gloria of most maps, including sheet N.G–14 of the Millionth Map (Lat. 26°48′N., long. 101°15′W.). I am informed by Dr. Ivan M. Johnston that a spring in these same mountains is locally called "Caracol," and it may be that the whole range has been called by the same name (*2; 142*).

Carey's Fort Reef, Florida (Monroe County)

1884. Said to have been visited August 6; see Florida. East of Key Largo, in latitude 25°13′N., longitude 80°13′W. Usually spelled "Carysfort"; listed as "Carysford" on the maps of the General Land Office (1911, 1926), but probably incorrectly so.

Carmen Island, Baja California

1870, 1890. See Isla Carmen, Baja California.

Carneros Pass, Coahuila

1880. Not mentioned by Palmer; see Sierra Madre.

Carpenter's Mound, Arkansas

1883. Near Arkadelphia, *q.v.*

Carson Lake Township, Arkansas (Mississippi County)

?1881. Palmer found skeletons in mounds on farm of Hugh Waller, 6 miles "a little southwest" of Osceola (*88*).

Carthage, Tennessee (Smith County)

1883. June 18, enroute to St. Louis, after visiting Nashville and probably other places enumerated under Tennessee, *q.v.* (*114b*).

Casa Grande, Arizona (Pinal County) GLO, 1933

1885. See Pima Indian Agency. Apparently Palmer did not visit the ruins of Casa Grande, but merely the station of this name on the Southern Pacific Railroad.

Cascada Station, Alabama

1884. Error for Coosada; see Elmore County.

Castillo Rapids, Nicaragua

1867. See Rápidos Castillo, and San Francisco, California.

Catalina Island, California

1888. See Santa Catalina Island.

Cedar City, Utah (Iron County) GLO, 1937

1870. See Cedarville.

Cedar Hammock Group (of mounds), Alabama

?1884. See Sumter County.

Cedar Keys, Florida (Levy County) GLO, 1926

1874. Arrived overland from Jacksonville (about April 25) and left by boat for Key West (about May 1). Returned to Cedar Keys, probably by boat from Key West, for the period August 3–12. Made about 37 collections of vascular plants and 16 of algae, the latter in August (*20; 22; 34a; 123a*).

1884. July 13; probably left July 14 by boat for Key West; see Florida (*114c*).

Cedar Ridges, Arizona

1877. Same as Juniper Mts., *q.v.* Not the same as the Juniper Mountains of his 1876 collection.

Cedarville, Utah

1870. Early June; see St. George. Not located on any map, and from Palmer's itinerary apparently the same as Cedar City, Iron County. The name Cedar City was current at an early date (*123a*).

Cedros (or Cerros) Island, Baja California

1889. See Isla de Cedros, Baja California.

Central City, Colorado (Gilpin County) GLO, 1934

1861, 1862. Palmer collected here; see Colorado. At the time of his visit this was the "metropolis" of the important Gregory Mines.[7]

Cerbat Mountains, Arizona (Mohave County) GLO, 1933

1876. According to Gray's list of Palmer's collections of this year, 2 numbers were collected May 6, "about 35 miles east of Hardyville, Cerbat Mountain Pass." See Arizona (*34a*).

Cerro del Pueblo, Coahuila

1904. Palmer collected here probably several times, from August to October. Not located on any map; actually a treeless ridge 50–75 m.

[7] O. J. Hollister, *Mines of Colorado* (Springfield, Mass., 1867).

high, crested with bare rock ledges, beginning near the western edge of the city of Saltillo and extending a short distance to the northwest. The lower slopes are sparsely covered with *Larrea* and *Agave lechеguilla.* Said by Palmer to be 3 miles north of the "Plaza de Armes," Saltillo, and called by him "Cerro del Puebla" or "Cierra de Puebla" *(34a).*

Cerro de Mercado, Durango 24°03′N., 104°40′W. N.G–13

1896. Same as Iron Mountain, *q.v.*, just north of the city of Durango.

Cerro de Santa Rosa, Chihuahua

1908. Not located on a map; a low rounded hill about at the southern edge of the city of Chihuahua, now (1951) bare and rocky, with a sparse covering of thorny shrubs. Visited by Palmer on April 24 and May 18; see Chihuahua (Estado).

Cerros Island, Baja California

1889. See Isla de Cedros, Baja California.

Chaco, Paraguayan

1853. See Asunción.

Chairs Mound, Arkansas

1882. Near Forrest City, *q.v.*

Chalco, México 19°16′N., 98°54′W. N.E–14

1878. Visited May 19, by canal from México, D. F., *q.v.* (*114i*).

Chapala, Jalisco 20°18′N., 103°11′W. N.F–13

1886. Nos. 701–28 collected here, October 27–November 3; this place is situated on the north shore of Lake Chapala (the largest lake in Mexico), at the foot of a semiarid mountain range which parallels the lake shore and descends steeply to it. Elevation at Chapala is about 1,400 m. above sea level, and the mountains along the lake west of the city rise to an average level of about 2,000 m. See Jalisco *(123a; 144).*

Charleston, Missouri (Mississippi County) GLO, 1891

1882. Palmer came here from Tennessee and spent June 26–30, investigating the making of spurious "mound pottery"; he went on to Osceola, Arkansas, about July 1 (*88; 114b; 114c*).

Charleston, Tennessee (Bradley County)
1882. April (?); see Tennessee.
1883. June (?); see Tennessee.

Chattanooga, Tennessee (Hamilton County)
1882. April 17–?20; see Tennessee.
1883. June 10; see Tennessee.

Cheatham County, Tennessee
?1883. Palmer reported stone graves near Ashland City, according to Thomas (*118*); see Nashville.

Cherokee Town, [Oklahoma] (Garvin County) GLO, 1876
1868. In the Chickasaw Nation at the junction of Rush Creek and Washita River, near the present site of Pauls Valley (4 miles from Smith Pauls—now Pauls Valley—according to Palmer). Palmer passed through here on February 17, on his way up the Washita to Fort Cobb, *q.v.* He returned on or before June 8; collected plants numbered 239–94 (June 8–12); made a trip southeastward through the Chickasaw and Choctaw nations to Boggy Depot, *q.v.*, and collected Nos. 295–441 (June 20 to July 2 or 3); collected in the vicinity of Cherokee Town (July 9–14); made a trip northeastward into the Seminole Nation (*ca.* July 18–20); and finally collected again in the vicinity of Cherokee Town (August 6–September 10). He collected Nos. 442–84 between July 9 and September 10. He was in Cherokee Town on September 22, recovering from an attack of fever and planning to leave for Leavenworth, Kansas, about the end of the month. See Indian Territory (*114b; 120; 123a*).

Cherry Creek, Colorado GLO, 1934
1862. A tributary of the South Platte River, which it enters from the southeast near Denver; see Colorado. Palmer was here during the summer, near the "headwaters of Cherry Creek . . . where gold was first discovered 35 miles south of Denver" (*114b*).

Cherry Valley, Arkansas (Cross County) GLO, 1886
1882. November 1, probably enroute from Harrisburgh to Forrest City, *q.v.* Palmer points out that at this time the settlement of Cherry Valley was but three months old (*88*).

Chester, South Carolina (Chester County)
1884. See South Carolina.

Chichimequillas, Guanajuato 21°02′N., 101°26′W. N.F–14

1898. August. Said by Palmer to be "in sight of Trinidad" (it is about 12–13 km. east of that place). Same as Rancho Chichimequillas; see Guanajuato (Estado) (*123a*).

Chickasaw Nation, [Oklahoma]

1868. See Indian Territory, and Cherokee Town; for a note on the boundaries of the Chickasaw Nation, see Choctaw Nation. Palmer's collections here were made mostly in the vicinity of Cherokee Town, but see also Boggy Depot; from March to May he collected west of the Chickasaw Nation, in the Leased Lands near Fort Cobb, *q.v.*

Chickasawba, Arkansas (northern Mississippi County) GLO, 1914

1881. October 31; see Mississippi County.

Chico, California (Butte County) GLO, 1928

1892. Arrived before June 3, from San Francisco. Collected Nos. 2,031–40 and 2,049–95, mostly in the bottoms of Chico Creek and the Sacramento River. The dates of collection are given in the field notes as June 7–12. See California (*114i; 123a; 123c*).

Chicot County, Arkansas

1881–83. Date uncertain. Palmer reported a mound at Lake Village, according to Thomas (*118*); see Arkansas.

Chihuahua (Ciudad) 28°38′N., 106°05′W. N.H–13

1885. Arrived late July, enroute from El Paso, Texas, to Parral (*123a*).

1908. Arrived from Washington, D. C., via El Paso, March 31; collected Nos. 1–125, 450, 451 (April 8–27); during this period botanized "along the river near the city," went by "coach to the hills east of the city," collected in the city market; collected many cacti. For other localities see Chihuahua (Estado). Left for Santa Eulalia (April 28, returning April 30); left for Aldama (May 13, returning May 16); collected Nos. 140–223, 452, 453 (May 1–21, chiefly May 4, 7, 12, 18, and 21); left for Madera (May 26, returning June 3); collected Nos. 331–80 (June 5–10); visited Santa Rosalía (June 13–15); left for Washington, D. C. (June 27). Nos. 389–437 were collected in the city market, between April 1 and June 26 (*34a; 114b; 123a; 123c*).

Chihuahua (Estado) N.H–12, N.H–13, N.G–12, N.G–13

1885. With the aid of Alexander Shepherd, general manager of the silver mines at Batopilas, Professor Baird of the Smithsonian Institution sent Palmer to study the culture of the Tarahumare Indians in Chihuahua. He left Washington about July 10, and traveled via El Paso, Texas (July 22), the city of Chihuahua, and Jiménez. From Jiménez to Parral he went by stage, and thence, with an escort sent by Shepherd, to Batopilas ("6 days journey by mule travel" across the mountains).

Safford says: "Journeying by stages from water to water, they reached Yerba Buena, on the eastern slope of the mountains, whence they ascended to the *cumbre* or summit, thence down a barranca by a winding road through Frailes to the Hacienda San Miguel, near Batopilas." Palmer reached Batopilas about August 1, and spent about two months as a guest at the hacienda San Miguel, the home of Governor Shepherd.

The details of Palmer's route from Parral to Batopilas remain obscure, and many writers have been content to cite his collections simply as from "southwestern Chihuahua," without inquiring into the specific localities. The modern road west from Parral, however, appears after examination and local inquiry to be approximately that over which Palmer traveled in 1885, and over which E. A. Goldman passed in the course of biological reconnaissance in 1898.[8] The first locality mentioned by Safford, namely Yerbabuena, is almost certainly the place of that name about 20 km. west of Balleza, at an elevation of about 2,000 m. West of Yerbabuena the country rises abruptly to an elevation of 2,200–2,300 m., and the road passes first across dry summits covered with oaks and piñon pines then west and southwest through a pine savannah for some 35 to 40 km. The modern road passes Baquiriachic and Agostadero; Goldman's route in 1890 was by way of Guasaráchic, in the same general direction. About 40 km. from Yerbabuena the road begins to climb to the summits of the Sierra Madre, reaching the summit pass at about 2,500 m. elevation, and continuing through the high pine forest for about 15 km. before dropping to a general level of about 2,200 m. or a little more.

Here, I take it, somewhere between Guasaráchic and Gabórachic, was Palmer's *cumbre*. West of this the road passes somewhat to the north of Gabórachic, and enters a more open pine forest in which

[8] Edward Alphonso Goldman, "Biological Investigations in Mexico," *Smithsonian Miscellaneous Collections*, Vol. CXV (1951), 117–29.

there are occasional flat areas which are entirely treeless. These *llanos,* which are often occupied by meandering streams, appear to be natural clearings. Small ranches are often located on or near them, and their grassland cover is heavily grazed. One such area, about 12 km. northeast of Guachóchic at an elevation of about 2,250 m., is known as "El Fraile." It is possible that this is Palmer's "Frailes," or "Frayles." Since the above was written, however, I have seen, through the kindness of Dr. I. W. Knobloch, an original large-scale map of this part of Chihuahua, prepared and processed in the city of Chihuahua in 1952 by Ing. E. Bronimann. This map shows a place called "Frailes" about 15 km. east of Batopilas, in the upper barrancas west of Tasajera. This may well be Palmer's "Frailes," as suggested by the wording in Safford's statement quoted above: "Down a barranca by a winding road through Frailes."

Actually the high plateau country continues about to Guachóchic, after which all roads to the westward begin to drop off into the barrancas. Palmer's route may have continued through Tónachic (still a passable road), or a little south of Tónachic by way of Tasajera, which was apparently Goldman's road.

Palmer left Batopilas soon after October 1. He seems first to have retraced his steps to the *cumbre,* as attested by the dates of collection at Cumbre as given in his field notes: "First ten days of October." From here he apparently took another road, that which leads northward, west of the divide, to Norogachic. Such a road leaves the Guachóchic road not far east of that place, but in 1951 I was informed that it was scarcely passable for motor vehicles, and I did not attempt it. Palmer apparently spent more than a month at Norogachic, *q.v.,* but the date of his departure from there is not known to me. According to Watson (*143*), plants were collected at Yerbabuena in November, presumably on the return trip to Parral from Norogachic.

From Parral, Palmer reached El Paso on December 14. The total plant collection of this year comprised about 522 numbers. See also Yerbabuena, Cumbre, Frailes, Hacienda San José (*3; 33; 34a; 114b; 123a; 143*).

1908. Reached the city of Chihuahua March 31. Visited Santa Eulalia (April 4), the Chihuahua city "water dam" (April 8–9), Quinta Carolina (April 10), La Junta (April 13), Hacienda Robinson (April 14), Cerro de Santa Rosa (April 24). Left Chihuahua for Santa Eulalia April 28, returning April 30; visited Ranchita Fresno

May 4; left for Aldama May 13, returning May 16; visited Cerro de Santa Rosa May 18; left for Madera May 26, arriving the same day; visited San Pedro Spring (May 28), Nahuarachic (May 29); left Madera by rail (June 2), reaching Temósachic the same day; left for Chihuahua (June 3), arriving the same night; visited Santa Rosalía [Camargo] (June 13–15), returning to Chihuahua before June 17; left for Washington, D. C., June 27. The collection of this year comprised about 455 numbers (*34a; 114b; 123a; 123c*).

Choctaw Mound, Arkansas (western Desha County)

?1882. Said by Palmer to be 4 or 5 miles south of east of Walnut [Lake] Station. The mound is described by Thomas (*88; 119*).

Choctaw Nation, [Oklahoma]

1868. See Boggy Depot, or Indian Territory. The Choctaw Nation occupied what is now southeastern Oklahoma, north to the Arkansas and Canadian rivers, and west to the 98th meridian. The Chickasaw Nation was originally established as a division within the boundaries of the Choctaw territory, and the boundary between the Choctaws and the Chickasaws was later fixed by treaty with the United States (November 4, 1854). The Chickasaw lands as delimited by this treaty extended westward to the 98th meridian, between the Red River and the Canadian River, from a line extending up Island Bayou "to the source of the east prong" and thence due north to the Canadian River. At this time the Choctaws also had claim to land west of the Chickasaws, but by treaty of June 22, 1855, they gave up all claims west of the 100th meridian and gave to the United States a permanent lease on all lands between the 98th and 100th meridians (between the Red River and the Canadian River). It was on these "Leased Lands" that the Wichitas, Kiowas, and Comanches and other Indians were subsequently settled.[9] The eastern boundary between the Choctaws and the Chickasaws, that running north from the source of Island Bayou, ran about 10 miles west of Boggy Depot, which Palmer visited in June; as far as known all his collections labeled as from the Choctaw Nation were made while he was on this trip, and in this vicinity only.

Chojo Grande, Coahuila

1904, 1905. Same as Chorro Grande; see Chorro de Agua. Spelled

[9] See Charles J. Kappler, *Indian Affairs—Laws and Treaties* (2 vols., Washington, 1904), II.

"Chojo" in Palmer's notes and on the labels distributed from the National Herbarium with his collections.

Chorro de Agua, Coahuila 25°23′N., 100°49′W. Atlas, 27

1904. Called by Palmer "Chojo Grande Cañon of the Great Waterfall 27 miles S.E. of Saltillo." Visited from Saltillo, August 29–31; collected Nos. 332–84, 450–52. Usually called El Chorro, and now accessible by a good road from Saltillo; the distance is a little over 16 miles (about 25 km.). Numerous large springs gush forth here from one rocky hillside in an otherwise extremely dry valley, forming a little oasis by the roadside (*34a; 123a*).

1905. July 16–19; collected Nos. 714–25 and 765. One of his notes states that No. 769 was collected here August 11, and so possibly Nos. 765–69 were all taken here on this date (*34a; 123a; 123c*).

Chuc-a-walla (Chuckawalla), California (southeastern Riverside County)

1870. ?September. A stage station on the Ehrenberg–San Bernardino route, shown on Bergland's (*126*) map in 33°27′N. latitude, 115°16′W. longitude. See Los Angeles.

Cierra de Puebla, Coahuila

1904. Same as Cerro del Pueblo, *q.v.*

City of Mexico

1877–78. See México, D. F.

Ciudad del Maíz, San Luis Potosí 22°24′N., 99°37′W. N.F–14

1878. Apparently first visited in February or March; see Río Verde. This is the place which often appears on maps as "Maíz," "El Maíz," or on some recent maps as "Gral. Magdaleno Cedillo"; Palmer often referred to it as Valle de Maíz. During his later visit here in this year, Palmer was a guest at the home of the brothers Arguinzonis, for whom he felt warm affection. Here at their home he attended to the final packing and shipping of his collections to Tampico in January, 1879.

1878–79. Arrived December 24, 1878, from Sabinito; left December 27 for San Nicolás ("an Indian settlement . . . 14 leagues E."). On the twenty-eighth he accompanied a "train" from San Nicolás to Gallinas ("9 leagues N. of San Nicolas"). About the twenty-ninth he

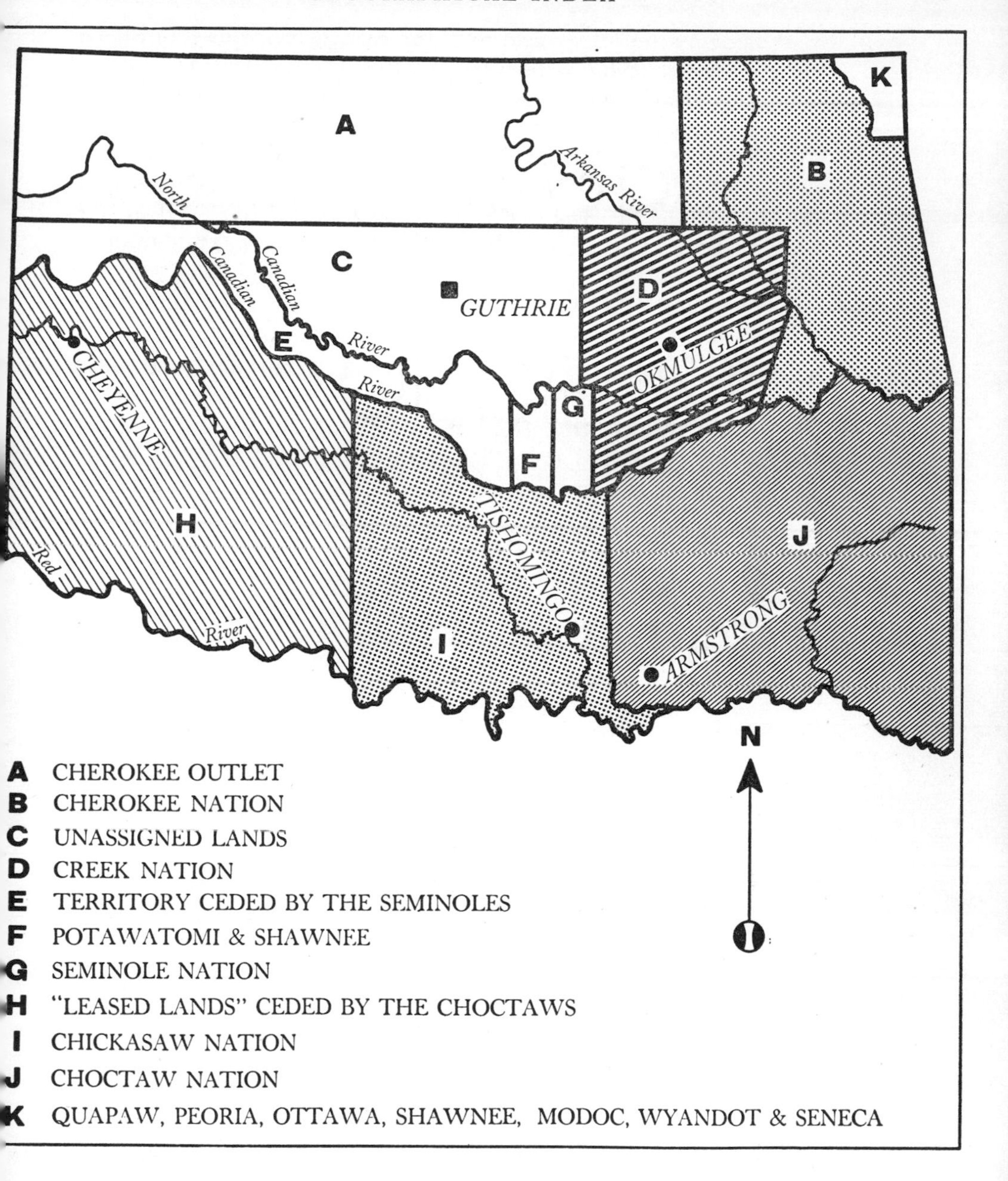

The Boundaries of the Indian Nations

approximately as they were at the time of Palmer's visit of 1868.

(Adapted from *Annual Report of the Bureau of American Ethnology, No. 18,* for 1896–97 [1899], plate 129.)

went alone by the "plain road to Tampico," via San Diego to Buena Vista, where he spent a short time with the Indians at and near a settlement called by him "La Machiguala." On January 1, 1879 he went from Buena Vista to Micos ("15 leagues N."), but found the burial mounds there too small to interest him, so went on January 3 to Minas Viejas ("15 leagues N."), where he was held up by rain until January 6, then worked in burial mounds for several days but found little, leaving January 13 and reaching Valle de Maíz the following day. Most of his travel on this trip was on muleback.

On January 17 he left Valle de Maíz on a horseback trip to Hacienda Custodio, about 40 km. to the northwest. He stayed at Custodio several days (noting that ice froze there each morning), returning in a coach, with a priest, on the twenty-fourth and reaching Valle de Maíz on the twenty-fifth, after collecting along the way.

On January 27 he left for Tampico; for discussion of the route, see Tamaulipas (*114i*).

Ciudad Victoria, Tamaulipas

1907. See Victoria, Ciudad, Tamaulipas.

Clarendon, Arkansas (Monroe County) GLO, 1886

1881. See Monroe County.

Clark County, Arkansas

1883. See Arkadelphia.

Clarke County, Alabama

1884. Palmer collected a few ethnological specimens at French's Landing. See Alabama (*114f*).

Clarks Creek, California (San Luis Obispo County)

1876. Probably due west of San Luis Obispo; also called Clarks Ferry; said to be "10 miles from San Luis Obispo and 4 from Morro Bay." Palmer visited here July 2 or 3, and made about 30 collections. See California (*34a; 123a*).

Clayton Mound, Arkansas

1882. Jefferson County, 16 miles southeast of Pine Bluff, in Section 36, T 6 S, R 7 W, according to Thomas (*119*, p. 242); see Jefferson County. Palmer's published account locates this mound "12 miles due east and west from Arkansas City, on Cypress Creek, 2.5 miles northeast of DeSoto mound" (i.e. in Desha County). This discrepancy may have arisen from an error in the transcription of Palmer's notes; I have not seen the originals (88).

Clear Creek, Arizona (Yavapai County) GLO, 1933

1866. Cited in the title of Item No. 21 of the Merwin Catalogue. Clear Creek entered the Río Verde about 5 miles below the mouth of Beaver Creek (the site of Camp Lincoln, *q.v.*) and, according to Palmer, "at the lower settlement" on the Verde. He describes the strata of which Clear Creek Canyon is formed (*45*, item 21).

Cleveland, Ohio (Cuyahoga County)

1849. First visited in 1849 soon after Palmer's arrival from England, via New York, Hudson River and Erie Canal, and a lake steamer from Buffalo. Palmer became an attendant of John W. Taylor, formerly speaker of the House of Representatives, and met Dr. Jared Potter Kirtland who encouraged his interest in natural history. Taylor gave Palmer a letter of introduction to Lt. T. J. Page, who was to lead the *Water Witch* expedition to Paraguay, *q.v.*, and Palmer came to Washington, D. C., probably early in December, 1852 (*123b*).

1855. Upon returning from South America, Palmer went from Washington to Cleveland, which he reached sometime between mid-June and July 30. He spent the summer working in Dr. Kirtland's library and collecting insects and returned to Washington, enroute to England, in September (*114a*).

1856–57. Probably reached Cleveland in late May 1856, from New York, after returning from England. Attended lectures in medicine at the Homeopathic College, probably from October or November 1856, until March or April, 1857. Left for Kansas to settle, mid-April 1857; for his route thither see Leavenworth (*114a; 114b; 123a*).

Cleveland, Tennessee (Bradley County)

1883. Palmer probably spent several days in this vicinity, perhaps in June. He explored certain prehistoric graves on the Blackburn Farm, 7 miles southeast, according to Thomas (*118*), who also identifies this locality with that discussed at some length in an earlier paper (Thomas, *117*, p. 94). See Tennessee.

Clinch River, Tennessee

1881. See Tennessee.

Coahuila N.H–13, N.H–14, N.G–13, N.G–14

1880. See Animas, Coyote, San Lorenzo, Sierra Madre, Saltillo, Monclova, Juárez (*2; 24; 34a; 34d; 114i; 123a*).

1898. Reached Saltillo about April 15; probably left for San Luis Potosí and Guanajuato about July 15; probably returned to Saltillo early in September and left on another trip early in October, visiting Parras (October 6–11), Torreón (October 13–20), Mapimí, Durango (October 21–23), and Zacatecas (October 24–November 2), probably returning to Saltillo about November 5. Probably left Saltillo for Washington, D. C., about November 15.

1902. See Saltillo.

1904. Reached Saltillo from San Luis Potosí about August 3; left for Concepción del Oro, August 11; returned about August 15 and left at once for General Cepeda, returning probably August 18; visited Chorro ("Chojo Grande") probably August 29–31. From September until early November Palmer seems to have stayed in or near Saltillo, engaged chiefly in collecting succulents for J. N. Rose. Perhaps visited Torreón, October 23–26. Apparently returned to Washington in November (*34a; 123a*).

1905. Reached Saltillo in early April, from Washington; visited San Lorenzo Cañon (April 16) and Agua Nueva (April 18), returning to Saltillo; left for San Luis Potosí late in April, returning about June 28; stayed in Saltillo until mid-August, visiting San Lorenzo Cañon (July 9) and Chorro (July 16–19). Probably left for Washington August 11 or 12 (*34a; 123a; 123c*).

Coahuila Valley, California (southwestern Riverside County)

1875. Probably about July 24; a single collection is listed from "Cuah. Valley" (*34a*). This is the valley of the Coahuila Indian Reservation, northwest of Warner Springs. The name Coahuila Valley appears on the map of San Jacinto Quadrangle, U.S.G.S. (1905). See Julian.

1889. May; see California.

Coahuillas Indians (of southern California)

1876. See San Bernardino.

Cobre, Cuba (Oriente) 20°03′N., 75°57′W. N.F–18

1902. February 21–24. Called "El Cobre" by Palmer's party. See Cuba.

Cocorit, Conora 27°35′N., 110°W. N.G–12

1890. April 10, enroute from Álamos, *q.v.*, to Guaymas.

Coimbra, Brazil

1853. See Forte do Coimbra.

Colima (Ciudad) 19°14′N., 103°43′W. N.E–13

1891. Arrived from Manzanillo, January 8 or 9; collected Nos. 1,097–1,273, and purchased Nos. 1,402–10 in the city market; visited Armería, *q.v.*, and apparently returned to Colima and collected Nos. 1,294–1,328. Left for Manzanillo, March 1, (*100; 123a; 123c*).

1897. Arrived from Manzanillo in June; collected Nos. 1–105 (?106) and 280–83 (in July), and (?106) 107–76 (August 1–19); probably left by steamer for Guaymas August 20. Also collected wood samples, Nos. 1–11 or more, in July, and herbarium specimens No. 267 and 267a (undated) (*114b; 123a; 123c; 125a*).

Colima (Estado) N.E–13

1890–92. See Armería, Colima (Ciudad), and Manzanillo (*100; 123a; 123c*).

1897. Reached Manzanillo June 17, probably by steamer from Mazatlán; spent July and a part of August at the city of Colima; visited the "Hortices district about 28 miles east from Colima"; returned to Guaymas by steamer, leaving probably August 20 (*114b; 123a; 123c; 125a*).

Colnett, Baja California 30°58′N., 116°15′W. N.H–11

1889. About June 7–22, on a trip from San Diego. See Ensenada, and San Diego.

Coloma, California (Eldorado County) GLO, 1928

1892. June 23–24, on a trip by stage from Placerville to Auburn; this is indicated by a note in Palmer's hand giving the date June 22, 1892, for a visit to Placerville, and the remark in his field notes that Cool "is a Stage Station 6 miles before reaching Auburn." At Coloma, collected Nos. 2,366–92 ("June 23 and 24th") and Nos. 2,421–22 ("June 23"). See California (*123a; 123c*).

Colonia Lerdo, Sonora 32°05′N., 115°W. N.H–11

1884–85. Palmer left Yuma, Arizona, with a party, for Lerdo, on December 21. Colonia Lerdo was the seat of what Palmer called

"Blythe Colony," settled according to him by the "Compania Mexicana Agricola Industrial Colonizadora de Terrenos del Colorado," which was organized in 1873.[10] Most of the party which visited it at this time, including General Andrade himself, G. E. Bateman the superintendent, and several others, returned to Yuma December 26, but Palmer seems to have stayed on a few days, as he notes happenings at Lerdo on December 31 and on January 1, 1885. He notes also that "Isabella Point or slough" is 25 miles southeast of Lerdo.

On this trip, as on that of 1889, Palmer's primary objective was to visit the "Grass Camp" of the Cocopa Indians, some 35 miles below Colonia Lerdo itself, and said to be at the Great Horseshoe Bend of the Colorado River, 12 to 15 miles from the mouth. Edward Potts refers to "Lerdo," saying it is approximately 59 miles south-southwest of Fort Yuma, California; this presumably refers to Colonia Lerdo itself, if distance is reckoned by river miles, not airline (*92; 114g; 123b*).

1889. Arrived about April 24 from Yuma, *q.v.*, by wagon; left April 24 by boat for the Horseshoe Bend. Probably returned to Yuma May 4 or 5. Vasey and Rose (*134*) gave the position of "Lerdo" as 31°46′10″N. lat., 114°43′30″W. long.; their figures evidently refer not to Colonia Lerdo but to the "Grass Camp," not far from the former site of the shipyard at Puerta Isabel. Plant specimens distributed as from Lerdo, doubtless including those from farther down the river at the Grass Camp, are Nos. 924–58; Palmer's field notes state that Nos. 924–31 were collected at the "Horseshoe Bend" during the "last three days of April," and Nos. 932–58 at Lerdo, April 24–26 *(34a; 114g; 114i; 134)*.

Colorado GLO, 1934

1859–61. Palmer left Stranger, Kansas, August 18, 1859, and Leavenworth, August 23; reached Denver September 26 and lived

[10] This land colony was formed as a result of a partnership between General Guillermo Andrade (who had holdings of more than a million acres, on both sides of the Río Colorado), and Thomas Blythe (a capitalist and land promoter in San Francisco). The colony was relatively short lived, and by 1890 there was only one Mexican family living at Colonia Lerdo. Part of this decline came about after the arrival of the railroad in Yuma in 1877. The Southern Pacific bought out the transportation rights and the boats belonging to the river navigation company; the shipyards at Puerta Isabel were dismantled in 1878, and regular navigation on the lower river and out into the Gulf of California was effectively ended.

there until August 6, 1861, when he left for San Francisco, California, by stage. Left "for the mountains," June 20, 1860; this may be the trip of which he wrote to George Engelmann (p. 15), "from the base of Longs Peak across the summit through Middle and South Park to the base of the mountains . . ." Probably he intended to provide Engelmann with a summary of his travels rather than an exact itinerary. In crossing the "summit," or Continental Divide from the base of Longs Peak to Middle Park, he must have crossed Rollins Pass, west of present Rollinsville; this pass, known in his day as Boulder Pass, was opened as a trail in 1860. In passing from Middle Park to South Park, Palmer could have crossed either Georgia Pass or Hoosier Pass, probably reaching the "base of the mountains" from South Park to Fountain Creek on the plains below, via the historic Ute Pass. Specimens from this trip are unknown, but if any exist they are probably at the Missouri Botanical Garden, as suggested above (p. 16). The specimens may have been among those whose sending was mentioned in a letter from Denver, November 27, 1860.

Palmer was in Denver on February 9, 1861. His field notes show that he spent the spring and early summer chiefly in the mountains west of Denver; the earliest date shown is April 21. He left for the "12 mile house in the mountains" on May 8; collected in the mountains in May, June, and July; on June 11 was in "mts 14 miles from Denver" (probably in lower Clear Creek drainage above Golden); June 25 he gives a definite locality: "10 miles up Cherry Creek." On July 10 he was at "Golden City edge of mts. 14 miles from Denver." Perhaps at this time he went up into the Front Range via the old stage road between Empire and Central City, for one of his mammals, a mouse (No. 17), is recorded as from "3 miles from Central City." Samuel Scudder (*112*) cites an insect collected by Palmer at Empire City, perhaps at this time. He was in Denver July 31, and left for San Francisco, *q.v.*, August 6 (*45*, item 87b); *114b; 123a*).

For the history of collections made in 1861, see above, p. 17.

1862–63. Reached Julesburg May 22, 1862, and Denver June 2, enroute from Fort Leavenworth, Kansas, *q.v.*, with the 2nd Colorado Volunteers. See Camp Weld, St. Vrain River, Fremonts Orchard, O'Fallons Bluffs, and Nebraska. Palmer was established at Camp Weld (within present limits of Denver) on June 6; on the seventh he was collecting animals near camp, and on the eleventh collecting plants "6 miles up the mts. from Denver." On June 14 he planned to leave for the mountains with the troops, and on June 20 he returned; he wrote

Baird soon after that his command had marched from Denver to the "region of perpetual snow" and back.[11] He left with his outfit for Fort Lyon, *q.v.*, on June 23, and returned to Camp Weld, August 8. On September 8, Palmer wrote Baird from Denver, shipping at the same time his collections for 1861 and 1862, and the field catalogue.[12] He was soon ordered back to Fort Lyon; left Camp Weld September 19 and reached his destination on September 25. He "overhauled and straightened" the hospital at Fort Lyon, and returned to Camp Weld probably December 8. On December 14 he sent Baird "one additional box . . . from headwaters of Cherry Creek whare gold was first discovered 35 miles south of Denver . . . also insects from Fort Craig, New Mexico . . . ," and added "am under marching orders for Fort Lyon . . . thence to the States." He was at Fort Lyon from January to May 6, 1863, when he left with his regiment for Fort Scott, Kansas, *q.v.* For collections made in 1862 see Nebraska, and other localities cited above.

1865. See Trinidad, and Fort Whipple.

1869. See Sheridan, Kansas.

1876. See Davenport, Iowa.

Colorado River, Arizona (Mohave County) GLO, 1933

1877. On May 5 Palmer wrote to Engelmann from St. George, Utah: "Returned yesterday from a very hard trip among the broaken mountains 75 miles little E of S from St. George and not far from the Colorado River." On June 15 he wrote of his most recent trip: "I went to the very edge of the Colorado River" (*24*).

Colorado River, Nevada

1870. June 25–27; see Hardyville.

Colorado River, mouth of 31°48′N., 114°40′W.

1869. Birds were collected October 6, 8, and 10 at a locality cited

[11] This hurried march to the mountains seems to have been his only opportunity to visit the high Colorado peaks during 1862. One of his collections, a mouse, was made at Gregory Mines in June, 1862, and could hardly have been collected so far from Denver except on this trip. The reference to "perpetual snow" suggests that his party went on as far as Mt. Audubon or even to Longs Peak, or perhaps turned to the southwest to the Mt. Evans region or James Peak above Central City. In any event he must have had small chance to collect while accompanying a squad of cavalry on a forced march.

[12] This is filed as Smithsonian Accession 291 for 1863, and is the important accession referred to above in various places with regard to the field notes of 1861 and 1862.

as "Mouth of Colorado, Ariz." and on October 6 and October 18 Palmer wrote to Joseph Henry from a locality which he called the "Mouth of the Colorado River." Palmer sent shipments from this place, and it is probable that his stopping place at the mouth of the river was at Puerta Isabel, Sonora [not Arizona as indicated above], and that he spent at least two weeks there (October 6–19). That this locality is the correct one is indicated by one of the entries in the catalog of the Division of Birds at the National Museum; in the series (Nos. 59,187–59,219) from "Mouth of Colorado," one collection (No. 59,211) is marked "Port Isabella," which is evidently Palmer's translation of Puerta Isabel, *q.v.* (*114b; 114e*).

1870. The records of the Division of Birds show that Palmer collected here September 4 (the year not given, but the collection entered in the museum records on March 11, 1871). The date 1870 is doubtless correct, as on August 9 Palmer was bound down the river for Adair Bay, and on August 13 he was in Yuma. August 26, according to the label on a specimen of *Cereus schottii* in the Missouri Botanical Garden, he was in "Lower California" (*114e*).

Colorado River Agency, Arizona (northwestern Yuma County) GLO, 1879

1870. Probably visited before August 1, from Camp Colorado, *q.v.* Here Palmer probably acquired the "six boxes of things collected from the Mohave Indians" about which he wrote while on the way to Yuma, *q.v.*, on August 9. The Mohave Agency was in 1870 about four years old; the reservation began 10 miles above La Paz and ran along the river for 41 miles. The agency building was 46 miles above La Paz (*45*, item 15; *114a; 124a*).

1876. Between March 14 and March 22, enroute from Williams Fork to Ehrenberg, *q.v.* About 10 numbers of plants were collected, according to the Gray Herbarium Manuscript (*34a; 123a*).

Colorado River Valley, Arizona

1876. Palmer sent for determination, to Engelmann, a series of specimens marked "Colorado River Valley Arizona March." These probably originated at Ehrenberg, at the Colorado River Agency, or at the mouth of Williams Fork. A similar series, of about 17 numbers, was labeled "Colorado Valley" by Asa Gray (*24; 34a*).

Columbia, Texas (Brazoria County)

1879. November 10; see Houston.

Comfort, Texas (Kendall County)

1879. September 4–10; a few collections were apparently made here, as the locality is included in the printed itinerary. Watson cites 2 collections from Kendall County, without definite locality (*2; 123a; 142*).

Compostela, Nayarit 21°13′N., 104°52′W. N.F–13

1892. Visited February 8, on a trip by coach from Tepic. Palmer's notes say: "15 miles E. of S. from Tepic, & 6 hrs. journey. The road runs along the Miravalles River which is crossed 19 times" (*45*, item 189; *123a*).

Concepción, Paraguay (Concepción) 23°27′S., 57°28′W. S.F–21

1853. On the east side of the Río Paraguay. Specimens were collected here on the trip of the *Water Witch* to Corumbá (November 12–15); also visited on the return trip (December 15–18); specimens were collected between Albuquerque, Brazil, and Concepción. See Río Paraná (*52; 123a; 125c*).

Concepción del Oro, Zacatecas 24°39′N., 101°28′W. N.G–14

1902. November 22. Palmer came here from Saltillo especially to collect a certain large *Sedum;* also collected Nos. 371–441 (*114i; 123a; 123c*).

1904. Visited August 11–14, on a hurried trip from Saltillo to collect succulent Crassulaceae. Collected Nos. 252–325 (or 326), 449, 466, 467 (*34a; 123a*).

On the labels distributed from the National Herbarium with Palmer's collections from this locality, the name is spelled "Conception del Oro."

Cool, California (Eldorado County) GLO, 1928

1892. June 24, enroute by stage from Placerville to Auburn. Collected No. 2,404. See California, and Coloma (*123a; 123c*).

Coosada Station, Alabama (Elmore County) GLO, 1882

1884. See Elmore County. In records of Division of Ethnology also listed as Cascada Station.

Copeland's Mill, Utah (Beaver County)

1877. July 12. According to Palmer this was "16 miles SE Beaver

City [,] head of Beaver Cr & near the base of the loftiest peak of the mountain called Balldey [,] Warsatch range"; see Beaver (*45*, item 282).

Copper Mines, Arizona (?Mohave County)

1870. Not the name of a settlement, but a mine said by Palmer to be 12 miles from the mouth of Williams Fork, *q.v.* This was the Planet Mine, worked from 1865 to 1873.[13]

Coraca, Sonora

1890. Not located. Palmer passed through April 9–10, enroute by stage from Álamos, *q.v.*, to Guaymas. Possibly the same as Cocorit, *q.v.*

Corinto, Nicaragua 12°28′N., 87°12′W. N.D–16

1862 or 1867. See Nicaragua.

Coronado Beach, California (San Diego County)

1888. On the peninsula west of San Diego Bay, between it and the ocean. Palmer's field notes show that in September he collected No. 21 (No. 268 of his principal series of this year). See San Diego (*114i*).

Coronados Islands, Baja California

1888. See Islas Coronados, Baja California.

Corpus Christi Bay, Texas (Nueces County)

1879. December 11–20; about 35 collections of plants, and some of insects, were made here about the Bay region. The dates of Palmer's visit to Lamar, Aransas County, are given in the printed plant-inventory as December 17–19, but some of his other notes indicate that he was in Corpus Christi on the eighteenth, and in Lamar on the nineteenth and twentieth. He left Corpus Christi by stage on December 23, leaving Sharpsburg at 4:00 the same afternoon and reaching San Antonio at 6:30 in the evening, "Christmas" [?day, i.e. December 25] (*2; 34b; 45*, item 269; *142*).

Corrientes, Argentina (Corrientes) 27°28′S., 58°47′W. S.G–21

1853. On the east side of the Río Paraná. Collections were made here September 23–25. See Río Paraná.

1854. Visited February 1; see Asunción. Later, the *Water Witch*

[13] Farish, *History of Arizona,* II, 296–97.

reached Corrientes July 16, from Asunción; left for Asunción September 17; reached Asunción September 20, left for Corrientes September 30; spent October 9–19 at Arroyo Atajo, *q.v.;* left Corrientes November 13, reaching Montevideo November 20 and leaving again December 17; reached Corrientes December 31.

1855. The *Water Witch* left January 31, reaching Montevideo, February 14.

Palmer probably accompanied the *Water Witch* on most or all the above trips; specimens were collected in 1854–55 at Corrientes, Arroyo Atajo, and probably at Montevideo (*52; 114i; 123a; 125c*).

Corumbá, Brazil (Mato Grosso) 19°S., 57°39′W. S.E–21

1853. West of the Río Paraguay; the highest point reached on that river by the *Water Witch.* Specimens were collected, November 30–December 3. See Río Paraná (*52; 123a; 125c*).

Cottonwood Creek, Arizona (Mohave County) GLO, 1933

1876. About 39 numbers were collected here, May 4; see Hardyville. The site of a tollgate, said to be 75 miles west of Prescott, but in actuality probably northwest; the creek probably the same as White Cliff Creek, which flows into the Big Sandy in T 20 N, R 13 W (*7; 34a; 123a*).

Cottonwood Island, Nevada (Clark County) GLO, 1941

1870. In the Colorado River at about 35°25′N. lat. Palmer spent the night of June 27–28 here; see Hardyville.

Council Grove, Kansas (Morris County) GLO, 1925

1863. June, while enroute to Fort Scott, *q.v.* (*114b*).

Cow Creek, (?Kansas)

1863. Probably May 17, enroute to Fort Scott, *q.v.* Perhaps crossed in or near the present Rice County, on the way from Fort Larned (*114b*).

1865. "On Cow Creek, in Kansas, in 1865 . . ." (67).

Coyote, Coahuila 25°41′N., 103°18′W. N.G–13

1880. May 15, according to a note by Palmer. This is his "Hacienda de Coyote"; he called it also "San Antonio del Coyote," *q.v.*, or simply "Coyote." The hacienda of Palmer's time has been divided into four contiguous ranches; the principal settlement (which retains the name) was and is on the plain, near the western end of the Sierra de

San Lorenzo. Item No. 175 of the Merwin Catalogue (*45*) [not seen by me] purports to be a description of a ceremony witnessed here by Palmer. In the Peabody Museum are collections from Coyote Cave, which is in the Sierra de San Lorenzo, probably near the western end. For information relative to the place names in this area, I am much indebted to Dr. Blas Rodríguez Ibarra and to Dr. Bulmaro Valdes Anaya, both of Torreón. See also San Antonio del Coyote, and San Lorenzo de la Laguna.

Crafton, California (San Bernardino County) GLO, 1900

1876. About 10 miles south of east of San Bernardino. Safford states that Palmer met C. C. Parry and J. G. Lemmon here, May 23. After a trip to San Bernardino Mountain, Palmer returned to Crafton May 31, stayed until June 8 and then left for the upper Mojave River, returning June 14 and leaving for San Bernardino probably the same day. See San Bernardino (*123a*).

Creek Agency, [Oklahoma] (Muskogee County) GLO, 1876

1868. Early February, and again in October. A few miles (about 10) up river from Fort Gibson. See Indian Territory (*123a*).

Crittenden County, Arkansas

?1881. See Oldham.

?1883. Palmer mentions visits in this year to Gilmore Station and to Pacific Place. He reported mounds from Gilmore Station, according to Thomas (*118*). Both Palmer and Thomas mention the former's work at the Roman Mounds, said by Thomas to be in Cross County, 6 miles southwest of Tyronza Station; actually a locality this distance and direction from Tyronza would be in Crittenden County. I have not been able to learn anything more about the work in this county *(88; 118)*.

Crook Mound, Arkansas

1882. Near Forrest City, *q.v.;* described by Thomas (*119*, p. 228).

Crump Cave, Alabama

1883. See Blountsville.

Cuah. Valley, California

1875. See Coahuila Valley.

Cuba N.F–18

1902. A trip from Washington, D. C., in company with C. L.

Pollard and William Palmer. Few details of the trip are known, but the work was confined to the province of Oriente. Some collections were made jointly by the three men, some by Pollard and William Palmer, and some by Edward Palmer alone. The party seems to have left Havana for the eastern end of the island by steamer about January 19 or 20, reaching Baracoa about January 24. They originally planned a trip of a month but apparently extended the time to six weeks, going from Baracoa to Santiago about February 10, and returning thence to Havana about the end of the month. Plant collections comprised more than 400 numbers, originating at Gibara (January 23), the vicinity of Baracoa (January 24–29, February 1–7), El Yunque, near Baracoa (January 30–31), Santiago de Cuba (February 14–24), San Luis (February 15–18), and El Cobre (February 21–24). Palmer was back in Washington by March 21 (*114i; 122; 123a*).

Cubero, New Mexico (Valencia County) GLO, 1886

1869. See Fort Wingate.

Cuernavaca, Morelos 18°55′N., 99°14′W. N.E–14

1878. Left Mexico City by coach May 29, arriving in Cuernavaca the same day. He collected some archaeological material, visited the "Indian town" of San Antonio "one and a quarter miles from Cuernavaca," and probably returned to Mexico City June 4, having had an attack of fever. See México, D. F. (*45*, item 190).

Cuero, Texas (De Witt County)

1879. November; see Victoria (*123a*).

Culhuacán, D. F. 19°20′N., 99°06′W. AMS, E–14–N–II

1878. May 19; see México, D. F. Spelled "Culguacan" by Palmer (*114i*).

Culiacán, Sinaloa 24°49′N., 107°23′W. N.G–13

1891. On August 3 Palmer wrote from Guaymas: "Expect to start in two days for Mazatlan there take another Steamer for Altatta thence Rail Road 60 miles to Culiacan." Reached Culiacán about August 15; left August 16 for Imala; returned about August 27; left for Imala about September 25; returned before October 25; left for Guaymas November 20–25. Collected at Culiacán Nos. 1,476–1,559 (August 27–September 15), and 1,767–1,809 (October 25–November 18). See also Imala, and Lodiego (*114i; 123a; 123c*).

Cullen's Well, Arizona (northeastern Yuma County)
GLO, 1879

1869. August; enroute to Ehrenberg (*45*, item 14); said to be 250 feet deep. Animals were watered at twenty-five cents each (gold); men free.

1869. September, enroute to Ehrenberg. According to Barnes (*7*, p. 119) it is 38 miles west of Wickenburg. According to a War Department map of the Department of Arizona (Sheet 3, revised, 1875, 1 inch equals about 10 miles), it was about 4.5 miles west of Wickenburg, at the junction of the roads to Wickenburg and Prescott. Spelled "Cullins" on the GLO map of 1921. See Yuma (*123a*).

Cumbre, Chihuahua

1885. Not located on a map; the name refers simply to the area at the summit of the Sierra Madre, probably near the road between Guasarachic and Gabórachic. See Chihuahua (Estado). Palmer seems to have collected here after leaving Batopilas; the dates of collection are given in his field notes as "first ten days of October." Nos. 314–21, 323–29, 331, 333–41, 358–63, and 365–68 were collected; in the National Herbarium are preserved the field notes for Nos. 21–30, pertaining to grasses only, some of which were reported by Watson as a part of the series of duplicate and supplementary numbers (*114i; 123a; 143*).

Custodio, San Luis Potosí 22°39′N., 99°58′W. N.F–14

1879. January ?18–24; see Ciudad del Maíz. This locality is on the desert plain in an area dominated by species of *Yucca, Opuntia, Larrea,* and various members of the Mimosoideae. The gasoline station of Tepeyac, on the modern highway from San Luis Potosí to Ciudad del Maíz, is approximately on the site of Custodio. Also spelled "Custodia" by Palmer (*114i*).

Cuyamaca Mountains, California (San Diego County)

1875. Palmer made his headquarters at Talley's Ranch, *q.v.*, July 7–17. See also California.

Dahlonega, Georgia (Lumpkin County)

1884. Palmer visited the gold mines here in May (*114c*).

Dallas, Texas (Dallas County)

1879. July; see Longview.

Dandridge, Tennessee (Jefferson County)

1881. September 2; see Tennessee.

Dasaic, Arkansas

1883. Evidently Palmer's corruption of Des Arc (Prairie County). His published notes mention the beautiful flower gardens here (*88*).

Davenport, Iowa (Scott County) GLO, 1885

1876. The home of C. C. Parry. Palmer arrived about September 10, from San Francisco; leaving Camp Halleck, Nevada, about the last of August, he had joined Parry at Graymont, Colorado for a proposed collecting trip. The trip was abandoned and the men returned to Davenport. Palmer left for Cambridge, Massachusetts, October 5, returning via New Haven, New York, and the Centennial Exposition at Philadelphia, reaching Davenport November 5. Left December 18 for St. George, Utah, having been engaged by the Peabody Museum to excavate mounds there (*24; 34d; 114b; 114i; 123a*).

1877. Arrived September 1, from Salt Lake City, to stay with Parry while arranging his collections for distribution. Left for Cambridge, Massachusetts, October 8 (*24; 34d; 114i*).

Davidson's Springs, Arizona (southeastern Pima County)

1867. Palmer collected No. 205 here August 4, in "ravines in mountains on the Wallen Road." This is apparently the place listed as "Davidsons" on the GLO map of 1883, in R 16 E, T 17 S. The principal (if not the only) road from Camp Grant to Tucson ascended the Río San Pedro to near present Benson before turning northwest, and it may be that Palmer passed this way enroute to Tucson after leaving Camp Grant about August 1. See Yuma, and Camp Grant (*48*, Vol. 20, p. 780).

Dayton, Tennessee (Rhea County)

1882. April 15; see Tennessee (*114a*).

Deep Fork, [Oklahoma] (Okmulgee County) GLO, 1876

1868. See Indian Territory. This is the Deep Fork of the Canadian River. The road from Fort Gibson to Cherokee Town crossed the river here near Okmulgee; Palmer noted that the crossing was about halfway between the Creek Agency and the Seminole Agency (*45*, item 297).

Demopolis, Alabama (Marengo County) GLO, 1915
1884. March; see Alabama.

Denver, Colorado (Denver County)
1859–62. Palmer lived here from about September 26, 1859, to August 6, 1861. After joining the army in 1862 he was stationed here a part of the time from May to December. See Colorado; see also discussion in Part I, page 15, of this book (*45*, item 87b; *114b; 123a*).
1870. Arrived October 22, enroute from San Francisco, *q.v.*, to Washington.
1893. See Idaho, and Washington, D. C.

DePriest Mound, Arkansas
1882. Same as De Soto mound, *q.v.*

Des Arc, Arkansas (Prairie County) GLO, 1886
?1883. Hill Bayou Mounds, 2 miles southeast of here, were explored by Palmer, according to Thomas (*118*); mentioned in Palmer's published notes as "Dasaic" (*88*).

"Desert of the Colorado, Arizona"
1870. See White Water.

Desha County, Arkansas
1882. Arrived from Drew County about December 1. Work done in the county is described by Thomas (*119*, pp. 237–39). Palmer may have made Arkansas City a shipping base, as he visited here briefly December 6, after a trip to Jefferson County, and arrived again on January 10, 1883, after work in Jefferson and Pulaski counties, returning to Woodson, Saline County, before January 15. See Franklin Mound.

De Soto Mound, Arkansas
1882. Jefferson County, 13 miles southeast of Pine Bluff and 2.5 miles northwest of the Clayton Mound, according to Thomas (*119*, p. 243). Also called "De Priest's Mound" by Palmer, who stated it was located 13 miles northwest of Arkansas City, i.e. in Desha County; see Jefferson County. I have not seen Palmer's original notes from which the printed account (*88*) of his Arkansas travels was taken, and it may be that seemingly egregious errors like the above location given for this mound are to be blamed on the transcribers.

De Witt County, Texas

1879. Palmer made archaeological collections here; see Victoria (*34d*).

Diamond Valley, Utah (Washington County) GLO, 1876

1877. Palmer passed through here May 19, doubtless on his return from Mountain Meadows, *q.v.*, to St. George. Diamond Valley lies east of the Santa Clara River, about 10 miles northwest of St. George (*114i*).

Diegueño Indian villages, California (San Diego County)

1875. July 24; said by Safford to be at the hot springs near Warner's Ranch. See Julian.

Distrito Federal

1877–78. See México, D.F.

Doniphan County, Kansas GLO, 1925

1857–58. Palmer lived at Highland, *q.v.* In a letter of April 9, 1858, he writes of a trip through Doniphan, Brown, Nemaha, and Marshall counties, Kansas, thence to the Big Blue River, Gage County, Nebraska, and also to Pawnee and "Richerson" counties, Nebraska. He says that on all of these trips the weather has prevented the collection of everything except minerals and fossils (*114b*).

Dos Cajetes, Durango [24°11'N., 104°57'W.]

1896. November 3–5; collected Nos. 771–834, 951–56, 961, 962, and perhaps Nos. 891 and 892. Not located on a map; said by Palmer to be 30 miles nearly west of Durango on the road to Otinapa at an elevation of about 8,500 feet. The distance from Otinapa to Durango is given by Palmer as 35 miles, so that we may suppose Dos Cajetes to have been no more than a few kilometers from Otinapa. I visited the now nearly abandoned Hacienda de Otinapa in 1951, and found through local inquiry that Dos Cajetes was unknown there, but an (also abandoned) ranch named Las Cajetas was well known. This was said to be on an old road to Durango, 8 or 9 kms. from Otinapa, and in the hills northeast of Trigo, distant one and one-half hours by horse. I have no doubt that this is Palmer's locality. See Durango (Estado) (*123c*).

Dos Palmas, California (Riverside County) GLO, 1907

1870. A stage station on the Ehrenberg–San Bernardino route, shown on Bergland's (*126*) map in latitude 33'°30'N., 115°51'W. longitude. (?)September; see Los Angeles.

Dresden, Missouri (Pettis County) GLO, 1878

1864. See Missouri.

Drew County, Arkansas

1882. See Jefferson County, and also Tiller Mound, Winchester, and Hollywood.

Dry Creek (near Boundary Monument)

1875. See Boundary Monument.

Dry Creek, Idaho

1893. See Dubois.

Dry Tortugas, Florida (Monroe County) GLO, 1911

1884. See Fort Jefferson.

Dubois, Idaho (southeastern Clark County) GLO, 1939

1893. Visited July 10–15, after leaving Blackfoot, *q.v.* Nos. 307–43, 564, 566, 571, 588, and 599 were collected here, July 12–13. Specimens from Dubois and vicinity were labeled "Dry Creek"; on July 8 Palmer wrote of his plans to go to Dry Creek, "now renamed Duboise"; in his diary he explains that Dry Creek was the railroad name, and Dubois the name of the post office (*114i; 123a*).

Durango (Ciudad) 24°02'N., 104°40'W. N:G–13

1896. Arrived March 23; collected Nos. 1–30 (April 1-8); left for Santiago Papasquiaro about April 9, returning before April 26; collected No. 90 (April 26); visited Nombre de Dios April 27–30, and returned May 2 or 3; probably spent the month of May at Durango, and was ill at least a part of the time; collected Nos. 125–300, and 894 (June 1–24), and 301–91 (July 1–25); visited Santiago Papasquiaro (August 1–11); returning to Durango, collected Nos. 473–556 (August 14–31), 557–743, 895, 896, 900, 912, 925, 931, 963, 966, 966½, 974 (September), 744–70 (October 1–22), 883–90, 893, 901, 903, 913, 918–20, 923, 924, 926–29, 936, 937, 940, 948, 959, 960, 965 (October), 957–58 (November 2); visited Dos Cajetes (November 3–5); collected at Durango Nos. 835–73 and 880 (November 8–10) and 897–99, 906–10, 914–17, 921, 922, 934, 935, 938, 939, 941, 964 (November), 874–79, 881–82, 902, 904, 905, 911, 930, 932, 933, 942–47, 949, 950 (undated). Left for Washington, D. C., about November 15. See Durango (Estado) (*34a; 114i; 123a; 123c*).

1906. Arrived about March 12, from Washington, D. C. Collected Nos. 1–8 (March 12–15); left for Tepehuanes about mid-March, returning June 26; was more or less incapacitated for a time by an arm injured at Tepehuanes. Visited Otinapa about July 25 to August 5, returning to Durango August 7; visited Tejamen August 21–27, returning about August 29; collected Nos. 556–58 at "Iron Mountain" (September 15); left for Washington probably in September.

Durango (Estado) N.G–13, N.F–13

1880. See San Antonio del Coyote.

1896. Reached the city of Durango March 23; left about April 9 to visit Santiago Papasquiaro (April 11–15) and Mina Tres Reyes (April 16–19), returning to Durango before April 26; visited Nombre de Dios (April 27–30); probably remained at Durango most of May, June, and July; perhaps visited New San Pedro (June 5); visited Santiago Papasquiaro (August 1–11); collected about Durango (August 14–November 2); visited Dos Cajetes (November 3–5); returned to Durango and left for Washington, D. C., via San Pedro, Coahuila, Eagle Pass, Texas, and perhaps Eustis, Florida, about November 15 (*34a; 114i; 123a; 123c*).

1898. See Mapimí.

1906. Reached the city of Durango, from Washington, D. C., via Torreón, about March 12; left for Tepehuanes about March 24 or 25; probably left Tepehuanes for San Ramón April 17, returning about May 24, and on the return trip collecting at Quebrada Honda (May 20–21); visited Tovar (May 28–31); returned from Tepehuanes to Durango (June 26); went to Otinapa about July 25, returning August 7; visited Tejamen August 21–27, returning to Durango August 28 or 29; collected at Durango at least until September 15. Returned to Washington, D. C., sometime before December 12, probably in September.

Eagle Pass, Texas (Maverick County)

1880. September 26–October 2, en route from Monclova to San Antonio. Collected about 15 numbers of plants (*2; 125a; 142*).

1896. About November 19, en route from Durango and San Pedro to Washington (*114i*).

Eagle Rock, Idaho

1893. Name used by Palmer for Idaho Falls, *q.v.*

East Florida

1874. More than 200 numbers of plants are so designated in Gray's list of this collection. See Florida.

Eastern Dry Rocks, Florida (Monroe County) CGS, 1251

1884. Collections from here are cited by Mary J. Rathbun (*94*). These are low rocks 6–7 miles southwest of Key West.

Eastport, Maine (Washington County) CGS, 801

1872. Palmer spent the summer here, as assistant to Spencer F. Baird, the commissioner of fish and fisheries; most of his work was at Eastport, and he received his pay there, for the period from July 1 to October 24, inclusive. He doubtless visited a few other localities; Eaton (*21*) notes that "Dr. Edward Palmer collected a few species on Grand Menan." Eastport is located on the eastern edge of the county, on Moose Island, across the channel from Deer Island and Campobello Island, New Brunswick, and is one of the easternmost localities in the United States (*21; 124b; 125b*).

Edgewood, California (Siskiyou County) GLO, 1928

1892. Reached from Sisson, *q.v.*, on the San Francisco and Portland Railroad, and said to be 25 miles north of Sisson. Palmer collected Nos. 2,574–2,606 and 2,668–71 here, July 28–31, and returned to San Francisco about August 5. On the printed labels distributed with the collection from the National Herbarium the name was spelled "Edgwood," and this spelling was also used on the GLO map, 1900 (*114i; 123a; 123c*).

Ehrenberg, Arizona (Yuma County) GLO, 1933

1869. August; Palmer came here overland by stage from Fort Whipple, *q.v.*, and descended the river to Yuma. He returned in September, overland by the same route (starting from Camp Date Creek); he shipped some of his collections from here and left for the mouth of the Colorado River on the steamer *Cocopah*, September 22. Ehrenberg, a new town in 1869, is on the Colorado River in about 33°35′N. Lat. (*45*, items 14, 57; *114b; 123a; 123b*).

1870. About August 10; see Yuma. His steamer to Yuma doubtless stopped at Ehrenberg (*45*, item 15; *114a*).

1876. Arrived March 3 or 4, by coach from San Bernardino, California; left March 9 on the steamer *Colorado* up the Colorado River to the mouth of Williams River (March 11–12) and visited the Mohave Reservation (March 14 or 15–22); returned to Ehrenberg and left for Wickenburg by coach April 8 at 5:00 P. M. to travel under "a good moon." Collected about 24 numbers of plants at Ehrenberg (*24; 34a; 34d; 45*, item 24; *114i; 123a*).

El Boludo, Tamaulipas 23°N., 99°54′W. N.F–14

1878. Visited December 3; see Sierra Naola. This place is nearly on the boundary between Tamaulipas and San Luis Potosí, and on most maps it is located in the latter state (*114i*).

El Cajon, California (San Diego County) GLO, 1928

1875. About 10 miles northeast of San Diego. Gray cites a single collection from "Cajon," doubtless referring to this locality (*34a*).

1889. May; see California.

El Carro, San Luis Potosí 22°32′N., 101°55′W. N.F–14

1878. April 10, enroute from San Luis Potosí to Zacatecas. The site of a well-known deposit of cinnabar, and referred to by Palmer as the "Carro Quicksilver Mine"; because of a misinterpretation of his handwriting, the name appears as "Cano" in his transcribed notes (*45*, item 190).

El Cobre, Cuba

1902. February; see Cobre and Cuba.

Eldorado Cañon, Nevada (Clark County) GLO, 1941

1870. Empties into the Colorado River at about 35°43′N. lat. Palmer spent the night of June 26–27 here; see Hardyville.

El Marqués, Guerrero 16°48′N., 99°50′W. Atlas, 11

1895. Visited from Acapulco, *q.v.*, January 9–14; called by Palmer "Portraro Ranch" and said to be on the sandbar across the bay from Acapulco (*123a*).

Elmore County, Alabama

?1884. Palmer explored the Parker Mound on the Coosa River near its junction with the Tallapoosa, and remains of the old French Fort Toulouse and the United States Fort Jackson, near the same river junction; these explorations are mentioned by Thomas (*118*) and apparently yielded more specimens than Palmer's other work in this state. Catalog Nos. 91,451–91,601 of the Division of Ethnology, U.S. National Museum, are mostly from this area: near Coosada Station (4 collections); near junction of Coosa and Tallapoosa rivers (about 40); island on Jackson Lakes, 6 miles from Montgomery (12); 8 miles north of Montgomery (3); old Fort Jackson (75); 2 miles south of Fort Jackson (10). See Alabama.

Elm Springs, [Oklahoma] (Garvin County)
GLO, 1876, 1879

1868. A variant of Erin Springs; see Fort Cobb.

El Ojito, Nuevo León 26°45′N., 99°51′W. N.G–14

1880. February, enroute to Monterrey, *q.v.;* called "Ojito" by Palmer (*45*, item 193).

El Paso, Texas (El Paso County)

1885. July 22, enroute to Chihuahua, and also December 14, on the return trip to Washington, D. C. (*114b; 123*).

1897. June 1, enroute from Washington, D. C., *q.v.*, to Mazatlán; Palmer and J. N. Rose met C. G. Pringle here at this time (*123a*).

1908. March 31, enroute to Chihuahua, *q.v.* (*123a*).

El Salto, San Luis Potosí

1878. See Salto del Agua, San Luis Potosí.

El Sauz, Tamaulipas 27°08′N., 99°36′W. N.G–14

1880. February, enroute to Monterrey, *q.v.;* called "Saus" by Palmer (*45*, item 193).

El Yunque, Cuba (Oriente) 20°22′N., 74°34′W. N.F–18

1902. January 30–31. A mountain near Baracoa; see Cuba.

Empire, Colorado (Clear Creek County) GLO, 1934

?1861. Palmer collected insects here, at "Empire City"; see Colorado (*112*).

England

Palmer was born at Hockwold cum Wilton, near Brandon, County Norfolk. According to Safford (*123b*) his mother was Mary Ann Armiger, and his father was William Palmer, a commercial gardener (but see above, p. 7). Edward came to New York in 1849 (*123b*).

1855–56. Left New York for England late in September or early in October, 1855. On September 19, 1855, he wrote to Baird: "All my immediate friends have died except my mother." He was married on March 29, 1856, and left London on the *Amazon* for New York, accompanied by his wife, on April 16, 1856 (*114a*).

Ensenada, Baja California 31°52′N., 116°38′W. N.H–11

1889. Arrived from San Diego, early June; was delayed a day and a night, and caught cold; on reaching Colnett was confined to bed fifteen days; see San Diego (*123a*).

1890. Touched here enroute from San Francisco, *q.v.*, to Guaymas, about August 27 or 28.

Enterprise, Florida (Volusia County) GLO, 1911

1874. April; apparently visited by Palmer on his return from Lake Okeechobee; the place is now called Benson Springs. See Florida (*114i*).

Erin Springs, [Oklahoma] (Garvin County) GLO, 1883

1868. A locality on the road along the Washita River between Fort Arbuckle and Fort Cobb, *q.v.* Called Elm Springs in Palmer's transcribed notes, and appears as "Elm Spr. Stage Sta." on the GLO maps of 1876 and 1879.

Escalerilla, San Luis Potosí 22°08′N., 101°04′W. N.F–14

1878. A small settlement in a stream valley about 15 km. southwest of the city of San Luis Potosí, on the modern highway. The valley lies in the midst of rugged dry mountains, now grazed almost to the bare rocks by goats. See Escobillo Mountains.

Escobillo Mountains, San Luis Potosí

1878. Mountains near Escalerilla, *q.v.* Also spelled "Escobrillos," "Escabrillos," or "Escobrillo." Numerous references to mountains of this name appear among Palmer's and Safford's notes. Palmer's own pencilled notes suggest that he collected 27 specimens there. The several variants ending in "-billo" or "-brillo" are evidently corruptions of the word "Escalerilla," and all based upon mistaken interpretation of handwritten memoranda. I am indebted to Professor Nereo Rodríguez Barragán, of San Luis Potosí, for confirmation of this suggestion (*114i, 123a*).

Eufaula, Alabama (Barbour County) GLO, 1882

1884. Palmer collected a few ethnological specimens here, perhaps on his way to Georgia, *q.v.* (*114f*).

Eureka Valley, [Oklahoma] (Caddo County)

1868. South of the Washita River, in R 10 W; see Fort Cobb.

Eustis, Florida (Lake County) GLO, 1926

1884. Visited in October, according to notes in the National Herbarium collection; see Florida (*114i*).

1888. January 26. Enroute from Guaymas to Washington.[14]

1896. Palmer wrote from Durango on October 15 that he planned to stop for a visit at Eustis while on his way to Washington; there is no other evidence that he made such a visit (*114i*).

Fabrica de la Fama, Nuevo León

1880. February 17–?26. Not located, but apparently just west of Monterrey, *q.v.* Called by Palmer the "New Bleaching Factory" or "Groom's Factory" (*45*, item 193).

False Bay, California (San Diego County) GLO, 1928

1888. On the coast about 5 miles northwest of San Diego, *q.v.* Palmer's field notes indicate that Nos. 28 and 29 (or 275 and 276 of his principal series of this year) were collected in September on the "east side of False Bay," and No. 30 (277) about 2 miles away on the "west side" (*114i*).

False Washita, Indian Territory

1868. Same as Washita River, *q.v.*

Fernandina, Florida (Nassau County) GLO, 1926

1874. September 1–3, probably just before leaving Florida for Boston (*123a*).

Filler Mound, Arkansas

1882. Same as Tiller Mound, *q.v.*

Fillmore, Utah (eastern Millard County) GLO, 1937

1870. About June 1, enroute from Salt Lake City to St. George, *q.v.* Palmer wrote "I stopped two days at Fillmore and made a nice

[14] See *Eustis Lake Region,* January 26, 1888.

collection." A specimen of *Opuntia erinacea* at the Missouri Botanical Garden is labeled "13 miles south of Fillmore, June 2, 1870" (*123a*).

Fishmouth Highland(s), Arkansas

1881. Said by Palmer to be "an old river cutoff" (?of Little River); probably in Mississippi County; see Mississippi County, and Little River (*88*).

Flat Rock Creek, [Oklahoma] (?Johnston County)

1868. See Boggy Depot. Palmer collected plants here, probably July 2. Not located, but probably the same as Rock Creek of GLO map, 1876 (see also U.S.G.S., Tishomingo Quadrangle, edition of 1898).

Florence, Alabama (Lauderdale County) GLO, 1882

1883 or 1884. Thomas (*118*) states that Palmer's field notes for 1883 describe mounds near here, but ethnological specimens from here (Cat. Nos. 90,485–90,508) were catalogued by the Division of Ethnology in March 1884. See Alabama.

Florida GLO, 1866, 1876, 1911, 1926

1874. Palmer reached Jacksonville February 4, a member of an expedition to Lake Okeechobee; he probably came from Boston, via Providence, Rhode Island. From Jacksonville the party at once ascended St. Johns River by boat to a point opposite Sand Point (Titusville), where they made the narrow crossing to Indian River and continued their southward journey by boat to St. Lucie (Old Fort Pierce), which they reached February 14. Here they loaded their boat and supplies, and traveled by wagon to Fort Bassinger, where they again embarked, descended the Kissimmee to Lake Okeechobee, circled the lake, returned to St. Lucie, Sand Point, and Jacksonville, by the same routes. Palmer then left his companions, crossed the state to Cedar Keys, took boat to Key West, made a trip to the Bahamas, and returned to Key West. He botanized at Pine Key, Cape Florida, and along Biscayne Bay; he returned (?by boat) to Cedar Keys in August, he was in Jacksonville August 16, in Fernandina September 1–3, and was back in Boston September 14.

Little is known of the details of Palmer's itineraries between the time of his departure from St. Lucie on the return trip (i.e. probably about March 20) and that of his departure from Cedar Keys (about

May 1). It appears, however, that his return to Jacksonville was slower than the trip out in February, and he seems to have collected at various points along the way. He probably went by water to New Smyrna, thence crossing by stage to Enterprise on the St. Johns and continuing north via Sulphur Springs and Tocoi, which he reached April 16 (*9; 10; 20; 22; 34a; 35; 123a*).

1884. Palmer was in Cedar Keys July 13; he left by steamer for Key West July 14, reaching Tampa Bay the following day; he was based at Key West until October 4; he left for Washington, D. C., October 5, reaching Jacksonville October 9. He visited Fort Jefferson in the Dry Tortugas (July 25 or 31); left Key West for Key Largo (August 3); was at Carey's Fort Reef (August 6), Key Largo (August 7), French's Reef (August 8), Old Fort Dallas (September 5), Miami (September 8) and Biscayne Bay (September). Left Miami for Key West (September 9). He was probably continuously at Key West from September 20 to October 5, and he seems to have gone north by the St. Johns River route, stopping over at Eustis and Orlando. See also Caesar Creek, Eastern Dry Rocks, Rodriguez Creek, Salt Pond Key, Stock Island (*94; 114a; 114b; 114c; 123a*).

1888. See Eustis.

1896. See Eustis.

Forrest City, Arkansas (St. Francis County) GLO, 1886

1882. January; see Phillips County. Called by Palmer Forest City.

1882. November. Arrived probably November 1, from Harrisburgh and Cherry Valley; left for Madison November 3, and was in Little Rock on November 11. According to Palmer's account he visited a number of mounds and house sites within a radius of about 10 miles from Forrest City, but whether during his first visit, in January, or later the same year in November, I do not know. Neither visit appears to have been a long one. He mentions the Crook Mound ("10 miles southeast"), Chairs Mound ("4 miles southeast"), mounds at Lake Anderson or Mud Lake (2 miles northeast according to Thomas [*119*, p. 228]), and a site on the St. Francis River ("12 miles northeast"). Thomas says Palmer explored several sites on the Robert Anderson farm, on the river 4 miles northeast of Forrest City (*88; 118; 119*).

Fort Apache, Arizona (southern Navajo County)
GLO, 1933

1890. Arrived about June 20, from Willow Springs; collected Nos.

575–613; left for Willow Springs July 5. The dates of the visit to Fort Apache are given by Rose (98) as June 21–30 (*98; 114i; 123a*).

Fort Arbuckle, Oklahoma (Garvin County) GLO, 1898

1868. Near the site of present Hoover, 6 miles west and one mile north of Davis. Palmer probably visited here about June 10, when he came east from Fort Cobb, *q.v.*, and again on August 6, from Cherokee Town, *q.v.* For plants collected "between Fort Cobb and Fort Arbuckle" see explanation in text, p. 39. Fort Arbuckle was occupied by troops in 1868, but after the establishment of Fort Sill it was abandoned June 24, 1870.[15]

Fort Bassinger, Florida (eastern Highlands County) GLO, 1926

1874. On the west side of the Kissimmee River, about 20 miles above Lake Okeechobee. Arrived February 20, from St. Lucie, after they had "walked 60 miles, swimmed two creeks and *waded over 20 miles.*" Their route was: 10 miles west to Ten-mile Creek, then north of west 24 miles over Alpattie Flats; from a point 26 miles from St. Lucie they followed the prairies of the St. Johns to the old road between Fort Capron and Tampa, and then due west 5 miles to the Kissimmee Prairies and thence southwest to the river. A letter was written from "Fort Bassenger Ford on the Kissimmee," February 21. Upon returning from Lake Okeechobee the party seems to have spent a few days at Fort Bassinger before leaving for St. Lucie. The name was invariably spelled "Bassenger" by Ober and his party, but the correct spelling (which appears on some maps) seems to be "Basinger," after Lt. Wm. E. Basinger, who was killed by the Seminoles at Dade's Massacre, Florida, December 28, 1835 (*9; 10*).[16]

Fort Blunt, Cherokee Nation

1863. July and August; see Fort Scott. This was a short-lived name, used in 1863 for the post known before and after the Civil War as Fort Gibson (now Muskogee County, Oklahoma). Fort Gibson was in Cherokee territory, and United States troops were withdrawn in 1857 at the urging of the Cherokees. When Union troops gained possession of the post during the war, the newly fortified establishment

[15] See *Chronicles of Oklahoma,* Vol. V (1927), 221–33, and Vol. VI (1928), 26–34.

[16] F. B. Heitman, *Historical Register and Dictionary of the United States Army, 1789–1903,* (2 vols., Washington, 1903), I, 197.

was renamed in honor of General James G. Blunt, the commander in this area. Palmer was stationed here with his army unit for about two months, and found time in the midst of active military service to collect at least a few plants, e.g. *Clitoria mariana,* as evidenced by a specimen in the National Herbarium.

Fort Bourbon

1853. See Fuerte Olimpo.

Fort Buchanan, Arizona (northeastern Santa Cruz County) GLO, 1921

Collections were made here, "south of Tucson," according to Scudder; no date is indicated on the specimens cited by him, which are now in the Museum of Comparative Zoology. The locality is listed on the GLO map (1921), as "Old Fort Buchanan," and also appears on the Riecker map of 1879[17] (*34b; 113*).

Fort Capron, Florida (northeastern St. Lucie County)

1874. On the coast (on the mainland side of the Indian River lagoon), about 4½ miles north of Fort Pierce and approximately opposite the Indian River Inlet just north of St. Lucie. Shown on J. C. Ives's map[18] at 27°29′ north latitude. Visited February 14; see Florida (*9; 123a*).

Fort Casseina, Florida

1874. Probably Palmer's variant of Cassina. Not located, but visited, according to notes in the National Herbarium collection, in February, and so apparently on or near the St. Johns, or Indian, River. See Florida (*114i*).

Fort Cobb, [Oklahoma] (Caddo County) GLO, 1876

1868. Palmer arrived early in March at the newly founded Kiowa-Comanche Indian Agency, with which he was connected as medical officer; collections were made "11 miles below Fort Cobb" on March 5 and 10. The agency was permanently established at this time in Eureka Valley, south of the Washita River and (according to Palmer)

[17] Engineer Office, D. A. *Map of Arizona Territory,* prepared by authority of Brevet Major General O. B. Willcox (under direction of 1st Lieutenant Fred A. Smith). Compiled and drawn by Paul Riecker. 18 miles equal 1 inch. 1879.

[18] J. C. Ives, *Memoir to Accompany a Military Map of the Peninsula of Florida South of Tampa Bay* (Washington, War Department, 1856. 42 pp.) and Map, 1/400,000.

17 miles southeast of the site of old Fort Cobb. Plants numbered 1–114 were collected in the vicinity of the Agency, between March 14 and May 5.

Fort Cobb had been abandoned by the federal forces at the outbreak of the Civil War and subsequently destroyed. Because of Indian depredations in this vicinity and along the Texas border, there was demand for the remilitarization of a fort here, and Fort Cobb was temporarily re-occupied in 1868, pending the completion of permanent quarters at Camp Wichita (later Fort Sill). Few of Palmer's collections were from the original site, but he refers in some notes to Fort Cobb as being but 3 miles from the agency, and it may be that another temporary encampment in 1868 was also called Fort Cobb.[19]

The site of Fort Cobb (as shown on many modern maps, and on the GLO maps of 1876, 1879, 1883, and 1885) was on the Washita River in R 12 W. Palmer's headquarters in Eureka Valley were south of the river in R 10 W, near present Anadarko. The Wichita Agency (see below) is shown in R 10 W on the GLO map of 1876 and (as "Old Wichita Agency") on the GLO map of 1883. The GLO map of 1885 shows, in R 10 W, both Anadarko and the "Kiowa, Comanche and Wichita Agency."

About May 8, Palmer changed his residence from the Kiowa Agency to the Wichita Agency immediately adjacent, having been discharged from his medical duties by his superior, Col. Jesse H. Leavenworth. He seems to have made a trip up river to the site of "old" Fort Cobb, about May 19–24, and to have collected some bird skins, and plants Nos. 115–74. He collected along the Washita, near the Wichita Agency, Nos. 175–223, May 26–31.

About June 1, he discovered that the Indians were plotting to kill him, and left at once for the east, traveling again the route along the Washita. The stations and distances as he gives them are as follows: Fort Cobb (i.e. "new" Fort Cobb?) to Kiowa-Comanche Agency (3 miles southeast); Fort Cobb to Shirley's old store (4½ miles); old store to Shirley's new store (17 miles east); New Store to Line Creek (10 miles); New Store to Little "Washata" [River] (18 miles); New Store to Elm (i.e. Erin) Springs (40 miles); New Store to Smith['s] Pauls (60 miles); Smith['s] Pauls to Cherokee Town (4 miles). Palmer collected plants numbered 224–38, on this trip to Cherokee

[19] See "Military Reminiscences of Captain Richard T. Jacob," *Chronicles of Oklahoma,* Vol. II (1924), 9–36.

Town, *q.v.*, June 3–6. See Indian Territory (*45*, item 297; *114b; 114e; 120; 123a; 125b*).

Fort Craig, New Mexico (southern Socorro County)
GLO, 1866, 1912

?1862. On the Río Grande in R2 W, T 8 S; the site of a brief battle of the Civil War, February 21, 1862. Specimens of insects from here were included in a shipment made by Palmer from Denver, as mentioned in a letter of December 14, 1862. Two companies of the 2nd Colorado Volunteers took part in the battle here, and possibly the insects in question were given to Palmer by someone else; he himself was enroute from Acapulco to Panama at the time of the battle, and I can find no record of any other trip to Fort Craig by the 2nd Colorado regiment in 1862. See Colorado (*114b*).

Fort Dallas, Florida (Dade County) GLO, 1866

1884. At the mouth of the Miami River, now in the city of Miami. Shown on Ives's map[20] at latitude 25°45′ North. Said to have been visited by Palmer September 5, and called by him "Fort Dallis." See Florida (*123a*).

Fort Defiance, Arizona (east-central Apache County)
GLO, 1933

1869. Palmer reached here probably about June 3, with a party, enroute to the Hopi village of Oraibi. He passed by again on the return trip, in mid-June. A specimen of *Echinocereus Fendleri* was collected June 16. See Fort Wingate (*114e; 114i*).

Fort Dodge, Kansas (Ford County) GLO, 1925

1865. May 29, enroute to Arizona. On this date Palmer wrote that he had been unable to collect any plants, owing to the danger from hostile Indians. See Fort Whipple (*114b*).

Forte do Coimbra, Brazil (Mato Grosso) 19°54′S., 57°48′W.
S.E–21

1853. West of the Río Paraguay. Specimens were collected (November 28) while the *Water Witch* stopped here, November 27–29, on the way up river to Corumbá; specimens were probably collected on the return trip as well, December 8–11; on this second visit Palmer,

[20] See Ives, *Memoir to Accompany a Military Map.*

accompanying a party, visited a near-by cavern, the Gruta do Inferno, and specimens were collected there. See Río Paraná (*52; 123a; 125c*).

Fort Gibson, "Arkansas" (now northeastern Muskogee County, Oklahoma) GLO, 1876

1868. About February 1, while enroute to Fort Cobb, and probably also early in October of the same year; see Fort Blunt, and Indian Territory (*123a*).

Fort Hall, Idaho

1893. See Portneuf River.

Fort Huachuca, Arizona (southwestern Cochise County) GLO, 1933

1890. Arrived from Guaymas about April 20; collected Nos. 416–78 (450–59, inclusive, are duplicated). Also bought a collection of about 25 numbers made in 1889 by a man living in a "canon" near the post. See Tombstone. Left for Fort Apache, May 29. The dates of Palmer's collections at Fort Huachuca are given by Rose (98) as April 26 to May 21. See Arizona (*34a; 98; 123a; 123c*).

Fort Jackson, Alabama (Elmore County)

1884. A site said by Thomas (*118*) to have been at the junction of the Coosa and Tallapoosa rivers, but shown (as Old Ft. Jackson) on the GLO map of 1889 as located between the rivers and 3–4 miles northeast of their junction. Palmer collected ethnological specimens here; see Elmore County.

Fort Jefferson, Florida (Monroe County) GLO, 1911

1884. July 25 (or 31). Palmer collected here and perhaps at other localities in the Dry Tortugas. The old fort is on Garden Key; for a map see U. S. Coast & Geodetic Survey chart No. 1,351 (3rd edition, 1952). Its position is approximately latitude 24°38′N., longitude 82°52′W. See Florida (*94; 123a*).

Fort Kearny, Nebraska (Kearney County)

1862. May 10–14; see Fort Leavenworth and Nebraska. Listed on the GLO map of 1890, as "Old Fort Kearney" (*114b*).

Fort Larned, Kansas (Pawnee County) GLO, 1912

1862. Arrived July 23, from Fort Lyon, Colorado, *q.v.;* left for Fort Lyon July 25 (*114b; 123a*).

1863. May 15, enroute to Fort Scott, Kansas, *q.v.*

Fort Leavenworth, Kansas (Leavenworth County)
GLO, 1925

1862. Palmer reached here from Washington, via Cleveland, Ohio, on March 22, as surgeon in the 2nd Colorado Volunteers, Colonel Jesse H. Leavenworth. His actual enlistment in the army was as of April 14, 1862. Left for Denver April 26, via Fort Kearny, Nebraska (May 10–14), Julesburg, Colorado (May 22–23), and Camp Evans, Colorado (June 2). The route seems to have followed the Platte River; see Nebraska (*114b; 123a*).

Fort Lyon, Colorado (eastern Bent County)

1862–63. Palmer arrived from Camp Weld, *q.v.*, July 2, 1862, and left for Fort Larned, Kansas, July 11, with the troops to negotiate with a band of unruly Pawnees. Returned August 2 and reached Camp Weld August 8. Ordered back to Fort Lyon; arrived about September 25, and was detailed to "overhaul and straighten" the hospital. Probably left for Camp Weld December 4. Returned about January 1, and remained until May 6, 1863, when he left for Ft. Scott, Kansas, *q.v.* A few collections were made along the Arkansas River between Denver and Fort Lyon, June 26, and others near Fort Lyon on July 3, 6, 8, and 10. July 18 a collection was made "150 miles east of Fort Lyon," and (July 23) 1 near Fort Larned. These specimens were sent to Washington on September 8, 1862 (see Colorado), but those collected at Fort Lyon in the winter and spring of 1863 were apparently sent from Fort Scott on June 16 of that year (*114b; 123a; 125d*).

The Fort Lyon of modern maps is near Las Animas, Bent County, some 30 miles west of the site in Palmer's time. In the 1860's, Fort Lyon was located on the north side of the Arkansas River, opposite present Prowers, in R 48 W. It was first known as Bent's Fort; it was said to be a large stone structure, covering about an acre, with space inside for 500 men. Old Bent's Fort, built in 1832, was about 40 miles west of this in eastern Otero County.[21]

The post called Fort Lyon in Palmer's time was located at the mouth of Little Sandy Creek, just west of longitude 102°30′W., according to the surveyor general's map of 1865.[22] Bent's Fort [i.e. the

[21] L. R. Hafen, ed., *Pikes Peak Gold Rush Guidebooks of 1859* (Cleveland, 1941).

[22] "Map of Public Surveys in Colorado Territory" (13 miles=1 inch), accompanying *Report of the Surveyor General* (1865); Surveyor General's Map (1866) in 37 Cong., 3 sess., *House Ex. Doc. No. 1.*

post at or near the site of twentieth-century Fort Lyon] appeared on these maps near the mouth of Purgatory Creek and a few miles west of the 103rd meridian; Bent's Old Fort (or Old Bent's Fort), as noted above, was still farther west.

Fort Mohave, Arizona (Mohave County) GLO, 1879

1869. Palmer came here overland from Fort Whipple, probably in August; see Yuma. Often referred to as Camp Mohave; it appeared on the GLO map of 1903 as "Old Fort Mohave." It was east of the Colorado River, about 70 miles north of Williams Fork and 7½ miles from Hardyville, according to Palmer (Latitude ca. 35°03′N.).

1870. Palmer arrived about July 1, from Hardyville, *q.v.*, and left for Williams Fork, *q.v.*, July 4 (45, item 15).

1876. Perhaps visited from Hardyville, *q.v.*, in May.

Fort Pierce, Florida

1874. Same as Old Fort Pierce; see Florida.

Fort Riley, Kansas (Geary County) GLO, 1925

1863. May 23, enroute to Fort Scott, Kansas, *q.v.* (*114b*).

Fort Scott, Kansas (Bourbon County) GLO, 1925

1863. Arrived about mid-June from Fort Lyon, Colorado, via Fort Larned, Cow Creek, Fort Riley, and Council Grove. Palmer's company of the 2nd Colorado Cavalry left Fort Scott about June 21, took part in the battle of Cabin Creek (July 2), reached Fort Blunt, C.N. (July 5), were in the battle of Honey Springs (July 17). Palmer probably was at Fort Blunt continuously until at least August 17. His unit was at Fort Smith, Arkansas, from September to November, leaving November 19 and reaching St. Louis December 17. Palmer probably was with his company most or all of this time (*114b; 125d*).

1868. See Indian Territory.

Fort Smith, Arkansas (Sebastian County) GLO, 1914

1863. Palmer probably was here from September 16 to November 19; see Fort Scott.

Fort Trumbull, Arizona

Same as Mt. Trumbull, *q.v.* In the original description of *Townsendia arizonica*, Gray erroneously cited Palmer's locality as Fort Trumbull (32).

Fortuna, Nayarit

1892. See La Fortuna.

Fort Wallace, Kansas (eastern Wallace County)
GLO, 1884

1869. See Sheridan, Kansas.

Fort Wallen, Arizona (southwestern Cochise County)
GLO, 1897

1867. See Wallen.

Fort Whipple, Arizona (central Yavapai County)
GLO, 1876

1865. At this time the fort was "one and a half miles from Prescott." Palmer arrived July 26, from Kansas City. His contract as acting assistant surgeon, U. S. A., had been annulled at the end of March, at his own request, to enable him to accompany a party including some "dignitaries" to Arizona. Travel from Kansas City was by way of Fort Dodge, Kansas (May 29), Trinidad, Colorado and the "Ratoon" Mountains (both June), and probably thence to Santa Fé, Albuquerque, up the route along the San Jose River to the Continental Divide, to the Zuni country, thence down the Little Colorado River. Palmer notes that "our road from Zuni to Fort Whipple Arizona runs along the Little Colorado River for 60 miles."

He was at Fort Whipple until October 20, when he rejoined the army as acting assistant surgeon and went at once to Camp Lincoln, *q.v.* Dr. Elliott Coues had been at Fort Whipple for some months previous to Palmer's arrival, and all plants collected that summer (about 600 numbers) were sent to Engelmann for identification and were distributed by him under the joint names of Elliott Coues and Edward Palmer, although a considerable number had been collected by Coues before Palmer's arrival, and some were collected by Palmer after Coues's departure (*114b; 123a; 123b*).

1866. Palmer was confined to the hospital here, probably September to November, leaving hurriedly to go to his next post, Camp Grant. No plants are known to be extant from Palmer's 1866 collections, although on November 26 he wrote to Engelmann that he was sending two boxes at the first opportunity. On April 20, 1867, he wrote that because of leaving Fort Whipple so hurriedly he had left his field notes at the post. Neither the notes nor the plants are known to have reached Engelmann (*24; 125d*).

1869. Arrived July 9, from Fort Wingate, and stayed until after

August 1, making in the interim a trip to Bill Williams Mountain. On August 19, after buying provisions for a long journey, he left for the Colorado River, perhaps first making a trip to Camp Lincoln.

The first day's travel from Fort Whipple was westerly to Mint Valley, then to Skull Valley, 23 miles in all. The route then passed through Bell's Canyon, "a few miles" to Cullen's Well, then to Johnson's Well, then Hanniger, then "passing out of the mountains" to Tyson's Station and Ehrenberg. (Safford states that Palmer went from Fort Whipple to Fort Mohave in August, but I can find nothing to confirm this.) From Ehrenberg he descended the Colorado River to Yuma and Puerta Isabel. He returned to Yuma, went up the Gila River past Gila Bend to the Pima villages, visited Camp McDowell and Fort Whipple again, and then stayed and collected at Camp Date Creek until September 16, when he set out again for Ehrenberg by the same route he had traveled in August. Leaving Ehrenberg September 22, on the *Cocopah,* he repeated his trip to Yuma, Puerta Isabel, and return to Yuma, then went to Tucson by coach.

Palmer's travels of 1869, after his departure from Fort Whipple on August 19, are not well documented, but it appears that he actually made two trips to Ehrenberg and Puerta Isabel as outlined above. His own account of the August trip is in Merwin item No. 14, while his account of the September trip, as quoted by Safford, differs in so many details that it seems almost certainly an authentic description of a second passage over the same route, starting from Camp Date Creek instead of Prescott. During the September trip he was able to collect at Puerta Isabel and to make at least one considerable trip beyond there, and it is possible that he met unfavorable conditions for work or travel in August, and so returned a month later for a second, and as it turned out more successful, attempt. Safford's account of the September trip from Camp Date Creek gives the itinerary: To Cullen's Well, 45 miles, south; Johnson's or Knapp's, 15 miles, south; Granite Wash, 9 miles; Hanniger Wells, 12 miles, west; Tyson's Well, 27 miles, southwest; Ehrenberg, 21 miles, west. See Yuma (*45,* items 14, 19, 22; *114a; 114b; 123a; 123b*).

Fort Wingate, New Mexico (McKinley County)
GLO, 1886

1869. Arrived from Sheridan, Kansas, *q.v.,* April 16, having come by way of Santa Fé and Albuquerque. A note among the manuscripts in Merwin item No. 223 (*45*) is undated, but gives the following

"Distances in New Mexico," and from the route outlined it may be inferred that Palmer followed in 1869 the road that was later followed by the railroad and the modern highway: "Cubero to Blue Water—35—to the Divide—20—to Bacon Spr. 15—to Ft. Wingate 15." Fort Wingate had been moved to this location (its present one) very shortly before Palmer's visit. A letter from Parry to Engelmann, dated May 13, 1869, emphasizes this by referring to a note from Palmer at "New" Fort Wingate. The original site was in the modern Valencia County, on Río San José about 70 miles west of Albuquerque (see GLO map, 1866). On the GLO map of 1886 "Old Ft. Wingate" is shown in T 10 N, R 10 W. From Ft. Wingate Palmer visited the Navajo Agency (before May 1) and also made visits (about May 5) to "nearby Pueblo Indian villages," possibly the villages of the Acoma Indians, *q.v.*

Leaving Fort Wingate about the first of June, and Fort Defiance on June 4, Palmer accompanied Commissioner Vincent Colyer on a fortnight's trip to the "Moqui" village of Oraibi. Colyer's party included a detail of soldiers and four Navajo guides. Palmer's sketchy account of the trip tells us that the first day's march was 12 miles southwest, then 11 miles generally west; the second day the party traveled 30 miles west and southwest; the third day (Sunday) was one of rest, and Colyer preached to his fellow travelers; the sixth day water was getting low; the seventh day the travel was 25 miles to Bird Spring, and the eighth day Oraibi was reached after a trip of 10 miles. The return trip to Fort Defiance was by way of Canyon de Chelly (June 13). The party reached Fort Defiance June 16, and Fort Wingate about June 18. Palmer then left for Fort Whipple, Arizona, June 22; see San Francisco Mountain (*24; 45*, item 221; *114a; 114b; 114e; 114i; 123a; 123e; 124a*).

Fort Worth, Texas (Tarrant County)

1879. July; see Longview.

Fort Yuma, California (southeastern Imperial County)

GLO, 1900

1875. From San Diego, Palmer wrote on August 8: "The Mail contractors will be hear in a few days then I will try to get a pass to Fort Yuma and back." He is not known to have reached Fort Yuma, but he may have started with the mail contractors; he visited Tiajuana Valley (August 14), Wildcat Station, Baja California (August 15),

Tecate Valley Station (August 16), Campo or Milquatay (August 17), Old Stone House or Larkens Station (August 18–19), and Mountain Springs (August 20). For his subsequent movements see Tantillas Mountains (*20; 123a*).

Fountain Green, Utah (Sanpete County) GLO, 1876, 1937

?1876. An incidental mention among Palmer's notes, with citation of this year. The year 1877 is more probable if Palmer stopped here for any length of time, as in July of that year he went from Paragonah to Spring Lake Villa by road; see St. George (*45*, item 282).

Frailes, Chihuahua

1885. Not certainly located on a map; for discussion see Chihuahua (Estado). Palmer passed through here first in late July, on the trip to Batopilas, and again in October after leaving Batopilas. In October he collected Nos. 245, 251–69, 271–85, 287–97. Also called by Palmer "Los Frailes," or "Frayles" (*123b; 143*).

Franklin Mound, Arkansas (?Desha County)

?1882. Not located, but said by Palmer to be in this county, near the junction of Opossum Fork and Cypress Creek, 6 miles northwest of Arkansas City. The junction is actually 8–9 miles nearly north of Arkansas City, as shown on USGS, Lamont Quadrangle (1939).

Fredericksburg, Texas (Gillespie County)

1880. October 16, apparently enroute from San Antonio to Palestine; the details of the trip are unknown; see Texas (*123a*).

Fremonts Orchard, Colorado (Morgan County)

1861–62. Mentioned in Palmer's field notes. One of the stopping places along the Platte route to Denver, near the South Platte River east of present Orchard and south of Goodrich (*114b*).[23]

French Lick, Indiana (western Orange County)
GLO, 1886

1882. August; see Indiana.

Frenchman's Bayou, Arkansas (Mississippi County)

?1881. In the southeastern part of the county, 6 miles west of Golden Lake P. O. on the Mississippi River (see GLO, 1886). Mounds

[23] L. R. Hafen, *Overland Routes to the Gold Fields* (Glendale, Calif., 1942).

here are described by Thomas (*119*, p. *221*), but Palmer states that he did no digging at this locality (*88*).

French's Landing, Alabama (Clarke County)

1884. Palmer collected a few ethnological specimens here; see Alabama (*114f*).

French Reef, Florida (Monroe County) CGS, 1249

1884. August 8; called "French's Reef" by Palmer. This is about 10 miles east of the southern end of Key Largo, in latitude 25°02'N., longitude 80°21'W. See Florida (*123a*).

Friar('s) Point, Mississippi (Coahoma County) GLO, 1915

1883. Palmer visited the Rozell Mounds, said to be 6 miles east of here, late in March. See Vicksburg (*114c*).

Frio River, Texas

1880. See Río Frio.

Fuerte Olimpo, Paraguay (Chaco) 21°01'S., 57°50'W. S.F–21

1853. West of the Río Paraguay. Specimens were collected here November 22. Also called Fort Bourbon by the members of the La Plata Expedition. See Río Paraná (*52; 123a; 125c*).

Gage County, Nebraska

1858. See Doniphan County, Kansas.

Gallinas, San Luis Potosí

1878. December 28 29; see Ciudad del Maíz. Not located on any map, but probably the same as Paso Real Gallinas, which appears in latitude 22°N., longitude 99°16'W., where the road from Montes (San Nicolás) crossed Río Gallinas just north of Rascón station [Map AMS, F–14–N–V]. Professor Nereo Rodríguez Barragán informs me that this is substantially correct; that is, that Gallinas of Palmer's time was near present Rascón, *q.v.*, and that the river is known either as "Río Rascón" or "Río Gallinas" (*114i*).

Gardner Mound, Arkansas

Said by Palmer to be one mile east of the Menard mounds, *q.v.*; here he obtained specimens from the surface only; the date of his visit probably was 1881 or 1883. See Arkansas County.

Garretson's Landing, Arkansas (southeastern Jefferson County) GLO, 1886

1882–83. A landing on the south side of the Arkansas River, in R 6 W, T 6 S, from which Palmer probably visited the Houson, Snuggs (or Smuggs), and Linwood mounds; for descriptions and comment see Thomas (*119*, p. 242); see Jefferson County (*88*).

Gay Head, Massachusetts (Dukes County) CGS, 1210

1871. The western end of Martha's Vineyard. Ethnological specimens were collected here (*114f*).

General Cepeda, Coahuila 25°22′N., 101°28′W. N.G–14

1904. Visited August 16–17, on a hurried trip by rail from Saltillo; collected Nos. 326–30, and 454 (*34a; 123a*).

Georgetown, Tennessee (Meigs County)

1882. (?)April; see Tennessee.

Georgetown, Texas (Williamson County)

1879. About 30 collections of plants made here, October 12–19; insects were collected October 12–16. On October 21, Palmer wrote of an archaeological collection he had just made at Georgetown, so that the above dates are at least approximately correct. They overlap, however, the supposed dates of his visit to Bluffton (October 10–15) and the correct sequence is unknown. A fragmentary list of expenses preserved among Palmer's papers suggests that his trip to Williamson and Burnet counties was made from Austin, by way of Fredericksburg, Llano (where he "laid over" one day), Burnet, and Georgetown, in that order. Apparently he returned to Austin from Georgetown (*2; 34b; 34d; 142*).

Georgia

1884. As an assistant in the Bureau of Ethnology, Palmer investigated mounds near Blakely (March 20 to about May 1), and in White and Habersham counties (about May 1 to about ?May 15), proceeding thence to Chester County, South Carolina, and to Washington, D. C. (May 26) (*34a; 114b; 114c*).

Gibara, Cuba (Oriente) 21°07′N., 76°07′W. N.F–18

1902. January; see Cuba.

Gibson County, Tennessee

?1882. Palmer reported mounds at Trenton and Brazil, according to Thomas (*118*). This may have been in May or June of this year, when he was in several counties in western Tennessee; see Tennessee.

Gibson Jack Creek, Idaho

1893. See Big Canyon, Idaho.

Gila Bend, Arizona (southern Maricopa County)

1869. August or September. Where the Gila River bends very abruptly to the west, about 50 miles southwest of Phoenix. See Yuma.

Gila City, Arizona (Yuma County) GLO, 1897

1867. On the Gila River, 17–18 miles above Yuma. Visited in (?)August, probably while Palmer was traveling down the Gila from Maricopa Wells. Some ethnological collections were made here. See Yuma (*114f*).

Gila River, Arizona

1867. See Camp Grant.

Gilmore Station, Arkansas (Crittenden County) GLO, 1886

?1883. See Crittenden County.

Glen Lake Mounds, Arkansas (Jefferson County)

1882–83. Palmer explored these mounds, said to be 9 miles southeast of Pine Bluff, according to Thomas (*118*); see Jefferson County.

Golden, Colorado (Jefferson County) GLO, 1934

1861. Some collections of plants and animals were made here during this season. Also called Golden City. See Colorado (*114b*).

Goliad, Texas (Goliad County)

1879. December 3; see Victoria.

Gomes Farías, Tamaulipas 23°05′N., 99°10′W. N.F–14

1907. Arrived from Xicoténcatl by wagon, April 13; collected Nos. 268–359, 562, 582, 583. On April 16 visited a canyon a league northwest of Gomes Farías. Left on the return trip to Ciudad Victoria, *q.v.*, April 21. Spelled Gómez Farías by Palmer and on most Mexican maps.

Gran Chaco, Paraguay

1853. See Asunción.

Grand Manan Island, New Brunswick 44°40′N., 66°50′W.

1872. Palmer collected a few algae here; see Eastport. He seems not to have collected any vascular plants; at least his name is not mentioned in the recent account of the flora of Grand Manan by C. A. Weatherby and John Adams.[24] See U.S. Coast & Geodetic Survey Chart No. 1,201 (edition of 1921).

Grand Prairie, Arkansas

1881. Not located; see Arkansas County.

Granite Wash, Arizona (Yuma County)

1869. September. Said to be 9 miles from Johnson's and 12 miles east of Hanniger Wells; see Fort Whipple. On War Department map of the Department of Arizona, Sheet 3 (Revised 1875, 1 inch=ca. 10 miles), this is shown crossing the Ehrenberg-Wickenburg road just west of the Granite Wash Mountains (*123b*).

Graymont, Colorado (Clear Creek County) GLO, 1897

1876. A few miles southwest of Georgetown, and 3 miles west of Silver Plume. Probably early September. Safford says Palmer joined C. C. Parry here to collect, but that they abandoned the project and returned to Davenport, Iowa, *q.v.* (*123b*).

Greeneville, Tennessee (Greene County)

1881. July 29–August 8; see Tennessee.

Greenhorn Mountains, California (north-central Kern County) GLO, 1928

1888. Palmer made a trip here from Kernville, *q.v.* The dates of the visit are given by Vasey and Rose (*133*) as June 7–15, but a letter from Sereno Watson to George Vasey, November 19, 1888, states that Palmer and W. G. Wright visited these mountains on June 12 (*114i*).

Greensboro, Alabama (Hale County) GLO, 1915

?1884. About January 10; Palmer visited Sereno Watson's brother[25] here at this time. See Alabama.

[24] *Contributions from the Gray Herbarium*, Vol. CLVIII (1945), 1–96, and map.

[25] Henry Watson (?–1889), a native of Connecticut who first came to Alabama in 1830, after a year's post-graduate study at Harvard. He was successful in law and in business, and by 1841 was a leading citizen of Greensboro. See

Greenville, Mississippi (Washington County) GLO, 1915

1883. About March 19–20. See Vicksburg.

Gregory Mines, Colorado (Gilpin County)

1862. See Colorado. Approximately at present site of Central City, *q.v.*, where the first important discovery of gold was made by John H. Gregory, in May, 1859.[26]

Greytown, Nicaragua 10°56′N., 83°42′W. N.C–17

1867. See San Francisco, California. The eastern terminus of the transisthmian route across Nicaragua from San Juan del Sur. Also called "San Juan," "San Juan de Nicaragua," or "San Juan del Norte."

Grief Hill, Arizona (Yavapai County)

1866. June; Palmer, with a party of soldiers, visited a small settlement 7 or 8 miles below here, on the lower Río Verde at the junction of that stream with Clear Creek, *q.v.*; see also Camp Lincoln (*114g*).

Gruta do Inferno, Brazil (Mato Grosso) 19°52′S., 57°49′W. S.E–21

1853. Visited December 9; near Forte do Coimbra, *q.v.* Called "Grotto Inferno" by Palmer and the others of his party.

Guadalajara, Jalisco 20°40′N., 103°21′W. N.F–13

1886. Palmer arrived about June 1, from Washington, D. C., and made the city his headquarters until November. Except for a trip of ten days to Tequila, and one of a week to Chapala, all his collecting was done near Guadalajara. For a summary of his movements see Jalisco (Estado). He collected at Guadalajara July 15–August 3 (Nos. 214–300), September 6–16 (Nos. 425–500), September 25–October 5 (Nos. 612–42), October 21–25 (Nos. 690–700); also collected Nos. B, and 765.

In the U. S. National Herbarium are field notes for certain numbers, as follows; these bear the actual date of collection (indicated below in parentheses), which may not agree exactly with the inclusive dates as stated in the published account (*144*) of this year's collection: 210 (4 Jl), 225 (12 Jl), 230–34 (11–16 Jl), 240–50 (14–19 Jl),

William Pratt Dale, "A Connecticut Yankee in Ante-Bellum, Alabama," *Alabama Review*, Vol. VI (1953), 59–70.

[26] For location and description see Hollister, *Mines of Colorado*.

253–55 (14–26 Jl), 270–71 (26–28 Jl), 284 (12 Jl), 286, 290, 293–96 (29–30 Jl), 429–31 (8–10 S), 433–35, 444, 454, 457, 459, 463, 466–68, 474–76, 479–84, 499 (7–14 S), 516, 615–16 (1–4 Oct), 765 (5 Jl).

The city of Guadalajara lies on a level plain at an elevation of 1,545 m. A short distance to the west are low rocky hills which in Palmer's time supported some oak and pine forests. Collections labeled as from Guadalajara may have come from the grasslands of the plains, or from the forested or shrub-covered hills outside the city.

North and east of the city, and distant less than an hour's walk, the Río Grande de Santiago lies in a great trough, or barranca, 600 m. in depth. Most of the barranca is rugged, with steep lower slopes and precipitous upper walls. There are several springs and tributary streams in the barranca, and the vegetation is abundant and varied, more tropical in aspect than that of the plains and hills above. Different parts of the gorge have received local names, and in one area, the so-called Barranca de Ybarra, Palmer spent a week (June 15–23). This was his locality which Watson's published account called "La Barranca," *q.v.*[27]

In the same drainage system, at the head of a branch barranca about 15 km. north and slightly west of the city, lies Río Blanco, *q.v.* Palmer worked more than a month here. The vegetation is very similar to that in the immediate vicinity of Guadalajara, but is now in a slightly less disturbed condition. The city has grown rapidly in population since 1886, with consequent severe pressure upon adjacent areas.

Guadalupe, "San Luis Potosí" [19°29′N., 99°07′W.]

1878. January 15, according to a note by D. S. Correll.[28] On this date Parry and Palmer were in or near Mexico City, so the locality cited is presumably the well-known Guadalupe (Guadalupe Hidalgo of map sheet N.E–14), at the present northeastern edge of México, D.F., *q.v.*

Guadalupe, Texas (La Salle or Webb County)

1879. September 17–18, apparently enroute from Laredo to San Antonio; his next stopping place (September 18–19) was a "High oak section with sandy soil, 30 miles west of San Antonio." About 20

[27] Rogers McVaugh, "The Barranca of Guadalajara and Its Place in Botanical Literature," *Asa Gray Bulletin* (New Series), Vol. I (1953), 385–90.

[28] See United States Department of Agriculture, *Agriculture Monograph No. 11* (1952), 99.

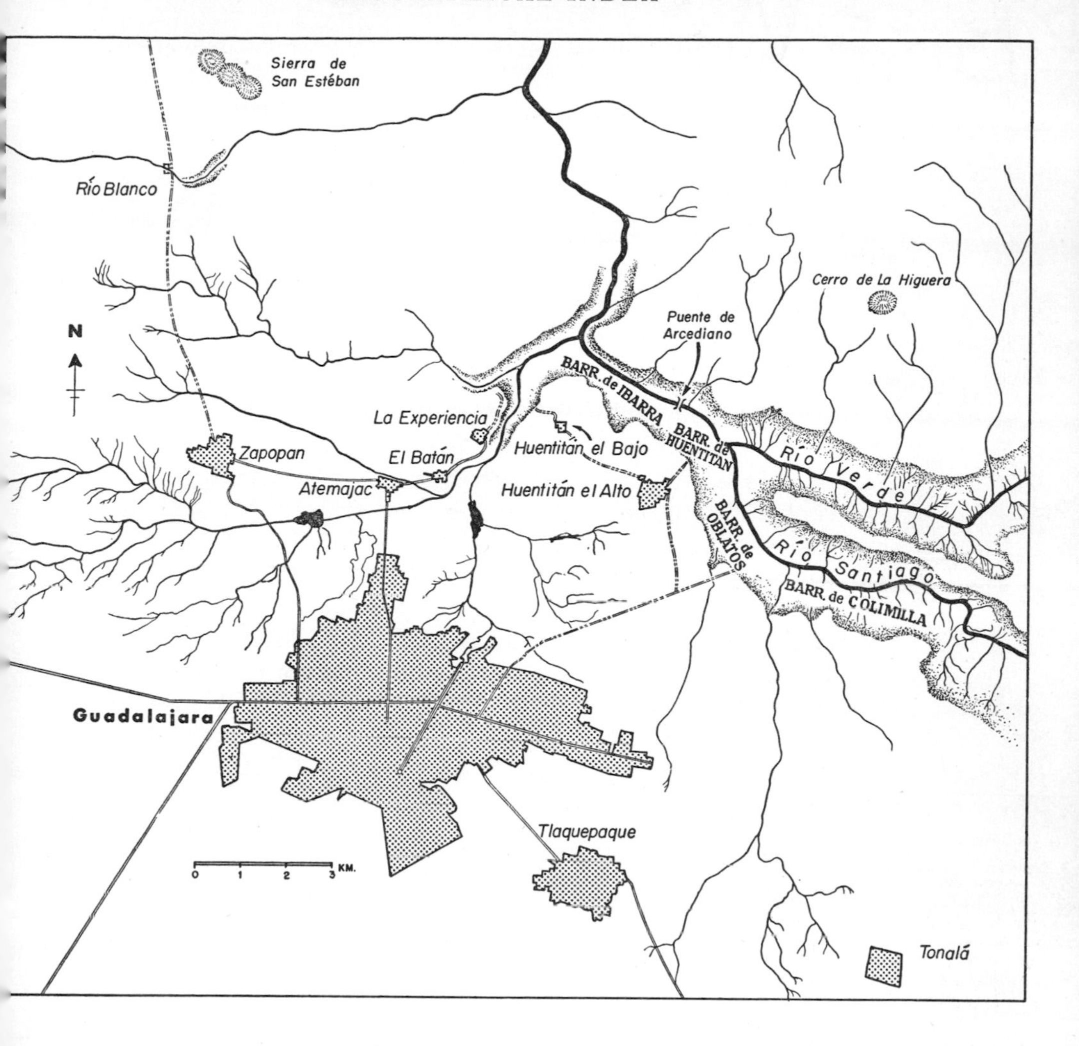

Map of Guadalajara and Vicinity

Palmer's principal collecting grounds were at Río Blanco and in the Barranca de Ibarra. (Map adapted from *Asa Gray Bulletin,* Vol. I [new series, 1953], 389).

numbers collected at Guadalupe, which is said to be "a mail station, 105 miles southwest of San Antonio, Texas; on the road to Laredo." Not to be confused with the modern Guadalupe, Victoria County. See Laredo (*2; 142*).

Guadalupe, Zacatecas 22°46′N., 102°31′W. N.F–13

1878. April 10, enroute from San Luis Potosí to Zacatecas, *q.v.* (*45*, item 190).

Guadalupe Island, Baja California

1875, 1889. See Isla de Guadalupe, Baja California.

Guajuco, Nuevo León 25°25′N., 100°09′W.

1880. Referred to by Palmer as the "Guajuco Rancheria, 10 leagues from Monterey by coach"; now called "Santiago" or "Villa Santiago" (see, e.g., map N.G–14). Palmer spent several days here early in March, but the exact dates are uncertain; he collected about 55 numbers of plants, and the dates usually given for this are March 1–8. He was in Monterrey, however, on March 3, and among his notes is one referring to Guajuco: "March 8—1880. Visited this place, 27 miles S.E. from Monterey & presented letter [of introduction]." The inference is that he arrived in Guajuco on March 8; he collected insects there March 8–10, and returned to Monterrey about the thirteenth (*2; 34b; 123a; 142*).

Guanajuato (Ciudad) 21°01′N., 101°15′W. N.F–14

1878. See Guanajuato (Estado).

1898. August; see Guanajuato (Estado).

Guanajuato (Estado) N.F–13, N.F–14

1878. Palmer collected archaeological material at the city of Guanajuato and at San Felipe, probably on one of his trips between San Luis Potosí and México, D. F., *q.v.* He is also said to have visited the "Santa Rosa Mts." and "Santa Ana Pacneco," Guanajuato (*34d; 114i*).

1898. August; Palmer apparently collected no plants, but obtained pictures and notes relative to their economic uses; visited Guanajuato (Ciudad), León, Silao, Villa Santiago, Trinidad, and "Rancho Chichimequillas." He probably came to this state from San Luis Potosí, and returned in September to Saltillo (*123a*).

Guardia Vermejo, Argentina

1854. Probably near the mouth of Río Bermejo; Vermejo is a variant used by the members of the La Plata Expedition. Visited February 1. See Asunción (*125c*).

Guascama, San Luis Potosí 22°14′N., 100°16′W.

1878. February or March, on a trip to Río Verde from San Luis Potosí. An hacienda, where Palmer made some excavations in ancient ruins, said by him to be 5 leagues west of Angostura. Appears, as Huascama, on Hoja 14-I-(U) of the *Carta de le República Mexicana a 100,000*[a], (edition of 1903). Also spelled "Huacama" and "Guazcamán." See Río Verde (*34d*).

Guaymas, Sonora 27°56′N., 110°54′W. N.G-12

1869. Arrived about November 10, by coach from Tucson, via Padrones (November 3), Altar (November 4), and Hermosillo. Left Guaymas for the Yaqui River November 21, and returned December 16. At Guaymas collected some plants and shells and birds. Left for San Francisco December 31, by steamer. Alexander Willard, who assisted and befriended Palmer during this and succeeding visits to Guaymas, had just taken office as United States Consul at this time (*114e; 114i; 123a; 125e; 136*).

1887–88. Arrived May 31; spent June 3–10 at Mulegé, Baja California; on June 14 moved "9 miles" north to Rancho de Guaymas (San José de Guaymas or "Old Guaymas"), where he lived at least until mid-October; left about October 23 for San Pedro Mártir Island and returned to Guaymas November 7; left by steamer *Ometepec* for Bahía de los Angeles on November 22 and returned late in December. Left for Washington, D. C. January 12, 1888, by train. At Guaymas collected Nos. 50–85 (June), 86–140 (July), 141–79 (August), 180–241 (September), 242–351 (October 1–22), 621–28, 634–56, 658, 659, 661–74, 677–96 (November 10–20). See Sonora (*34a; 114i; 123a; 145*).

1890. Arrived January 8, by steamer from San Francisco; left by steamer for La Paz, January 18; returned February 8; left about February 11 or 12 on a trip to the islands of Raza and San Pedro Mártir, returning February 14 or 15; left for Santa Rosalía by steamer February 21, returning March 17; left by stage for Álamos March 19, returning April 12. Left for Arizona about April 15. At Guaymas collected Nos. 145–47 (February 11), 162–76 (February 15–17), 274–75 (March 17–19) (*34a; 123a; 135*).

1890–91. Arrived about September 5–7, 1890, by steamer from San Francisco, *q.v.;* left for Agiabampo September 10, by steamer; returned October 31 and left the same day for Carmen Island; returned to Guaymas about November 10; left about November 25 for Manzanillo, Colima; returned in late March or early April, 1891; left by rail for Washington, D. C., April 14; returned July 24; left about August 5 for Culiacán via Mazatlán and Altata; returned November 30; left for San Blas, Nayarit, about December 19 (*100; 114i; 123a*).

1897. Arrived early in June, enroute from Washington, D. C., *q.v.*, to Mazatlán and Colima. Returned probably late in August and stayed until October 21; visited Topolobampo (September 15–25), San José de Guaymas (October 1–6), and Nacapuly (October 12). Left for San Diego, California, October 21. Collected Nos. 261–66 at San José de Guaymas, 268, 272 and perhaps 276–79 at Guaymas (*123a; 123c*).

Guerrero

1862; 1894–95. See Acapulco.

Habersham County, Georgia

1884. May; see Georgia.

Hacienda de Álvarez, San Luis Potosí

1878. Same as Álvarez, *q.v.*

Hacienda de Angostura, San Luis Potosí

1878. March; same as Angostura; see Río Verde.

Hacienda Bledos, San Luis Potosí

1878. September 25; same as Bledos, *q.v.*

Hacienda de Coyote, Coahuila

1880. Same as Coyote, *q.v.*

Hacienda Custodio, San Luis Potosí

1878. Same as Custodio, *q.v.*

Hacienda de Guascama, San Luis Potosí

1878. Same as Guascama, *q.v.*

Hacienda Peotillo(s), San Luis Potosí

1878. Same as Peotillos, *q.v.*

Hacienda de las Pilas, San Luis Potosí

1878. Probably same as Pila, *q.v.*

Hacienda de la Quemada, Zacatecas

1878. See Quemada.

Hacienda Robinson, Chihuahua

1908. Not located on a map. Visited April 14, from the city of Chihuahua, and said by Palmer to be 5 miles southeast of the city. Now a railroad loading point in the valley of the Río Chuvíscar, and actually about 2 miles (3 km.) east of the city. See Chihuahua (Estado) (*123a*).

Hacienda Rosario, Coahuila

1880. See Rosario.

Hacienda San José, Chihuahua

1885. See San José.

Hacienda San Miguel, Chihuahua

1885. See San Miguel.

Hale County, Alabama

?1884. January. Palmer was in Greensboro the early part of this month. Possibly at this same time he visited the Prince Mounds near Carthage, which he reported to the Bureau of Ethnology (Thomas, *118*). See Alabama.

Half Moon Lake, San Luis Potosí

1904. This is apparently Palmer's version of Laguna Media Luna, near Río Verde, *q.v.*

Hangtown, California (Eldorado County)

1861. Palmer came here late in August as "passenger by Ben Holladay's Stage—took breakfast and washed it being customary not to wash until after the sink of the Humboldt was passed." The name of the town was later changed to Placerville. See San Francisco (*123a*).

Hanniger Wells (or Hanniger), Arizona (Yuma County)

1869. August and September; see Fort Whipple. Said to be 12 miles west of Granite Wash and 27 miles northeast of Tyson's Well. Perhaps "Hanegras"; the War Department map of the Department of Arizona (sheet 3, Revised, 1875, 1 in.=10 mi.) shows "Hanegras Plain" *ca.* 10 miles west of Granite Wash, *q.v.* This becomes Ranegras Plain on modern maps, e.g. GLO, 1933.

Hardyville, Arizona (Mohave County) GLO, 1912

1870. Palmer left St. Thomas, Nevada, on June 25, on muleback, accompanying the mail carrier. Passed the Salt Mountains, then after several miles left the Virgin River, turned left by Bitter Springs and followed Callville Wash so as to reach Callville that night. June 26 followed the Colorado River for an estimated 8 miles, then overland to Eldorado Cañon for the night. June 27 followed the mountain trail near the river to the night's camp at Cottonwood Island. Reached Hardyville June 28, left Fort Mohave for Williams Fork, *q.v.*, July 4. See also Yuma, and Los Angeles (*123b*).

1876. Arrived May 8, from Prescott, on the toll road via (?)Juniper Mountains, the toll gate at Cottonwood Creek (May 4), Camp Willow Grove, Hualpai Valley, the Cerbat Mountains (another toll gate, May 6), and Union Pass. While at Hardyville perhaps visited Camp Mohave. Left Hardyville at noon, May 13, for Crafton and San Bernardino, California. About 20 numbers of plants collected at Hardyville (*34a; 45*, item 24; *114b; 114i; 123a*).

Harpswell, Maine (Cumberland County)

1873. See Peak's Island.

Harrisburgh, Arkansas (Poinsett County) GLO, 1886

?1882. Palmer gives no year for his visit, but mentions digging, probably in late October, in the Stone Mound 3 miles east of here, and in the Brookfield Mound nearby (88).

Harwood, Texas (Gonzales County)

1879. November; see Victoria.

Hassayampa Creek, Arizona (Yavapai or Maricopa County) GLO, 1933

1865. Collections labeled as from Hassayampa Creek came doubtless from the vicinity of Fort Whipple (*48*, Vol. 20: 281).

1876. Palmer sent to Engelmann, for identification, a series of plants marked "Hass-ay-ampa valley central Arizona . . . beginning of April." These probably came from near Wickenburg or from the area between Wickenburg and Prescott (*24*).

Havana, Cuba

1902. See Cuba.

Hayden's Ferry, Arizona (Maricopa County) GLO, 1876

1885. January 29; Palmer visited here one day probably from headquarters at Mesa. For history of name see Tempe (*7; 45*, item 24; *123a*).

Heckatoo, Arkansas (Lincoln County) GLO, 1886

1883. Visited January 3, from Jefferson County, *q.v.* On the south side of the Arkansas River, in R 5 W, T 7 S. Here Palmer went to what he called the Sarassa Mounds and to the Smith and Adams' mounds described by Thomas (*119*, p. 241).

Helena, Arkansas (Phillips County) GLO, 1914

1882. About January 1 to January 11; see Phillips County.
1883. Probably early November; see Little Rock.

Hell('s) Canyon, Arizona (Yavapai-Coconino County) GLO, 1921

1869. The type-specimen of *Morus grisea* Greene, in the United States National Herbarium, came from Hell Canyon. Palmer passed through here on his trip to Bill Williams Mountain, *q.v.*, about July 21 and probably again July 29 or 30 on the return trip. The canyon, according to Barnes (*7*), rises on the southwest slope of Bill Williams Mountain and drains into the Verde River in T 18 N, R 1 E.

Hermosillo, Sonora 29°05′N., 110°58′W. N.H–12

1869. November; enroute from Tucson to Guaymas, *q.v.*

Hesperia, California (San Bernardino County) GLO, 1907

1888. Probably late June, on a trip to Victor; see San Bernardino. Palmer stated that this was a "new town, on the A. & P. RR., San Bernardino branch"; it was probably a few years old at least at the time of his visit, however, for Hesperia appears on a map of the state of California (*ca.* 31 miles to 1 inch) compiled expressly for the Immigration Association of California about 1885 (*45*, item 57).

Hickman Mills, Missouri (Jackson County) GLO, 1878

1865. See Missouri. Also called Hickman's Mills.

Hidalgo (Estado)

1878. See Tula.

Highland, Kansas (Doniphan County) GLO, 1925

1857–58. Palmer moved here to practice medicine late in April, 1857, and remained about a year, making some collections. He then moved to Leavenworth, *q.v.* Spelled "Highlands" by Palmer. See also Doniphan County (*114b*).

Holbrook, Arizona (Navajo County) GLO, 1933

1890. Arrived early June, enroute from Fort Huachuca to Fort Apache; left about June 7 by stage for Fort Apache; returned July 9 and left for San Francisco July 11. See Arizona (*114i; 123a*).

Holcomb's, California (southwestern San Bernardino County)

1876. Visited June 11, enroute from Crafton to the Mojave Desert. See San Bernardino. Not located on a map, but probably on the stage route to Hardyville, Arizona; Holcomb Valley is shown on Bergland's (*126*) map in latitude 34°17′N., 117°W.

Hollands Ranch, California (?San Luis Obispo County)

1876. Visited July 2, probably soon after leaving San Luis Obispo, *q.v.* (*34a*).

Holly Grove, Arkansas (Monroe County) GLO, 1886

1881. See Monroe County. Sometimes referred to as Holly Wood (or Holley Wood) in the printed version of Palmer's Arkansas notes (*88*).

Hollywood, Arkansas (Drew County)

1882. November 22; see Jefferson County. The plantation of Dr. J. M. Taylor, called "Hollywood," was 4 miles west of Winchester Station. The Taylor Mounds are described and illustrated by Thomas (*119*, p. 239, fig. 149).

Holl(e)y Wood, Arkansas (Monroe County)

Palmer's version of Holly Grove; see Monroe County.

Honey Springs, [Oklahoma] (McIntosh County)
GLO, 1876

1863. July 17. The site of a Civil War battle, the most important in this theater of the war, which resulted in the defeat of the Confederate forces on this date; see Fort Scott. This was in present McIntosh County, about 4½ miles northeast of Checotah, and 15 miles south of Muskogee, in what was then the Creek Nation.[29]

Hoorez Mountains, [San Luis Potosí]

1878. Not located, but evidently a corruption of "Juárez Mountains," that is, probably the range east of Juárez, as shown on Hoja 13-II-(Z) of the *Carta de la República Mexicana a la 100,000*[a] (edition of 1903) in Lat. 22°10′N., Long. *ca.* 100°50′W. The same settlement is listed as "Portezuelo" on map sheet N.F-14.

Horseshoe Bend (of the Colorado River), [Sonora]

1885. See Colonia Lerdo.

1889. April; said to be 12 to 15 miles above the mouth of the river, in Sonora. See Colonia Lerdo, or Yuma (*130*).

Hortices District, Colima

1897. Said to be 28 miles east of the city of Colima, but not located there. "Hortices" appears to be Palmer's variant of "Ortices"; a locality called "Los Ortices" (American Geographic Society map, N.E-13) lies about 15 km. south of Colima, and is very probably Palmer's locality (*114b*).

Hot Spring County, Arkansas

?1883. See Arkansas. Palmer reported mounds southwest of Malvern, according to Thomas (*118*).

Hot Springs, Arkansas (Garland County) GLO, 1914

1883. September 30. Palmer came here in an endeavor to cure his rheumatism; his itinerary between St. Louis, which he visited June 24, and Hot Springs, is unknown.

Hot Springs, California (San Diego County)

1875. July 24; apparently the same as Agua Caliente, *q.v.*

Houston, Texas (Harris County)

1879. Palmer seems to have spent several days in this vicinity, making short trips by rail to investigate reports of Indian remains; the records of the Peabody Museum, however, fail to note any collections made in the area. He was in Houston (November 8), Columbia and West Columbia (November 10), Orange (November 14), and Liberty (November 17). See Texas (*34d; 123a*).

Huacama, San Luis Potosí

1878. See Guascama.

[29] See *Chronicles of Oklahoma,* Vol. XIII (1935), 154-68.

Hualpai Valley, Arizona (Mohave County)

1876. May; probably the pass north of the Hualpai Mountains, 25 or 30 miles west of Cottonwood Station. See Hardyville (*34a*).

Huatabampo, Sonora 26°50′N., 109°41′W. N.G–12

Gentry (*28*) says: "Dr. Edward Palmer collected a few specimens on the coast at Huatabampo on his way to Alamos." He gives no date for these collections. It is possible that he refers to Agiabampo, *q.v.*, which Palmer visited in 1890 on his way to Álamos.

Humboldt River, Nevada

1861. August; Palmer passed the "sink of the Humboldt" in a stage; see Hangtown.

Huntsville, Alabama (Madison County) GLO, 1882

?1883. Palmer reported the existence of shell heaps here, according to Thomas (*118*); see Alabama.

Idaho GLO, 1899, 1939

1893. Collected plants for the United States Department of Agriculture. Reached Pocatello May 6, from Washington, D. C., via Kansas City, Denver, and Ogden, Utah. Visited Market Lake May 14–16; visited Shoshone and Blue Lakes (May 31–June 14), Blackfoot, Arco and Big Butte (June 16–July 10), Idaho Falls and Dubois (July 10–19); made a second visit to Blackfoot and Big Butte (August 8–16) and a second to Shoshone and Blue Lakes (August 18–27). Left for Washington, D. C., September 13. See also Pocatello (*45*, item 128; *114i; 123a; 123d*).

Idaho Falls, Idaho (Bonneville County) GLO, 1939

1893. Arrived July 16, from Dubois, *q.v.* Left for Pocatello July 20. For collections see Blackfoot (*114i; 123a*).

Illinois GLO, 1885

1882. After investigating mounds in the vicinity of Vincennes, Indiana, in August and September, Palmer worked for a time in Lawrence County, Illinois. He examined, according to Thomas (*118*), the Brown Mill Mounds on the Embarrass River, 8 miles southwest of Vincennes. Collections were made at Russellville on October 4. See Indiana.

Imala, Sinaloa 24°52′N., 107°15′W. N.G–13

1891. Arrived August 16, from Culiacán; collected Nos. 1,413–75 and returned to Culiacán August 25 or 26; returned to Imala about September 24 or 25; collected Nos. 1,668–1,766; left October 8 or 9 for Lodiego and probably passed Imala again, after mid-October, enroute to Culiacán. Also spelled "Ymala" (*114i; 123a; 123c*).

Independence, Missouri (Jackson County) GLO, 1878

1865. See Missouri.

Independence County, Arkansas

1883. Palmer reached Newport, Jackson County, on October 28 from Lonoke, and left for Batesville the same day. After a visit to Jamestown, a probable visit to mounds at Akron, and possibly also a visit to mounds on the G. R. Stevens farm in Jackson County 6 miles south of Newport, he returned from Jamestown to Little Rock, October 31; probably he did little during this period beyond locating certain mounds for future work; excavations in Independence and Jackson counties are described by Thomas (*119*, pp. 224–25, and *118*, p. 19).

Indiana GLO, 1886

1882. As an assistant in the Bureau of Ethnology, Palmer investigated mounds, chiefly within a radius of 15 miles from Vincennes. Left Washington, D. C., August 10; made a side trip by stage to French Lick; stopped at Shoals, Martin County; reached Vincennes about August 16 and stayed until at least September 24 before going on to Arkansas in October; visited Oaktown, Knox County (September 7), and worked in Knox and Pike counties, Indiana, and Lawrence County, Illinois (*34d; 114a; 114b; 114c; 114f; 118*).

Indian Bay, Arkansas (southeastern Monroe County)
GLO, 1886

1881. See Monroe County.

Indian Bayou, Arkansas (southern Lonoke County)
GLO, 1886

1883. See Lonoke County. This was a bayou on which Palmer collected, some 22 miles from Lonoke.

Indian River, Florida GLO, 1926

1874. Palmer reached Titusville (Sand Point) early in February, reached Fort Capron February 12, and St. Lucie February 14; returned to St. Lucie from Lake Okeechobee March 17, and to Sand Point April 7. Collections labeled as from Indian River doubtless came from somewhere between Sand Point and St. Lucie, or perhaps from as far north as New Smyrna. He collected about 230 numbers of vascular plants and 24 of algae at "Indian River." See Florida (*20; 22; 34a; 123a*).

Indian Salt Works, Arkansas

1883. Near Arkadelphia, *q.v.*

Indian Territory GLO, 1876, 1879, 1883, 1885, 1894, 1898

1863. See Fort Scott.

1868. As doctor to the then newly established Kiowa-Comanche Indian Agency, Palmer left Leavenworth, Kansas, late in January. He traveled with a party by way of Fort Gibson, "Arkansas," and the near-by Creek Agency, thence by way of Deep Fork to Cherokee Town in the Chickasaw Nation (February 17), then up the Washita River to the vicinity of Fort Cobb, *q.v.* He left Fort Cobb and vicinity about June 1, descending the Washita to Fort Arbuckle and Cherokee Town, *q.v.*, where he made his headquarters until autumn, making in the meantime at least one trip southeastward to the Choctaw Nation, June–July (See Boggy Depot), and a trip northward to the Seminole Nation, mid-July. He left Cherokee Town after September 22, and reached Leavenworth before October 10. The stations and distances along this route, as outlined by him, are as follows: "Cherokee Town to Spring Brook–12–to Canadian [River] 15–to Seminole Agency–30–to Deep Fork 45–to Creek Agency 45–to Fort Gibson 10–to Cabin Creek 55–to Backsteer's Spring [i.e. Baxter Springs, Cherokee County, Kansas] 45–to Fort Scott 56–to Ottawa (terminus of the RR) 70" (*43; 45*, item 297; *114e; 120; 123b*).

Indian Wells, California (Imperial County)

1867. ?August. A station on the stage route from Yuma to Los Angeles, *q.v.* It appears on the Immigration Association map of California (*ca.* 1885), in R 12 E, T 16 S, that is, not far from the present highway US 80, near Dixieland and Seeley. From here the road turned northwest toward Vallecito (*123a*).

Iowa GLO, 1885

1876, 1877. See Davenport.

Ioway Point, Nebraska

1857–58. A locality said by Palmer to lie on the Big Blue River in Gage County, Nebraska; visited by him during the winter of his residence in Doniphan County, Kansas, *q.v.* (*114b*).

Iron Mountain, Durango

1896. Safford states that Palmer used this name for the Cerro de Mercado, *q.v.*, 2 km. north of the city of Durango. This imposing red hill, which dominates the view north of the city, is rich in iron, and mining operations have stripped much of the vegetation from it since Palmer's time. His field notes of this year indicate that many of the specimens came from Iron Mountain, but most of these were distributed merely as from the vicinity of the city of Durango (*123c*).

1906. Nos. 556–58 collected here, September 15 (*123c*).

Iron Springs

1876. Not located, but mentioned in Gray's list of the collections of this year. See Arizona, and California (*34a*).

Iron Springs, Colorado (southwestern Otero County)
GLO, 1910

1869. See Sheridan, Kansas. In R 58 W, T 40 N, at or near the present Mindeman P. O. (*114g*).

Isla Carmen, Baja California 26°N., 111°10′W. N.G–12

1870. Arrived January 1, enroute from Guaymas to San Francisco. Palmer landed and collected a few specimens; these are numbered at least to 10, *Ayenia compacta* (*114e; 114i; 123a*).

1890. Reached by the steamer *Romero Rubio*, from Guaymas, October 31; collected Nos. 816–85 (November 1–7); returned to Guaymas about November 10 (*99; 114i; 123a*).

Referred to as "Carmen Island" by Palmer, and so written on his herbarium labels and in papers in which they are cited.

Isla de Cedros, Baja California 28°15′N., 115°15′W. N.H–11

1889. Palmer arrived from Lagoon Head March 17; embarked for San Benito Island March 20, but was held at anchor by weather until March 22. Collected Nos. 659–66, 676–764. Nos. 659–741 duplicate those from San Quintín. See San Diego. Called "Cedros Island" by

Palmer and so written on his herbarium labels; called also "Cerros Island" on some maps (*114i; 123a; 134*).

Isla de Guadalupe, Baja California 29°N., 118°15′W. N.H–11

1875. Arrived about February 1, by boat from San Diego; collected about 140 numbers of plants, which were distributed under 119 numbers by the Gray Herbarium and reported upon by Sereno Watson. Returned to San Diego soon after May 20. Not only plants but also several of Palmer's collections of other groups were the subjects of special papers (*11; 34a; 39; 95; 109; 114b; 123a; 139*).

1889. March 27–April 3. Palmer's field notes show that he collected Nos. 656–58 and 858–905 on the south end of the island, March 29 and 30, and Nos. 667–75 and 831–57 on the north end of the island, April 1–3. See San Diego (*23; 123a; 134*).

Isla de Juana Ramírez, Veracruz N.F–14

1910. The island lies inside the coastal bar in the Laguna de Tamiahua, extending from about latitude 21°44′N. to 21°54′N., and so is about 30 to 50 km. south of Tampico. Visited March 8–9; collected Nos. 451–71 (*123a; 123c*).

Island of San Pedro Martin

1887. See Isla San Pedro Mártir.

Isla Rasa, Baja California 28°50′N., 113°W. N.H–11

1890. February 12; collected Nos. 151–61. See Guaymas. Called "Raza Island" by Palmer and so written on his field notes and herbarium labels (*123a; 135*).

Isla San Benito, Baja California 28°19′N., 115°35′W. N.H–11

1889. Arrived March 24; collected Nos. 906–23 on March 25. Vasey and Rose say this was on "West San Benito Island," a note by Safford says it was on the largest island of the San Benito group, and Palmer's field notes state that it was the easternmost island of the group. Called "San Benito Island" by Palmer and so written on his herbarium labels. See San Diego (*123a; 134*).

Isla San Pedro Mártir, Baja California 28°23′N., 112°20′W. N.H–12

1887. Arrived from Guaymas October 23 or 24; collected Nos. 400–

19; returned to Guaymas, arriving November 7. The herbarium labels distributed with this collection were of two sorts; one bore the legend "Island of San Pedro Martin" and the other "Plants of San Pedro Martir." Watson, in his report on the collection used the name "San Pedro Martin"[30] (*123a; 145*).

1890. February 13; collected Nos. 148–50. See Guaymas. The labels distributed with these plants bore the legend "San Pedro Martin Island" (*123a; 135*).

Islas Coronados, Baja California 32°26′N., 117°16′W. N.H–11

1888. Palmer's field notes show that Nos. 13–20 (or 260–67 of his series of this year), were collected on August 18, on the "north east side of the largest of the Coronados Islands 20 miles South from San Diego." These islands are listed on Map Sheet NH–11 (Baja California, Norte), published in 1928, as "Islas Coronadas." This is corrected in the index (Index to Map of Hispanic America 1: 1,000,000 2: 48. 1944) to Islas Coronados. See San Diego (*23; 114i; 123a*).

Isla Tiburón, Sonora 29°N., 112°25′W. N.H–11, N.H–12

1869. Safford states in a note that Palmer visited the island while enroute from Tucson to Guaymas. In his completed account of Palmer's trip, however, he discusses the latter's visit, near Hermosillo, to a tribe of Indians (the Seris) that were later moved to Tiburon Island. It is probable that some misconception arose in this way, and that Palmer never visited the island (*123a; 123b*).

Jacksboro, Tennessee (Campbell County)

1881. September. Palmer reported mounds from near this place, according to Thomas (*118*). See Tennessee.

Jackson County, Arkansas

1883. See Independence County.

Jackson County, North Carolina

1881. See North Carolina.

Jackson Lakes, Alabama (Elmore County)

1884. A locality at which Palmer collected ethnological specimens; see Elmore County.

[30] See also C. S. Sargent's note, *Garden & Forest*, Vol. II (1889), 64, Fig. 92.

Jackson Mound, Arkansas

Said by Thomas (*119*, p. *222*), to be on the Little River cutoff, about 16 miles northwest of Osceola. Palmer mentions his work there, but gives no date; see Mississippi County (*88*).

Jacksonville, Florida (Duval County) GLO, 1926

1874. Arrived February 4, enroute to Lake Okeechobee; returned from Lake Okeechobee in April, via "Tacoy," and after two days' rest "took cars" for Cedar Keys. Palmer seems to have returned from Key West via Cedar Keys before mid-August. On August 16 he took part in a regular Sunday excursion to Mayport and Pilot Town, the latter stated by him to be opposite Mayport and to be famous for its shell heaps; see Florida (*20; 114g; 123*).

1884. Arrived by steamer from Key West in the morning of October 9, expecting to leave for Washington by the 5:20 P. M. train (*114g*).

Jacumba Mountains, California (southeastern San Diego County)

1875. See Larkens Station.

Jalisco (Estado) N.F–13, N.F–14

1886. Reached Guadalajara about June 1, and collected until about mid-November. Visited Río Blanco (June 3–10), La Barranca (June 16–23), Río Blanco (July 1–8 and again August 15), Tequila (August 25–September 5), Río Blanco (September 17–23 and October 12–20), and Chapala (October ?23–November 3). Made archaeological and ethnological collections (Nos. 132,356–132,426) at Old San Pedro, San Pedro (October), Old Tonalá, and Chapala. Left about November 20–25 for Washington, reaching the railroad by stage on November 28 (*45*, item 192; *114f; 123a; 144*).

Jalisco, Nayarit 21°27′N., 104°55′W. N.F–13

1892. Palmer notes: "Left Tepic January 16, for the village of Jalisco 5 miles s. of Tepic." The following day, after reaching Jalisco, he says: "Early in the morning I collected in the pass through the mountains, and in the afternoon along the water way to near its source . . . Jan 18 worked over plants to air them." From Jalisco he doubtless returned to Tepic (*45*, item 189).

Jamestown, Arkansas (Independence County) GLO, 1886

1883. Left October 31 for Little Rock. In Palmer's published notes on Arkansas, reference is made to this visit to Jamestown, "Jefferson County," but I believe the county reference is an error, for (on November 1) Palmer wrote Cyrus Thomas from Little Rock, announcing his arrival that day and telling of his unsuccessful work just terminated "about Batesville and New Port Independence Co Ark." (*88; 114c*).

Jamul (and Jamul Valley), California (San Diego County)
GLO, 1907

1875. June 25–26; about 42 collections were made here, in an area said by Palmer to be 20 miles east of south of San Diego. Jamul (spelled "Jamuel" by Palmer), however, is in T 17 S, R 1 E, almost due east of San Diego; see California (*34a; 123a*).

Jefferson County, Arkansas

1882–83. Palmer came to the Pulaski–Jefferson County areas from northeastern Arkansas early in November, 1882; see Arkansas; he was in Little Rock November 9 and 11, in Pine Bluff on November 13. On November 22 he visited Winchester, Drew County, the nearby Tiller Mounds and the mounds at "Hollywood," the plantation of Dr. J. M. Taylor. On December 1 he was in Arkansas City (possibly to make shipments of material), but on the sixth he was back at the De Priest's (or De Soto) Mound, on the twenty-fifth he was working at the Knapp Mounds, and on the thirtieth he was in Pine Bluff, where he stayed at least until January 1, 1883. January 3 he visited Lincoln County, *q.v.;* January 10 he went to Arkansas City from Garretson's Landing, and January 15 he went from Woodson to Reed's Landing. On the twentieth he visited a locality, probably the Thibault mound, 8 miles southeast of Little Rock, and on the twenty-seventh of January he began a trip to Saline and Clark counties, *qq. v.*

It seems evident from the above (which is practically all I have been able to find out about Palmer's movements during this period) that the collector was engaged in exploratory work, traveling from one area to another in an effort to locate as many promising sites as possible and to eliminate the poorer ones. Apparently he concentrated his activities in the area around Pine Bluff, but made frequent trips down the Arkansas River to Arkansas City. It was probably during this period that he visited the Clayton Mound and the Glen Lake Mounds (*88; 114c; 118; 119*).

Jiménez, Chihuahua 27°08′N., 104°55′W. N.G–13

1885. Arrived late in July, enroute from El Paso to Parral. See Chihuahua (Estado) (*123a*).

Johnson, Utah (southwestern Kane County) GLO, 1937

1877. Palmer probably left St. George, *q.v.*, about March 1; visited Johnson March 12 and Kanab March 14, returning to St. George about March 26 or 27. Collected archaeological material, but apparently no plants (*34d; 123a*).

Johnson's (or Knapp's) (Well), Arizona (northeastern Yuma County)

1869. August and September; not located, but said to be 15 miles south of Cullen's Well, *q.v.* (*123a*).

Jolley's Island, Tennessee (Meigs County)

1883. (?)June; said to be at the junction of the Tennessee and Hiawassee rivers; this is evidently the island described, but not named, by Thomas (*119*, p. 405), and the same as that called "Jolly's Island" by Thomas (*118*, p. 209). See Tennessee (*114c*).

Jolon, California (southwestern Monterey County) GLO, 1928

1876. About 7 collections made here July 31; see San Luis Obispo (*34a*).

Jonestown, Mississippi (Coahoma County) GLO, 1885

1882. January 3, by ferry and train from Helena, Arkansas, *q.v.*, with letters of introduction to "ex-Governor Alcorn."[31] (*88*).

Jonesville, Louisiana (Catahoula Parish) GLO, 1930

1883. See Louisiana.

Juárez, Coahuila 27°37′N., 100°47′W. N.G–14

1880. About 25 numbers of plants collected here, September 23–24; for itinerary see Monclova. From Juárez, Palmer probably went to Eagle Pass, Texas. Called "Juraz" by Palmer and so written by Watson in his report on the 1879–80 collections (*2; 142*).

[31] James Lusk Alcorn (1816–94) was prominent in Mississippi and national politics, 1843–90; retired in 1877 to his plantation in Coahoma County, Mississippi. See *Dictionary of American Biography* (1937), I, 137–39.

Juárez ("Hoorez") Mountains, [San Luis Potosí]

1878. See Hoorez Mountains, and San Luis Potosí (Estado).

Judsonia, Arkansas (White County) GLO, 1886

1883. October 3, arrived at 2:30 A.M. by train from Malvern; left for West Point, October 5; see White County (*88*).

Julesburg, Colorado (Sedgwick County) GLO, 1934

1861. Visited August 7, enroute from Denver to San Francisco, *q.v.* See also Colorado (*123a*).

1862. May 22–23; see Fort Leavenworth.

Julian, California (San Diego County) GLO, 1928

1875. Palmer came here from San Diego. His own manuscript itinerary of this year says: "July 18–20 Julian 15 miles beyond Tighes in Cuyamaca Mountains." A few collections were made here. Palmer then made trips out from Julian to the north, visiting the Diegueño Indian villages near Warner's Ranch (July 24) and the hot springs near the ranch (?Warner Springs). He collected sparingly at these places and in "Cuah." (i.e. ?Coahuila) Valley. He then made his way to the San Felipe Ranch (July 26), San Felipe Canyon (July 27), the Oriflamme or Stonewall mine (July 28) and Mesa Grande (July 30). He returned from Julian to San Diego about August 7 (*123a; 123b*).

Juniper Mountains, Arizona (northwestern Yavapai County) GLO, 1933

1876. A few specimens collected here, late April or early May; mountains said by Palmer to be 30 miles west of Prescott, *q.v.*; they are probably northwest rather than west of that place (*34a*).

Juniper Mountains, Arizona (northern Mohave County)

1877. Visited May 1–2, and again on June 4; Palmer's letters indicate that this locality is about 10–20 miles south or east of south from Mokiak Pass, *q.v.* (*24; 110*).

Juraz, Coahuila

1880. Same as Juárez, *q.v.*

Kanab, Utah (Kane County) GLO, 1937

1875–76. Palmer collected archaeological material, and perhaps seeds, here, between October, 1875, and January, 1876; see St. George (*114b*).

1877. March; see St. George, and Johnson.

Kansas GLO, 1884, 1891, 1912, 1925

1857–60. Came from Cleveland, Ohio, to settle, in April, 1857. He lived at Highland for about a year, moving to Leavenworth, *q.v.*, about April 1, 1858. He lived in Leavenworth until about August 18, 1859, when he moved to Colorado. He made trips to Nebraska, *q.v.*, in March or April, 1858, and in December 1858 (*114b*).

1862. Reached Fort Leavenworth, *q.v.*, from Washington, D. C., March 22. Left for Colorado April 26, via Fort Kearny and the Platte River route. Arrived at Fort Larned, Kansas, July 23, with an army unit from Fort Lyon, Colorado, leaving on the return trip July 25 (*114b; 123a*).

1863. See Fort Scott.

1864–65. See Leavenworth, Kansas City, and Fort Dodge.

1868. See Indian Territory.

1869. See Sheridan.

Kansas City, Missouri (Jackson County)

1864–65. Palmer acted as Hospital Steward here, March and April, 1864, while still in the United States Army. From May to October he was incapacitated by illness most of the time. From December, 1864, to May, 1865, he worked on a (civilian) contract at the Kansas City General Hospital as acting assistant surgeon, U. S. A. He left for Fort Whipple, Arizona, q.v., soon after May 7, 1865. See Missouri; Leavenworth, Kansas; and Washington, D. C. (*123a; 125d*).

1893. See Idaho, and Washington, D. C.

Kendall County, Texas

1879. See Comfort.

Kentucky

1899. See Mammoth Cave.

Kern River, California (Kern and ?Tulare counties) GLO, 1928

1888. June 7–15; see Kernville.

Kernville, California (Kern County) GLO, 1928

1888. Palmer made two trips here from San Bernardino in unsuccessful attempts to reach Mt. Whitney. He arrived by stage from Caliente, June 5 or 6, in company with W. G. Wright; collected Nos. 18–30 and 107–50 on the north fork of the Kern River near Kernville, and Nos. 1–17, 31–106, and 151–60 in the Greenhorn Mountains, 10–12 miles west of Kernville. Left for San Bernardino, *q.v.*, June 15 or 16. On his second trip he reached Kernville early in July, and set out for the mountains to the north with a pack train and guide; a note among the Palmer manuscripts reads: "July 12, 1888. Left Kernville for the Sierra Nevada mountains." The third day out the guide refused to proceed, and the party turned back to "our first camp in the mountains hear was a long wet meadow"; this was probably the locality called "Long Meadow" by Palmer. Upon the return to Kernville it transpired that the guide was incompetent and himself unfamiliar with the mountains. The return to Kernville must have been on July 20 or 21 (*114i; 123a; 133*).

Key Largo, Florida (Monroe County) GLO, 1926

1884. Visited August 7; see Florida.

Key West, Florida (Monroe County) GLO, 1926

1874. Arrived by boat from Cedar Keys soon after May 1; left May 13 by boat for the Bahamas; returned to Key West June 6. During June and early July botanized along the coast, visiting Pine Key, Biscayne Bay, and Cape Florida. He was at Key West July 10–20, and then returned to Cedar Keys. He collected about 80 numbers of vascular plants and 30 algae at Key West (*20; 34b; 123a*).

1884. Mid-July to October 5; see Florida.

Kingston, Tennessee (Roane County)

1881. September and most of October; see Tennessee.

Kiowa Agency, [Oklahoma] (Caddo County)

1868. The Kiowa-Comanche Indian Agency at which Palmer was stationed in the spring of this year; see Fort Cobb. The records of the Division of Birds of the National Museum indicate that birds were collected at or near the agency on March 14, 18, 19, and 21, April 1 and 5, and June 10, 11, 13, 14, and 27. The dates given in June are certainly erroneous, for Palmer reached Cherokee Town, *q.v.*, on or before June 8 (*114e*).

Kissimmee Prairies, Florida (probably Okeechobee County)

1874. February 20 or 21. See Fort Bassinger.

Kissimmee River, Florida GLO, 1926

1874. Palmer's party descended the river from the site of Fort Bassinger to Lake Okeechobee, by boat, the trip taking two days (March ?23–?24). After making a circuit of the lake, they returned to Fort Bassinger by the same route. See Florida, and Fort Bassinger (*9; 10; 123a*).

Knapp's (or Johnson's), Arizona

1869. See Johnson's.

Knapp Mounds, Arkansas (Pulaski County)

1882. About December 25; see Jefferson County.

1884. July 1; came here from Little Rock to measure the mounds before going on to work near Natchez. The Knapp Mounds, according to Thomas, are on the east bank of Mound Lake, a bayou 16 (or 17) miles southeast of Little Rock, and "form, without doubt, the most interesting group in the state, and, in fact, one of the most important in the United States" (*119*, p. 243, and illustration, Plates IX, X). Palmer, according to his own account, did considerable excavating at this locality (88).

La Barra, Tamaulipas 22°15′N., 97°48′W. N.F–14

1910. At the mouth of the Río Pánuco, about 8 km. northeast of Tampico. Palmer's journal indicates that he botanized here February 1–8, February 20, April 2–3, May 17–18. Although the field notes imply that the visits to La Barra were long ones lasting as much as eight or nine days, the journal shows that he made the trip each day from Tampico, completing the sets of each number by repeated visits to the same locality. The correct dates of collections made here are mostly in doubt; see Tampico. Nos. 251–304, 561–62, 581, 590, 591 were collected here. Shown as "Barra" on some maps (*123a; 123c*).

La Barranca, Jalisco

1886. The great gorge of the Río Grande de Santiago, said by Watson to be "nine miles east by north from Guadalajara . . . where is the hacienda of Señor Portillo, and a ferry over the Rio Grande known as the Paso de Ybarra." Safford says Palmer reached the barranca by crossing level fields from Buena Vista on the northern edge of Guadalajara, *q.v.* Palmer collected Nos. 74–144 here, June 16–23. Spelled "Baranca" on the labels distributed with these specimens. Field notes for Nos. 82 and 144, both dated June 18, are preserved in the U. S. National Herbarium (*123a; 144*).

Ladrillera, San Luis Potosí 22°08′N., 100°59′W. Atlas, 42

1878. A few kilometers south-southwest of San Luis Potosí (Ciudad), *q.v.* Mentioned in a typewritten itinerary in the National Herbarium.

La Fortuna, Nayarit 21°34′N., 104°58′W. N.F–13

1892. Visited February 15, by coach from Tepic. Called "Fortuna" by Palmer. The trip was apparently of short duration, for on February 17 Palmer was back in Tepic (*45*, item 189).

Lagoon Head, Baja California 28°14′N., 114°06′W

1889. Said in Palmer's field notes (and thence copied by Vasey and Rose, *132; 134*) to be "the Cabo-Negro of the old Spanish charts, in latitude 28 degrees," on the Pacific Coast. The name appears in the above position on Chart No. 620 of the U. S. Hydrographic Office, a map of the west coast of Mexico and the Gulf of California, between the parallels of latitude 26° and 29°20′N (published 1877). Palmer arrived from San Diego, *q.v.*, about March 6; he visited the mines of Calmallí, traveling by mule wagon "45 miles inland" (March 11–12); Vasey and Rose note that he "finished" this trip at "Rosalia Bay"; he left Lagoon Head for Cedros Island at noon, March 15. Plants distributed as from Lagoon Head probably include those from the trip inland, and comprise Nos. 651–55, and 765–834. Nos. 651–55 duplicate those from San Quintín. Some of the numbers are not cited by Vasey and Rose, who reported upon the collection; field notes for Nos. 651–55, and 760–830, are in the National Herbarium collection (*114i; 123a; 132; 134*).

Laguna Media Luna, San Luis Potosí

1904. Not located, but near Río Verde, *q.v.*

Laguna Puerta, Tamaulipas

1910. March 23–24; Palmer's journal mentions collecting water plants here, and mentions also "a night journey in a second class coach." The lake lies east of the Río Tamesí, about 8 km. north of Tampico. Called by Palmer "Laguna de la Puerta." See Tamaulipas (*123a*).

La Junta, Chihuahua

1908. Visited April 13; said by Palmer to be the picnic grounds at the junction of the Chuvíscar and Nombre de Díos Rivers, near the city of Chihuahua. See Chihuahua (Estado) (*123a*).

Lake Anderson, Arkansas

1882. Near Forrest City, *q.v.*

Lake George, Florida (southern Putnam County)
GLO, 1926

1874. Visited February 4, soon after leaving Jacksonville for the trip up the St. Johns River. See Florida (*114i*).

Lake Harney, Florida (Seminole and Volusia counties)
GLO, 1926

1874. Apparently visited in February, during Palmer's trip up the St. John's River; see Florida.

Lake Okeechobee, Florida 27°N., 81°W. GLO, 1926

1874. Palmer, with a party, left Fort Bassinger February 22 or 23. They descended the Kissimmee River to the lake in two days, circled the lake and returned to Fort Bassinger by the same route after an absence of eight days and nights. About 12 collections of plants were made at the lake (*9; 10; 34a; 123a*).

La Machiguala, San Luis Potosí

1878. Visited about December 30–31; not located on any map, but see Ciudad del Maíz (*114i*).

Lamar, Texas (central Aransas County)

1879. About 7 collections of plants made here, December 17–19 (or 19 and 20). Lamar is said by Palmer to be on the "edge of Copano Bay." See Corpus Christi (*2; 45*, item 269; *142*).

Lamar County, Texas

1879. Archaeological collections were made here in this year *(34d)*.

La Paz, Argentina (Entre Ríos) 30°44′S., 59°38′W. S.H–21

1853–54. East of the Río Paraná. Specimens were perhaps collected here, September 14–?16, 1853; see Río Paraná. The *Water Witch* anchored "30 miles" above La Paz on February 3, 1854; she was delayed at a point not far from La Paz most of the following day; specimens were collected by Palmer on February 5 at La Paz, probably this same year (*52; 123a; 125c*).

La Paz, Arizona (Yuma County) GLO, 1912

1869. On the east bank of the Colorado River about 10 miles above Ehrenberg (7 miles according to Palmer). On October 6, Palmer wrote that he had just sent specimens from La Paz. W. C. Barnes (*7*, p. 238) says: "In 1870 the river during a rise cut away from the place and left La Paz without a landing"; this seems not to agree with Palmer's 1869 journal as quoted by Safford: "La Paz . . . is back from the river's bank a considerable distance owing to a change in the channel." See Fort Whipple, and Yuma.

The published title of Merwin Item No. 14, which contains a copy of Palmer's account of his trip from Prescott to Ehrenberg in August, 1869, is as follows: "Description of a Journey from Prescott to La Paz, made in 1869, by Dr. Palmer, and the Killing of Indians near La Paz on September 16th, 1869." The killing took place on September 16, 1868, as indicated in the manuscript itself, and had no relation to Palmer, who was not in Arizona at the time (*45*, item 14).

La Paz, Baja California 24°09′N., 110°18′W. N.G–12

1870. January 5; see Baja California (*45*, item 57).

1890. Visited January 6, enroute from San Francisco to Guaymas (*123a*). Arrived about January 19, by steamer from Guaymas; collected Nos. 1–144; returned to Guaymas February 8; made a trip to Rancho San José, January 24 (*123a; 135*). Palmer also touched here September 3, enroute from San Francisco, *q.v.*, to Guaymas (*123a*).

La Plata, Río de la

1853–54. See Paraguay.

La Puerta, Tamaulipas

1910. See Puerta.

Laredo, Texas (Webb County)

1879–80. About 70 collections were made here in 1879. The date of the visit is problematical, although given, in the printed itinerary of his collections, as August 1–20; Palmer was in Uvalde on August 4 (having just arrived from San Antonio), and probably remained there several days before returning to San Antonio and proceeding to Laredo, perhaps after visiting Sutherland Springs, *q.v.* The dates of his visit to Guadalupe, *q.v.*, are given as September 17–18, and he was back in San Antonio on September 19, so it is probable that he visited Laredo about September 12–17. On a second visit Palmer passed through Laredo, enroute by coach to Monterrey, *q.v.*, about January 29 or 30, 1880 (*2; 34d; 142*).

Larkens Station, California (southeastern San Diego County)

1875. August 18–19; about 25–28 collections were made here. Palmer's manuscript itinerary says: "Old Stone House (Larkens station) near Jacumba mountains 80 miles east from San Diego on the old Fort Yuma Road." The locality appears as Larkin in T 17–18 S, R 7 E, on the Immigration Association's map of California, *ca.* 1885; it is on the site of modern Buckman's Springs, on highway US 80. See Fort Yuma (*34a; 123a*).

Las Canoas, San Luis Potosí

1902. See Canoas.

Las Juntas, Baja California 32°29′N., 116°24′W. N.H–11

1875. This appears to be the locality of which Palmer wrote: "Lasjuantas Lower California is 43 miles above Tecate valley." At the time of his visit (September 7) he was enroute to the Tantillas Mountains, *q.v.* (*123a*).

Las Vegas, New Mexico (San Miguel County) GLO, 1936

1884. December; see Raton.

La Virgen, Nicaragua 11°22′N., 85°46′W. N.C–16

1867. See San Francisco, California, and Virgin City.

Lawrence, Arkansas

1881. Thought to be the same as Lawrenceville, *q.v.* (*88*).

Lawrence County, Illinois

1882. See Indiana.

Lawrenceville, Arkansas (southern Monroe County)

1881. December 7; see Monroe County. Said to be on the "edge of Maddox Bay." A Lawrenceville Ch[urch] appears on the Holly Grove Quadrangle (War Dept., Corps of Engineers, 1 /62500, edition of 1940) on Mattock Bay, a cutoff east of the White River, in Sect. 24, T 2 S, R 2 W. This is evidently Palmer's locality (*88*).

Leavenworth, Kansas (Leavenworth County) GLO, 1925

1857–59. Palmer came to Kansas from Ohio, leaving Cleveland about mid-April, 1857, and traveling by boat via the Ohio, Mississippi, and Missouri rivers. After living in Highland for about a year he settled in Leavenworth about the first of April, 1858. He lived here until about August 18, 1859, when he moved to Denver, *q.v.* On December 20, 1858, he wrote that he was living on the "Strainger River" a few miles from Leavenworth. He made some collections in the vicinity of Leavenworth. Safford states that he made "large collections" which were subsequently destroyed by fire (*45*, item 87b; *114b; 123a*).

1864–65. Palmer's army unit was stationed here (?at Fort Leavenworth) in 1864. He was on hospital duty at Pleasant Hill, Missouri, and Kansas City, Missouri; and was hospitalized at Kansas City for some months and discharged from the army for disability on November 30, 1864. He rejoined the army as acting assistant surgeon stationed at Kansas City, until March, 1865. In April he acted as examining surgeon for the Missouri state militia. He was in Kansas City until after May 7, but soon afterward left for Arizona (*123a; 125d*).

1868. January and October; see Indian Territory (*114b*).

Lee County, Arkansas

1882. See Phillips County.

León, Guanajuato 21°12′N., 101°40′W. N.F–14

1898. August; see Guanajuato (Estado).

Lerdo, Sonora

1884–85, 1889. Same as Colonia Lerdo, *q.v.*

Lerios, Coahuila

1880. Same as Lirios, *q.v.*

Liberty, Texas (Liberty County)

1879. November 17; see Houston.

Lincoln County, Arkansas

1883. See Heckatoo.

Line Creek, [Oklahoma] (Grady County)

1868. A locality (a creek) cited by Palmer, along the Washita River road between Fort Cobb, *q.v.* and Cherokee Town; enters the

Washita from the southwest near present Chickasha (USGS, Indian Territory–Oklahoma, Chickasha Quadrangle, 1/125000, edition of August, 1904).

Linwood, Arkansas (southeastern Jefferson County)
GLO, 1886.

1882–83. A railroad stop in R 7 W, T 6 S, called "Linwood Station" by Palmer. He visited what he called the Waldestein Mounds, "one and one-half miles north"; these are probably the same mounds mentioned by Thomas (*119*, page 242); see Jefferson County, Long Lake, and Garretson's Landing (*88*).

Linwood, North Carolina (western Davidson County)
1883. See North Carolina.

Lirios, Los, Coahuila 25°23′N., 100°38′W. Atlas, 27

1880. About 80 numbers of plants were collected here, July 10–13. The locality is east of Derramaderos, near the boundary between Nuevo León and Coahuila, about 45 or 50 km. east of Saltillo, in a high valley at an elevation of about 2,200 m. About 6 km. farther east is the pass, at about 2,400 m., where begins the steep descent into Nuevo León. North of the pass the hills are relatively arid; characteristic forest plants are species of *Pinus, Quercus, Ceanothus, Cercocarpus, Cowania.* South of the pass a moist mesophytic forest goes high on the slopes, which appear to rise 600 or 700 m. above the road. Characteristic plants are species of *Pinus, Cupressus, Pseudotsuga, Populus, Prunus, Cornus, Salix, Smilax, Rubus,* and *Pachystima.* Lirios (spelled "Lerios" by Palmer and in Watson's account of the 1879–80 collection) is a picturesque village of a few hundred people (*2; 142*).

Little Colorado River, Arizona (Navajo County)
GLO, 1933

1869. See Navajo Springs, and San Francisco Mountains.

Littlefield, Arizona (Mohave County) GLO, 1933
1877. At the time of Palmer's visit called Beaver Dam, *q.v.*

Little River, Arkansas (western Mississippi County)
GLO, 1886

1881. A river; see Mississippi County. Palmer left Osceola by mule team on October 27, stayed overnight with a Mr. Beggs on the bank of Little River, and went on to Big Lake on the twenty-eighth (*88*).

1882. October 13; a trip from Osceola to Little River (?and) Fishmouth Highland; several mounds were excavated. See Jackson Mound (*88; 119*).

Little River, [Oklahoma] (Seminole County) GLO, 1876

1868. See Seminole Nation.

Little Rock, Arkansas (Pulaski County)

1882–83. See Jefferson County.

1883. Arrived November 1, having just visited Batesville and Newport; he planned to leave the same day for Helena to work, thence to go to Washington, D. C. via Vicksburg and Jackson, Mississippi, and Talladega, Alabama.

1884. June 30; after measuring a mound Palmer planned to go to Natchez for ten days, thence to the "Gulf of Mexico to collect for New Orleans Exposition." This letter is undated to year, but can hardly be any year but 1884, the date of the exposition (*34a*).

Little Wood River, Idaho (probably Lincoln County) GLO, 1939

1893. August; see Shoshone.

Lodiego, ?Sinaloa

1891. According to Palmer's field notes he collected Nos. 1,560–1,667, October 9–15, near Rancho Lodiego, at the surveyors' camp of the Sinaloa & Durango R. R. Company, on the Culiacán River 55.5 km. northeast of Culiacán. If this distance was measured along a railroad survey line or even the road from Culiacán to Tamazula, Lodiego must lie well within the borders of Durango, probably along the Río Tamazula (here also called "Río de Topia") between Tamazula and Topia at about 25°N. lat., 106°45'W. long. That Lodiego lies in the vicinity of Topia, Durango, is implied by Jesús González Ortega (*51*) who, in an enumeration of localities—visited by himself in 1926—between Topia and Culiacán, puts Lodiego first: "De Topia bajé por todo el río hasta Culiacán visitando el punto llamado 'Lo de Diego' explorado por el Doctor Palmer." See Imala (*123a; 123c*).

In another article, however, Ortega maps the basin of the Río Tamazula, and places "Lo de Diego" on the north side of the river,

4 km. (airline) east of Imala and definitely in Sinaloa about 2.5 km. from the Durango border (50).

London, England

1855–56. See England.

Lone Mountain

1876. Not located; 5 collections from here are listed by Gray. See Arizona, and California (*34a*).

Long Lake, Arkansas (Jefferson County)

1882–83. The "Waldestein Mounds" near Linwood Station, *q.v.*, were said by Palmer to be on the bank of this lake. This is evidently the long winding cutoff of the Arkansas River which extends from near Linwood eastward into Lincoln County, and appears under this name on the topographic maps (Noble Lake Quadrangle, 1935; Varner Quadrangle, 1935). On the Noble Lake Quadrangle "Walstein Cemetery" is shown about 2 miles northeast of Linwood, near the river (88).

Long Meadow, California (Tulare County)

1888. Not located, but said by Vasey and Rose to be "8,000 to 9,000 feet above sea-level, 20 miles due north from Kernville, being two days' journey by a circuitous route in the Sierra Nevada Mountains"; for further discussion see Kernville. Palmer collected Nos. 161–223, and 231–47 here. On the printed labels distributed with Palmer's plants the dates of the visit are erroneously given as June 7–14, and Vasey and Rose give the dates July 7–14, as stated in Palmer's original field notes, but see Kernville; Palmer probably reached Long Meadow July 14 or 15 (*114i; 123b; 133*).

Longview, Texas (Gregg County)

1879. Arrived July 3, by rail from Memphis; visited Dallas and Fort Worth, and left Longview for San Antonio about July 26 or 27. Probably visited Longview again in November (*34d; 123a*).

Lonoke, Arkansas (Lonoke County) GLO, 1886

1883. October 27; see Lonoke County.

Lonoke County, Arkansas

1883. Early in October Palmer was in White County; on October 27 we find him at Indian Bayou, Lonoke County, where he had collected at mounds owned by A. J. Tait; these are evidently the "Tate Mounds" reported by Thomas (*118*). On this date Palmer drove in a wagon to Lonoke, "22 miles north," left at once from Lonoke for the Iron Mountain R. R., flagged a train late at night, and reached Newport October 28 (*88*).

Los Angeles, California (Los Angeles County)

1867. Palmer left Yuma, Arizona, *q.v.*, by stage, probably in mid-September. The Butterfield stage route, which usually took about four days to Los Angeles, was by way of Salton, Indian Wells, and Vallecito[32] then turned northward through the mountains to the Agua Caliente valley, Warner's Ranch, *q.v.*, and San Bernardino. From Los Angeles and its port of Wilmington (September 21), Palmer took a boat to San Francisco (*45*, item 62; *123a*).

1870. Palmer left Ehrenberg, Arizona, probably in September, for Los Angeles, traveling via Chuc-a-walla, Canyon Springs (Palmer collected here the second day out from Ehrenberg), the north end of the Salton Desert, Dos Palmas, Burnt Palm ("the terminus of the desert"), Martinez, Toros Station, Agua Caliente, White Water, San Gorgonio Pass, and San Bernardino. He was at Los Angeles October 2 according to a typed itinerary in the National Herbarium collection. The route is outlined in detail by M. M. Macomb who refers to the [?unpublished]Atlas Sheets 73D, 80B, 81A and 81B of the Wheeler Surveys.[33] Most of the localities appear on Bergland's (*126*) map of the route; see also San Francisco (*123a*).

1888. See California, and San Bernardino.

1889. April and May. Passed through enroute from San Diego to Yuma, *q.v.*, and again on the return trip.

Los Angeles Bay, Baja California

1887. See Bahía de los Angeles, Baja California.

Los Canos, San Luis Potosí

1902. See Canoas.

Loudon, Tennessee (Loudon County)

1881. About September 30; see Tennessee.

[32] M. M. Macomb, *Tables of Geographic Positions, Azimuths, and Distances, together with Lists of Barometric Altitudes, Magnetic Declinations, and Itineraries of Important Routes* (Washington, Engineer Department, U. S. Army, 1885. 261 pp.).

[33] *Ibid.*, 257.

Louisiana GLO, 1887, 1930

1883. From Natchez, Mississippi, Palmer went by steamer during a flood period (February or early March) to "Junction of Black [,] Washita [,] and the Tensaw Rivers"; he sent material to Washington from what is probably the same place, a mound at Jonesville ["Troyville, at the junction of Tensaw-Witchita & little River"]. Thomas (*119*, pp. 250–52) gives an illustration of the mounds here and a map of the area. Palmer also reported mounds at Monroe, Ouachita Parish, and may have visited these before returning to Mississippi. See Memphis (*114c*).

Lowndes County, Alabama

1883. Palmer's field notes for this year contain a description of a village site in the northwestern corner of the county, on the south bank of Alabama River, at the junction of Pentlala Creek, according to Thomas (*118*); see Alabama.

Lufty Creek, North Carolina

1881. See North Carolina.

Lynx Creek, Arizona (Yavapai County) GLO, 1933

?1869. Palmer collected the eggs of a species of wild turkey on "Upper Lynx Creek," in the "spring of 1870."[34] This locality is near Prescott, but Palmer is not known to have visited here in 1870. He worked at and near Prescott, however, in 1869, and collections made in 1869 and 1870 have been variously confused in other cases. See Fort Whipple.

McGinnis Ranch, California (San Luis Obispo County)

1876. About 30 collections made here July 10; said to be near the head of the Salinas River, 25 miles northeast of San Luis Obispo, *q.v.* (*34a; 123a*).

Machiguala, San Luis Potosí

1878. See La Machiguala.

Madera, Chihuahua 29°12′N., 108°07′W. N.H–12

1908. Arrived by rail from Chihuahua, May 26. Visited San Pedro Spring (May 28), Nahuárachic (May 29), a chicken ranch "15 miles" north of Madera (May 30), and a lumber camp (May 31). On this trip to Madera and vicinity collected Nos. 260–330, 438–49, 454, 455

[34] *Smithsonian Contributions to Knowledge,* Vol. XXVIII (1892), 119.

(all collections dated May 27–June 2). Left June 2, via the Sierra Madre and Pacific R. R., for Temósachic, where he stayed the night; left for Chihuahua June 3 (*123a; 123c*).

Madison, Arkansas (St. Francis County) GLO, 1886

1882. Arrived November 3, from Forrest City, *q.v.* (*88*).

Maine CGS, 801, 1201, 1204

1872. See Eastport, Grand Manan Island, Pleasant Point.

1873. See Peak's Island.

Maíz, San Luis Potosí

1878–79. See Ciudad del Maíz.

Malvern, Arkansas (Hot Spring County) GLO, 1886

1883. See White County. Palmer reported mounds (Clem Mounds) 3 miles southwest of Malvern, according to Thomas (*118*). Also called Malvern Junction (*88*).

Mammoth Cave, Kentucky (Edmonson County)

1899. Palmer made a small collection of plants here in May, on a trip from Washington, D. C.; 215 specimens were accessioned by the Smithsonian Institution, as a gift from Palmer, but the number of mounted sheets accessioned by the National Herbarium is about one-fourth this number, and it is probable that he made a collection of 50 or 60 numbers in three or four sets (*114b; 114i*).

Manzanillo, Colima 19°03'N., 104°20'W. N.E–13

1870. February. Touched here enroute from San Francisco, *q.v.*, to Panama (*45*, item 53).

1890–91. Arrived from Guaymas about December 1, 1890; collected Nos. 886–1,096 (not 816–1,096, as reported by Rose, *100*). The dates of the collection at Manzanillo are given in Palmer's field notes as December 1–31, 1890. He left for the city of Colima January 8, 1891, returning March 1 or 2 and leaving for Guaymas in March or early April. During his second stay at Manzanillo, March 2–18, 1891, he collected Nos. 1,329–1,401 (*100; 123a; 123c*).

1891–92. Arrived late in December, 1891, enroute from Guaymas to San Blas, Nayarit. Collected Nos. 1,810–12 (December 31); left January 1, 1892, by steamer for San Blas (*100; 123a*).

1895. April 7; collected No. 619 while his steamer was unloading; see Acapulco. Left soon for San Francisco (*114i; 123c*).

1897. Arrived June 17, from Mazatlán; probably went at once to Colima, returning sometime in August to proceed to Guaymas by steamer (*123a*).

Mapimí, Durango 25°50′N., 103°50′W. N.G–13

1898. Collected Nos. 516½–552, 555, 556, 586, 587, October 21–23. See Coahuila (*123a*).

Marianna, Arkansas (Lee County) GLO, 1886

1882. January 12–18; see Phillips County (*88*).

Maricopa Station, Arizona (northwestern Pinal County)

1885. March 7; see Phoenix. Maricopa Station, according to Barnes (7, p. 263), was then located in Section 28, T 4 S, R 3 E (*123a*).

Maricopa Wells, Arizona (northwestern Pinal County) GLO, 1897

1867. About 20 miles south of Phoenix, near the junction of the Gila River with the Santa Cruz. Palmer probably visited here in August, traveling overland from Camp Grant. See Yuma (*123b*).

Market Lake, Idaho (eastern Jefferson County) GLO, 1939

1893. Visited May 14–15, from Pocatello, via the Oregon Short Line R. R. Palmer found the ground still snow-covered, and collected one number only (No. 1, May 15). Market Lake, now dry, is a few miles northwest of Roberts, Jefferson County (*114i; 123a*).

Marshall County, Kansas GLO, 1925

1857–58. See Doniphan County.

Martinez, California (Riverside County)

1870. (?)September; a stage station on the Ehrenberg–San Bernardino route, shown on Bergland's (*126*) map in latitude 33°33′N., longitude 116°08′W.; see Los Angeles.

Masa Grande, California

1875. Palmer's variant of Mesa Grande, *q.v.*

Massachusetts

1871. See Woods Hole, Gay Head.

1873–79. See Cambridge.

Mayport, Florida (Duval County) GLO, 1911

1874. Palmer collected an alga (No. 83) here, perhaps August 16; see Pilot Town (*22*).

Mazatlán, Sinaloa 23°12′N., 106°26′W. N.F–13

1890. January 5, enroute from San Francisco to Guaymas (*123a*).

1891. August, enroute to Culiacán, *q.v.* (*123a*).

1897. June, enroute from Washington, D. C., to Colima, *q.v.* At this time Palmer was in company with J. N. Rose (*123a*).

Media Luna, San Luis Potosí

1904. Not located, but said to be near Río Verde, *q.v.* Visited in June; called "Laguna Media Luna" by Palmer (*34a; 123a*).

Memphis, Tennessee (Shelby County)

1879. July 2, enroute to Texas; see Cambridge (*34d*).

1883. February 16–18, and again March 27, visiting in the meantime mounds at Bradley's Landing, Arkansas, at Washington, Mississippi and at Natchez, Mississippi. Floods were raging at this time, and Palmer went by steamer to Troyville, Louisiana, thence probably to Monroe, Louisiana and Vicksburg, Mississippi (March 18), thence to Greenville, Mississippi (about March 19), Friar Point, Mississippi, and Memphis. During this time Palmer collected archaeological material but apparently no plants. He reported a mound at Fort Pickering, near Memphis, according to Thomas (*114c; 118*).

Menard Mounds, Arkansas

1881, 1883. See Arkansas County.

Mesa, Arizona (Maricopa County) GLO, 1933

1885. Also called Mesa City. Palmer came here by stage from Yuma, via Tempe, *q.v.*, where he visited over night with B. F. Johnson,[35] whom he had known in earlier years at St. George, Utah. According to Palmer, Mesa was at this time a Mormon settlement of six hundred persons. He wrote on January 20 that he had already been at Mesa for a "few days." On January 21, he left to visit ruins, owned by one La Tourette, about 50 miles north of Phoenix. His route lay 18 miles north of east to McDowell, then 12 miles north to Box

[35] Benjamin F. Johnson (1818–1905), a brother of Joseph Ellis Johnson. See p. 64. The brothers settled in Arizona in 1882. For these details I am indebted to Mr. Rufus D. Johnson of Washington, Utah.

Canyon Wash, then leaving the river, up a wash for 12 miles, then 10 miles to the River [?Verde], then 3 miles to the ruins, on a mesa on the west bank of the Río Verde. He returned to Mesa January 26, visited Tempe again on the twenty-ninth, and left Mesa again on February 3, this time for a trip by team to a cave in the Superstition Mountains, at the "First Water," 25 miles to the east. About February 7 he transferred his base of operations from Mesa to the Pima Indian Agency, *q.v.* (*34a; 45*, item 206; *114b; 114g; 123a*).

Mesa Grande, California (San Diego County) GLO, 1907

1875. Palmer's own itinerary says "July 30 Masa Grande 12 miles north of Julian." At least 4 collections were made here. Palmer's locality was not the Mesa Grande on the 1928 map of the General Land Office, which is nearly due west of Julian, but the one on the 1907 map, which is about 12 miles northwest of Julian on the road to Warner's Ranch. See Julian (*34a; 123a*).

Mesa Verde, San Luis Potosí

1902. Not located. Palmer wrote on September 23, from the city of San Luis Potosí: "I am going to Masa Virde near Alvarez to morrow." The dates of his visit to Álvarez are given as September 28 to October 3, so that if he left the capital on September 24, as announced in his letter, he may have spent a few days at Mesa Verde before going to Alvarez (*114i; 123a*).

Mesquite Flat, ?Nevada

1877. Safford says that Palmer collected at "Mesquite Flat, 12 miles from Beaver Dam." Not located, but probably in the valley of the Virgin River, between Mesquite and Bunkerville, in northeastern Clark County. Probably visited late in April, on a trip from St. George to St. Thomas (*123b*).

Mexicaltzingo, D.F. 19°21′N., 99°07′W. Atlas, 26

1878. Visited May 19; see México, D.F. Also spelled "Mexicalcingo" (*114i*).

México, D. F. 19°26′N., 99°08′W. N.E–14

1877–78. Palmer arrived December 23, 1877, from Veracruz, *q.v.;* he left for San Luis Potosí, *q.v.*, with Parry, January 19, 1878. He returned from San Luis Potosí May 10; on May 19 he went from Mexico City to Chalco by canal, passing Mexicalcingo and "Culguacan"

[Culhuacán], and the resort of Santa Anita. He intended to return at once to San Luis Potosí, but on May 22 he was attacked by intermittent fever, and was "detained two months." He visited Cuernavaca (May 29–June 4) and Toluca (June 15), and left by stage for San Luis Potosí at 5:00 A.M., July 23, stopping enroute the same day, at Tula, Hidalgo. While in the vicinity of Mexico City, Palmer collected a few plants, and collected archaeological material at Cuernavaca; Toluca; San Francisco; Texcoco; Teotihuacán; San Juan de Teotihuacán; Mexico City; and perhaps in the "Tierra Caliente" (*31; 34a; 34d; 45*, item 190; *96; 114i*).

México (Estado)
1878. See México, D. F.

Mexico City
1878. See México, D. F.

Mezquitic, San Luis Potosí 22°16′N., 101°07′W. N.F–14
1878. September 15. Called by Palmer "San Miguel de Mesquite," or "San Maguel de Mezquitic." See San Luis Potosí (Estado) (*114i*).

Miami, Florida (Dade County)
1884. September; left for Key West September 9; see Florida (*123a*).

Micos, San Luis Potosí 22°11′N., 99°15′W. Atlas, 42
1879. Palmer reached here January 1, by mule train from Buena Vista; left for Minas Viejas January 3; see Ciudad del Maíz. This place is a few kilometers northwest of Micos station on the present railroad (*114i*).

Mill Creek, California (San Bernardino County)
1876. May 29, enroute to San Bernardino Mountain. See San Bernardino.

Mill Creek, [Oklahoma] (Johnston County) GLO, 1876
1868. See Boggy Depot; Palmer collected plants here, probably July 2. In his day Mill Creek was within the boundaries of the Chickasaw Nation.

Milquatay, California (San Diego County)
1875. See Campo.

Minas Viejas, San Luis Potosí 22°24′N., 99°19′W. N.F–14

1879. Palmer reached here January 3, at dusk, by pack mule train from Micos. Searched for archaeological material until January 13, but found relatively little and left for Ciudad del Maíz, *q.v.* It is probable that the "Venis Mecas," *q.v.*, at which Palmer is supposed to have collected in 1878–79, is identical with Minas Viejas (*114i*).

Mina Tres Reyes, Durango

1896. Not located; visited April 16–19, and said by Palmer to be 13 miles west of Santiago Papasquiaro, *q.v.*

Mint Valley, Arizona (Yavapai County)

1869. See Fort Whipple.

Mississippi GLO, 1885, 1915

1882. See Phillips County, Arkansas.

1883. See Louisiana; Memphis; Vicksburg; and Washington (Mississippi).

1884. See Selsertown Mounds.

Mississippi County, Arkansas

1881. Palmer moved his headquarters from Tennessee to Osceola, Arkansas, about October 20; he was at Pecan Point, *q.v.*, October 21; visited Little River (October 27), Big Lake and probably Pemiscot Bayou ("22 miles northwest") on the twenty-eighth. On October 31, he visited a mound at Chickasawba, or Chickasawba Village ("24 miles north"). William H. Holmes (*38*) and Palmer mention a visit to Carson Lake Township, probably about November 1. November 10 he was in Osceola, on the twelfth he left for Pecan Point by train, and on November 18, after waiting "all night for a boat . . . on the river bank," he left by steamer for Arkansas Post; see Little River, Jackson Mound, Fishmouth Highland (*88; 114c*).

1882. Arrived in Osceola about July 4, from Charleston, Missouri, but found the river so high he was forced to abandon plans for work in the vicinity; possibly visited Pecan Point July 5; returned to Washington, D. C. (*88; 114c*). Revisited Osceola and Pecan Point in mid-October; see Arkansas (*88*).

Missouri GLO, 1878, 1891

1863. See Fort Scott.

1864–65. From Leavenworth, Kansas, *q.v.*, where he was on January 4, 1864, Palmer was sent to Pleasant Hill, Missouri, on hospital duty, during January and February; visited St. Louis January 13; was in Dresden January 28; on hospital duty in Kansas City from March to October; visited Washington, D. C., April 20; was in St. Louis October 23, and went thence to Kansas City to assume duties as contract surgeon, November 17, 1864, to March 31, 1865; perhaps visited St. Louis in November. Visited St. Louis March 11, 1865, in charge of delivery of a group of Confederate prisoners. About April 1 started from Kansas City to Washington, but in St. Louis (April 3) accepted post of examining surgeon of Missouri state militia (Jackson County) and returned to Kansas City. During April held examinations at Hickman Mills, Independence, Kansas City, and Westport. Early in May concluded work at Kansas City, and soon after May 7 left for Arizona. See Fort Whipple (*123a; 125d*).

1868. See St. Louis.

1880. See St. Louis.

1882. See Charleston, and Pemiscot County.

1883. See St. Louis.

Mobile, Alabama (Mobile County)

1884. About March 15–20, and perhaps also at an earlier date the same year. See Alabama. A few ethnological specimens were collected here from the Choctaw Indians (*114b; 114f*).

Mogollon Mountains, Arizona

1866–67. "On one occasion a detachment of the First Arizona Infantry Volunteers attacked a camp of Apaches in the Mogollon Mountains, northern Arizona; . . . the writer, being with the party as surgeon, examined the dead. . . ." See Camp Grant (*57*).

Mohave Reservation, Agency of

1876. See Colorado River Agency.

Mojave Desert, California (San Bernardino County)

1876. May and June; see San Bernardino.

Mojave River, California (San Bernardino County)
GLO, 1928

1876. May and June; more than 100 numbers of plants are so labeled in Gray's list of the 1876 collections. See Crafton, and San Bernardino (*24; 34a; 123a*).

Mojave River, sink of, California (San Bernardino County)

1876. A single collection, No. 219½, made here (*34a*). The Mojave River ends in the desert in central San Bernardino County, approximately in R 9 E, T 11 N, where the railroad crosses the southern end of the sink.

Mokiak Pass, Arizona (Mohave County)

1877. Not located on any map, but on the road to Wolf Hole, about 40 miles south of St. George, Utah. In his notes Palmer located it "20 miles east of south" of St. George, and described it as the "famous" Mokiak Pass "you pass over . . . to the Grand Gulch Copper Mine." Mokiah [*sic*] Mountain and Mokiah Wash appear on the GLO Map of 1933.

Palmer left St. George about April 27, visiting Mokiak Pass April 28–30, the Juniper Mountains (also called Cedar Ridges) May 1–2, and returning to St. George May 4. A second trip to Mokiak Pass and the Juniper Mountains was made about June 1–4. About 70 numbers of plants were collected at Mokiak Pass on the two trips together (*24; 34a; 45*, item 282; *110*).

Monclova, Coahuila 26°54'N., 101°25'W. N.G–14

1880. Probably arrived August 17 or 18, from Saltillo; visited the Caracol Mountain (August 19–22), the mountains "24 miles northeast by north from Monclova" (September 1–6 or 7), Arroyo de Chiva (September 5), Soledad (September 9–19). See Animas. Left for Juárez about September 21 or 22. At and near Monclova collected about 100 numbers of plants (*2; 113; 123a; 142*).

Monroe, Louisiana (Ouachita Parish) GLO, 1930

1883. See Louisiana.

Monroe County, Arkansas

1881–82. Removed here from Arkansas County about December 5, 1881; was in Lawrenceville December 7; visited Indian Bay, crossed the White River to St. Charles (Arkansas County) on December 8; probably worked several days following this at Indian Bay, and may have visited Big Cypress Mound 13 miles to the north. Left Indian Bay by stage, for Holly Grove, December 26; on the twenty-seventh visited mounds on Trotter's farm 4 miles from Holly Grove; left Holly Grove for Clarendon, December 29; left Clarendon for Helena, Phillips County, probably January 1, 1882. Collections made at Indian Bay are cited by Holmes (*38*), but Thomas (*119*) dismisses briefly the work done in this county, saying "no explorations were made" (*88; 114c*).

Montelovez, Coahuila

Scudder (*113*) cites this locality, with the date September 20 [year not given]; the collections cited by Scudder, now in the Museum of Comparative Zoology, are labeled "Montclovez." Both "Montelovez" and "Montclovez" are undoubtedly corruptions of Monclova, visited by Palmer in 1880.

Monterrey, Nuevo León 25°40′N., 100°18′W. N.G–14

1880. Palmer left San Antonio, Texas, January 26, by coach, via Tilden (about January 27), thence turning somewhat westward to cross the Río Nueces near Fort Ewell (about January 28) and going on to Laredo. From Laredo the route is indicated by the following note preserved by Palmer: "Leagues of 2⅗ miles each. Laredo. 12 Saus=Willow, lodging. 15 Ojito, dinner. 5 Vallecillo,=mines, lodging. 7 Sabinas, dinner. 7 Villaldama, lodging. 11 Palo Blanco, dinner. 10 Salinas, lodging. 10 Monterey." This route from Laredo to Monterrey is approximately parallel to, but somewhat east of, the modern automobile highway, as far as Vallecillo; it follows the highway as far as Sabinas Hidalgo, then crosses the mountain ridge to Villaldama and thence follows the present route of the railroad south to Monterrey.

Palmer probably reached Monterrey about the end of the first week in February. About 120 numbers of plants were collected at "Monterey," and for these Palmer gave the dates February 17–26; most of the collections during this period seem actually to have been made west of Monterrey, either in the vicinity of the "Fabrica de la Fama" [said to be within sight of the church at Santa Catarina] or at the "Potrero Pass" said to be 4 leagues from Monterrey. Palmer went out to the Fabrica de la Fama with a party on February 17; he noted that he "staid 3 days to collect plants," and he was still there on February 25, so it may be supposed that he spent the entire time there. He next visited Guajuco, *q.v.*, returning to Monterrey March 13 or 14; on March 17 he attended to the shipment of his collections ("6 boxes of live & dead plants for Cambridge, 1 box of live plants for Ag. dept., 1 box of live plants for Dr. George Englemann"), and soon thereafter he left for Saltillo (*2; 34d; 45*, item 193; *142*).

Montevideo, Uruguay 34°54′S., 56°11′W. S.I–21

1853–55. Palmer reached here, on board the *Water Witch*, in May, 1853, and stayed here and at Buenos Aires until August 31. On a second visit the *Water Witch* arrived from Asunción, *q.v.*, February 12, 1854, and left for Asunción April 17. For details of later visits to Montevideo, see Corrientes. Palmer remained at Montevideo with the ship until at least April 10, 1855, when he was discharged from his duties on board. After a short stay he returned to Washington, D. C. He is not known to have collected plants at Montevideo, but probably collected reptiles, fish, and insects (*52; 114d; 125c*).

Montezuma Well, Arizona (Yavapai County)

1866. See Camp Lincoln, and Beaver Creek. This name is quoted in the published title of Merwin Item No. 16 (*45*).

1869. For possible visit see Camp Lincoln; for specimens collected, see p. 46.

Montgomery, Alabama (Montgomery County) GLO, 1915

1884. March 12, enroute to Mobile, having finished collecting along the Tombigbee River. See Alabama.

Moqui Villages, [Arizona]

1869. See Fort Wingate.

Morales Mountains, San Luis Potosí

1878. Not located, but Safford and Palmer mention them, possibly referring to the mountains west of Morales, about 20 km. west of the city of San Luis Potosí. Palmer's own pencilled notes imply that he collected 136 specimens here (*114i; 123b*).

Morelos

1878. See Cuernavaca.

Mound Lake, Arkansas (Desha County)

?1882. Here, according to Thomas, (*119*, p. 239), are the Wyenn Mounds, "16 miles from the present mouth of the Arkansas River"; see Desha County (*88*).

Mound Lake, Arkansas (Pulaski County)

1882, 1884. See Knapp Mounds.

Mountain Meadows, Utah (northern Washington County) GLO, 1908

1877. About 7 miles east of Enterprise. Palmer probably left St. George about May 11 or 12, was at the Pine Mountains, *q.v.*, May 12, and at Mountain Meadows May 14–?18, collecting about 15 numbers of plants; returned to St. George about May 22, probably via Diamond Valley (May 19), *q.v.* (*24; 34a; 45*, item 207; *110; 114i*).

Mountain Springs, California (San Diego County)

1875. August 20. Said by Palmer to be 9 miles beyond Larkens Station (on the road to Fort Yuma, *q.v.*). A few plants were collected (*34a; 123a*). The locality is on highway US 80 at the eastern edge of San Diego County.

Mount San Bernardino, California (San Bernardino County)

1876. May 29–31. See San Bernardino.

Mount Shasta, California (Siskiyou County) GLO, 1928

1892. See Sisson.

Mount Tamalpais, California (Marin County) GLO, 1900

1892. Visited June 13. Collected Nos. 2,355–65, and 2,394–95 (in the field notes, 2,395 is written "3,395"). See California (*123a; 123c*).

Mount Trumbull, Arizona (Mohave County) GLO, 1933

1877. Palmer came here from St. George, Utah, probably along the old Mormon wagon road down the Hurricane Ledge. Collected about 27 numbers of plants, June 7–10; returned to St. George, about June 15 (*24; 34a; 110*).

Mount Whitney, California (Inyo-Tulare Counties) GLO, 1928

1888. See San Bernardino, or Kernville. Palmer made two unsuccessful attempts to reach Mt. Whitney.

Mouth of the Colorado

1869, 1870. See Colorado River, mouth of.

Muddy Creek, Nevada (Clark County) GLO, 1941

1875–76. Formerly emptied into the Virgin River near St. Thomas, at about 36°28′ north latitude; called Muddy River by Palmer. The area near St. Thomas where Palmer probably collected is now mostly submerged in Lake Mead. He collected archaeological material (and perhaps seeds), on a trip here from St. George, Utah, *q.v.*, sometime between October, 1875, and January, 1876 (*114b*).

1877. April. See St. Thomas.

Mud Lake, Arkansas

1882. Near Forrest City, *q.v.*

Mulegé, Baja California 26°53′N., 112°W. N.G–12

1887. June 3–10; probably reached by schooner from Guaymas. Nos. 1–49 collected here at this time. Nos. 421–24 were apparently collected during a later visit, December 25. Also spelled "Mulejé" (*114i; 123a; 145*).

Murphy's Canyon, California (San Diego County)

1875. About 6 collections made here, September 22. See San Diego. Said by Palmer to be "near Old San Diego Mission 6 miles from San Diego." A single collection from "San Diego Old Mission" is listed by Gray (*34a; 123a*).

Nacapuly, Sonora

1897. Nos. 255–60 collected here, October 12. Not located, but said by Palmer to be "a locality in the Rancho de Represo about 15 miles west of San José de Guaymas." See Guaymas (*123a*).

Nacoochee Valley, Georgia

1884. May; see White County.

Nahuárachic, Chihuahua 29°10′N., 108°05′W. N.H–12

1908. Visited May 29; spelled "Naguerochi" by Palmer and said by him to be a small Mexican settlement 1 league south of Madera, *q.v.* (*123a*).

Naola, Tamaulipas 23°N., 99°52′W. N.F–14

1878. December 3–6; see Sierra Naola (*114i*).

Nashville, Tennessee (Davidson County)

1879. Late June, enroute to Texas. See Cambridge.

1883. Early June. Probably also June 19, when enroute to St. Louis, *q.v.* Palmer perhaps visited Ashland City in this month; see Cheatham County (*114b*).

Nassau, Bahama Islands 25°05′N., 77°21′W. CGS, 1002

1874. Arrived in mid-May by boat from Key West, Florida. Collected about 33 numbers of algae; returned to Key West early in June. For location see U. S. Hydrographic Office Chart No. 1,377, New Providence Island (21st Edition, 1936) or U. S. Coast & Geodetic Survey Chart No. 1,002 (edition of 1917) (*20; 22; 123a*).

Natchez, Mississippi (Adams County) GLO, 1915

1883. February; see Memphis.
1884. Probably early July; see Little Rock.

Navajo Spring(s), Arizona 35°06′N., 109°29′W. GLO, 1933

1869. Central Apache County, in the valley of the Río Puerco. On June 27 Palmer collected birds on the "Rio Puerco, 3 days from Navajo Springs." His party, leaving Fort Wingate June 22, probably followed the valley of the Puerco to its junction with the Little Colorado, which was crossed farther down, perhaps near the modern Winslow, on June 30. See Arizona (*114e*).

Nayarit N.F–13

1892. Reached San Blas from Manzanillo, *q.v.*, by steamer, about January 2; left at once on horseback for Tepic; arrived January 4 (or 3); collected at Tepic until sometime in February (Nos. 1,813–2,040 [?2,067]); visited Jalisco (January 16–18), Compostela (February 8), Bellavista (February 11), and Fortuna (February 15). Was incapacitated two months by sciatic rheumatism; finally left Tepic by stage for San Blas April 28, and returned to San Francisco, California (*45*, item 189; *114i; 123a; 123c*).

Nebraska GLO, 1890, 1922

1858. See Doniphan County, Kansas, and Ioway Point, for trips to Nebraska during the winter of 1857–58. On December 20, 1858, Palmer wrote of a trip to northern Nebraska from which he had just returned to his home near Leavenworth, Kansas, *q.v.* (*114b*).

1862. Reached Fort Kearny May 10 and left May 14, enroute from Fort Leavenworth, Kansas, to Denver, via the Platte River route. Of the plants and animals collected in this year, some came from the vicinity of Fort Kearny, some from Walnut Creek, *q.v.*, and some from a locality "100 miles from Fort Kearney on platt rout towards mts." See O'Fallons Bluffs (*114b; 123a*).

Neches, Texas (Anderson County)
1879. October; see Palestine.

Negro, Río
1853. See Río Otuquis.

Nemaha County, Kansas GLO, 1925
1857–58. See Doniphan County.

Nevada GLO, 1876, 1894, 1930, 1941
1870. See St. Thomas, and Hardyville.
1875. See St. George, and Muddy River.
1876. Reached Wadsworth by train from San Francisco, about August 20; went on to visit Camp Halleck, August 26, and proceeded to Iowa.
1877. See St. George, and Mesquite Flat.

New Braunfels, Texas (Comal County)
1879. Probably visited late in September or early in October, enroute from San Antonio to Austin. See Texas (*34d*).

New Brunswick
1872. See Eastport, Maine, and Grand Manan Island.

New Haven, Connecticut (New Haven County)
1874. December 22. Left for San Diego, California, *q.v.;* see also Cambridge (*45*, item 57).
1876. Probably October; see Davenport, Iowa.

New Mexico GLO, 1866, 1886, 1912, 1936
1862. In December of this year Palmer sent to the Smithsonian Institution some insects collected at Fort Craig, *q.v.* See Colorado (*114b*).
1865. See Ratoon Mountains, and Trinidad.
1869. See Fort Wingate, and Albuquerque.
1884. See Raton.

New Orleans, Louisiana (Orleans Parish)
1910. June, enroute from Tampico to Washington, D. C. (*123a*).

Newport, Arkansas (Jackson County) GLO, 1886
1883. See Independence County (*88*).

Newport, Tennessee (Cocke County)

1881. About July 15–?25; see Tennessee.

New Providence Island

1874. See Nassau.

New San Pedro, Durango

1896. Not located. Possibly Palmer's version of a locality near the city of Durango. See Durango (Estado).

New Smyrna, Florida (Volusia County) GLO, 1926

1874. Palmer collected a few vascular plants and algae here; this was in April, according to the manuscript itinerary in the National Herbarium; see Florida (*22; 34a; 114i*).

New Wales, Utah

?1876. See Wales.

New York, New York (New York County)

1849. Arrived from England and went to Cleveland, Ohio, *q.v.* (*123b*).

1855–56. Arrived from Washington, D. C., about September 26–27, 1855; sailed for England; returned from London on the ship *Amazon*, arriving at New York May 20, 1856; probably left for Cleveland May 21 (*114a; 125g*).

1862. March 6; see Acapulco.

1867. November; see San Francisco, California.

1870. February. See San Francisco, California.

1876. October; see Davenport, Iowa.

1877. Probably arrived December 6, from Cambridge, Massachusetts; left December 8 by steamer *City of New York* for Veracruz (*90; 114i*).

1879. Arrived March 17, on schooner *Comet* from Tampico, and left at once for Cambridge, Massachusetts (*114a; 125g*).

Nicaragua N.C–16

1862. An itinerary and various notes among the Palmer manuscripts refer to a trip across Nicaragua in this year, after a stop at Acapulco, Mexico, a landing at Corinto, and the subsequent crossing by "ambulance" to "Virgin City" on Lake Nicaragua. Apparently none of the papers which were available to Safford mentioned Palmer's actual trip across Nicaragua in 1867, and it appears that Palmer himself in later years confused his trip of 1862, when he went from Acapulco to Panama, with that of 1867 when he seems to have gone directly from San Francisco, California, to San Juan del Sur, Nicaragua. There is no confirmatory evidence that Palmer stopped at all in Nicaragua in 1862, and certainly he did not cross the isthmus there in that year (*45*, item 53; *123a*).

1867. Palmer crossed the country while enroute from San Francisco, California, *q.v.*, to New York. For a map of the route across Nicaragua by way of the Río San Juan, see E. G. Squier's *Nicaragua*.[36]

Niles Ferry, Tennessee (Monroe County)

1881. September; at the junction of the Little Tennessee and Tellico rivers. See Tennessee.

1882. April 5. The mounds here are discussed by Thomas (*119*, p. 388). According to this account, Palmer made some preliminary investigations here, possibly at this time.

Nimaha County, Kansas

1857–58. Palmer's variant of Nemaha; see Doniphan County.

Nola, Tamaulipas

1878. See Sierra Naola.

Nombre de Dios, Durango 23°50′N., 104°16′W. N.F–13

1896. Palmer visited here from the city of Durango, April 27–30; collected Nos. 91–109, and 109½–124, and also landshells. He gives the location as "45 miles south of Durango"; actually it is about 30 miles (48 km.) east-southeast of that city. See Durango (Estado) (*19; 123c*).

Norfolk, Virginia (Norfolk County)

1879. Probably arrived by boat from Boston, about June 23 or 24, enroute to Texas. See Cambridge.

Norogachic, Chihuahua 27°14′N., 107°08′W. N.G–13

1885. Leaving Batopilas about the first of October, Palmer spent about 10 days at Cumbre, then made extensive ethnological and botanical collections at Norogachic. The plants were collected November 13–25, according to his field notes. He collected Nos. 322, 330, 332, 364, 369, 370, 373–79, 381–455, 500, BB, CC, and EE–VV,

[36] (New York, 1852), I, map facing p. 2; II, map facing p. 217.

and the following grasses for which the field notes are preserved in the National Herbarium: Nos. 1–4, 4A, 4B, 5–14, 16–19. Norogachic is said by Watson (*143*) to be 150 miles north of Batopilas, but is actually about 70 km. east-northeast of that place. See Chihuahua (Estado) (*114i; 123a; 143*).

North Carolina

1881. Palmer visited the Cherokee Indians at Yellow Hill Council House, "Jackson County," [now Cherokee, Swain County], about July 10. He collected a few plants which he sent to Sereno Watson. He called the locality "Lufty Creek," his version of Oconaluftee Creek. From here he went to Tennessee, *q.v.*, returning about August 10 to visit a mica mine at Bakersville (*34a; 114f*).

1883. An undated report by Palmer (received about July 2, 1883) mentions a recent visit to a mound at the old trading ford of the Yadkin River, near Linwood, Davidson County. This is evidently the Mars Mound mentioned by Thomas (*118*). Palmer also reported a mound near Salisbury, Rowan County, and may have visited it at this time (*114c; 118*).

North Creek, Utah (Beaver County) GLO, 1937

1877. July 17. Among Palmer's notes is one recording a "trip to North Creek 15 miles n. side of Baldey." Apparently this refers to the creek which heads on the west or northwest side of Mt. Baldy and runs off to the west, crossing the valley north of Beaver. I interpret Palmer's note to mean that he walked 15 miles on this trip to (and up) North Creek, and reached a point (as he thought) on the north side of Mt. Baldy; see Paragonah (*45*, item 282).

North Fork of Kern River, California (Kern County)

1888. See Kernville.

Nueces River, Texas

1880. See Río Frio.

Nuevo León N.G–14

1880. See Monterrey.

Nutt, New Mexico (Luna County) GLO, 1886

1884. December. A station on the Santa Fe Railroad, in T 20 S, R 6 W. This is presumably the station mentioned by Palmer, but spelled "Nut." See Raton.

Oakland, California (Alameda County) GLO, 1928

1892. Palmer collected Nos. 2, 396–98 in the "hills about Oakland," June 22. The date of this collection may be wrongly given, for Palmer seems to have been in Placerville on June 22. See Coloma, and California (*123a; 123c*).

Oaktown, Indiana (northern Knox County) GLO, 1886

1882. September 7; see Indiana.

O'Fallons Bluffs, Nebraska (Lincoln County)

1861–62. Mentioned in Palmer's field notes. Not located on a map, but along the South Platte River south of present Sutherland. Spelled "Othallens" by Palmer (*114b*).

Ogden, Utah (Weber County)

1893. See Idaho, and Washington, D. C.

Ojito, Nuevo León

1880. Same as El Ojito, *q.v.*

Ojo Caliente(s), Zacatecas 22°37′N., 102°15′W. N.F–13

1878. April 10, enroute from San Luis Potosí to Zacatecas, *q.v.* (45, item 190).

Oklahoma

1868. See Indian Territory.

Old Fort Cobb, [Oklahoma]

1868. Same as Fort Cobb, *q.v.*

Old Fort Dallas (Dallis), Florida

1884. See Fort Dallas.

Old Fort Hall, Idaho

1893. See Portneuf River.

Old Fort Pierce, Florida (St. Lucie County)

1874. Same as St. Lucie, *q.v.* First visited February 14 (*114i*).

Old Guaymas, Sonora

1887–88. See Guaymas

Oldham, Arkansas (Crittenden County) GLO, 1886

?1881. Descriptions and an illustration of the mounds here are given by Thomas (*119*, pp. 226–27). He calls the locality "Oldham (formerly Bradley's landing)"; on the GLO map Oldham P.O. is about north-northeast of Marion, in T 8 N, R 9 E. Palmer seems to have visited here first in the fall, for in describing his work he states that the "cotton was not yet gathered." He locates the mounds about a mile from the landing, near Wappanoke (or Wappanocka or Wappanoca) Creek (*88*).

1883. Palmer left Memphis for Bradley's Landing, February 6; he found the river so high he was unable to reach the hotel, and returned to his steamer (*88*).

Old San Pedro, Jalisco

1886. Said to be "3–5 mil. of present San Pedro"; see San Pedro (*45*, item 192).

Old Stone House, California

1875. See Larkens Station.

Old Tonalá, Jalisco

1886. Said to be on "outskirts of present Tonalá"; see Jalisco (*45*, item 192).

Old Town, Veracruz

1910. See Pueblo Viejo.

Oraibi, Arizona (Navajo County) GLO, 1933

1869. About June 9; the principal village of the "Moquis" (Hopi), visited by Palmer and a party led by a special Indian Commissioner. See Fort Wingate. Spelled "Uriba" by Palmer. No. 135, *Cereus fendleri*, was collected here June 9 (*45*, item 221; *67*; *124a*).

Orange, Texas (Orange County)

1879. November 14. See Houston.

Oriflamme Mine, California (San Diego County)

1875. Palmer's manuscript itinerary of his trip of this year says: "Oroflamme Mine 12 miles from Julian. July 28." At least 2 collections were made here. Said to be the same as the Stonewall Mine, but C. R. Orcutt locates the latter about 8 miles (southeast) from Julian,[37] and this seems to agree with the location given on the GLO

[37] *West American Scientist*, Vol. III (1887), 69.

map of 1876. The rich Stonewall gold mine was opened about 1870. See Julian (*34a; 123a*).

Orlando, Florida (Orange County) GLO, 1926

1884. See Florida.

Osceola, Arkansas (Mississippi County) GLO, 1886

1881. See Mississippi County.
1882. See Mississippi County.

Othallens Bluffs

1861–62. Same as O'Fallons Bluffs, *q.v.*

Otinapa, Durango 24°11'N., 105°W. N.G–13

1906. July 25–August 5; on August 7 Palmer wrote from the city of Durango: "I have to day returned to this city from the Hascienda of Otonapa 35 miles n.w. of Durango City . . . at which place spent 12 days." Nos. 332–465, 546–55, 559, and 560 were collected. The distance from Durango is not far from 35 km. (not 35 miles as stated by Palmer, nor 65 miles as given in the set of the field notes at the Gray Herbarium). The Hacienda de Otinapa is now (1951) nearly abandoned, but is accessible by a poor road from Otinapa station on the railroad. The site of the old hacienda, about 20 km. north of the railroad, is in a broad cultivated stream bottom, with grasslands and pine forests on the hills above it and some rough broken land in the canyons along the creek (*34a; 114i; 123c*).

Ottawa, Kansas (Franklin County) GLO, 1891

1868. See Indian Territory. At the time of Palmer's return to Kansas, this place was the terminus of the railroad from Leavenworth (*45*, item 297).

Otuquis, Río

1853. See Río Otuquis.

Ouachita River, Louisiana GLO, 1930

1883. See Louisiana.

Paces Landing, Alabama (?Marengo County)

1884. March; said to be on the Tombigbee River 9 miles northeast of Demopolis (Division of Ethnology, Cat. Nos. 75,002–75,011; here spelled "Pacas"). See Alabama.

Pacific Place, Arkansas

?1883. Not located, but said by Palmer to be in Crittenden County, *q.v.* (*88*).

Padrones, Sonora

1869. November 3. Safford quotes Palmer as follows: "On November 1, Dr. Palmer left Tucson by coach for Altar . . . 'A little before dark we stopped on the desert to eat our supper . . . At midnight we stopped again to rest the animals and we ourselves spread our blankets on the dry grass and slept soundly. The next day at noon we stopped at a water station, a miserable hut of mud and sticks; it was the only one on the road. Here we changed animals, having made seventy miles. Fifty-four miles farther on, at Padrones, we breakfasted.'" This is the type-locality of *Cereus palmeri.*[38] Not located, but probably the same as "Paredones," which is about 40 km. north of Altar (Atlas, 1; shown in 31°04′N., 111°44′W.). See Guaymas (*123b*).

Paint Rock Ferry, Tennessee (?Roane County)

1881. September; see Tennessee.

Palestine, Texas (Anderson County)

1879. October 21, enroute from Georgetown to Neches and Longview; specimens of insects in the Museum of Comparative Zoology are dated October 10 [year not given], but this date may be erroneous (*34b; 34d*).

1880. October 28, probably enroute from San Antonio to St. Louis, Missouri (*125b*).

Palm Springs, California (Riverside County) GLO, 1928

1876. Perhaps visited in mid-February, on a trip from San Bernardino, *q.v.* (*114i*).

1892. May and September; see California.

Palo Blanco, Nuevo León 26°16′N., 100°23′W. N.G–14

1880. February, enroute to Monterrey, *q.v.* (*45*, item 193).

Panama N.C–17

1862. See San Francisco, California.

1870. See San Francisco, California.

[38] *Contributions from the United States National Herbarium* (1896), III, 401.

Pão de Azucar, Brazil (Mato Grosso) 21°25′S., 57°52′W. S.F–21

1853. Visited by a party from the *Water Witch,* November 20–21, and by them called "Pan de Azucar"; specimens of plants were collected. This is a hill 493 m. high, about 1 km. east of the Río Paraguay. See Río Paraná (*52; 123a; 125c*).

Pánuco, Veracruz 22°03′N., 98°10′W. N.F–14

1910. Palmer came here from Tampico; collected Nos. 341–75 (April 22–25); returned to Tampico, April 25. Nos. 351–75 are duplicated by the series collected at Pueblo Viejo, February 10–25 (*123a; 123c*).

Paragonah, Utah (eastern Iron County) GLO, 1937

1877. Arrived from St. George June 25 or 26; collected about 40 numbers of plants and made archaeological collections in near-by mounds; collected at Parowan (July 3–10) went on to Beaver (July 12–21), Spring Lake Villa (July 25–August ?11), and Salt Lake City. The spelling "Paragoona" (or "Paragoonah") was current at least as late as about 1890 (GLO, 1876, 1893). Palmer used both "Paragoonah" and "Red Creek," apparently quite interchangeably (*24; 34a; 34b; 34d; 45,* item 283; *110; 113; 114i*).

Paraguay S.E–21, S.F–21, S.G–21

1853–55. Palmer accompanied the La Plata Expedition of the United States Navy in the Steamer *Water Witch;* the primary purpose of the expedition was that of exploration and of a "goodwill" mission to Paraguay, but much of the time was spent in Argentina and Brazil. In 1853, Palmer accompanied the vessel from Montevideo, Uruguay, to Corumbá, Brazil, and back to Asunción, Paraguay. Leaving Asunción January 30, 1854, the ship went to Montevideo, returned to Asunción, and dropped down river to Corrientes, Argentina. She made a round trip from Corrientes to Asunción, and spent thereafter a short time at anchor in the Arroyo Atajo. Returning to Corrientes, she made a round trip to Montevideo, returning again to Corrientes on December 31, 1854. She left again for Montevideo on January 31, 1855; Palmer stayed at Montevideo with the ship at least until April 10, 1855, and returned to the United States at his own expense. See Washington, D. C. For notes on the collections made by Palmer, see Río Paraná or any of the above places (*42; 52; 123a; 125c*).

Paraguay, Río

1853–55. See Río Paraná.

Paraná, Río

1853–55. See Río Paraná.

Paris, Tennessee (Henry County)

1882. Early May; see Tennessee.

Parowan, Utah (Iron County) GLO, 1937

1877. Collected insects here, July 3–10. See Paragonah (*34b*).

Parral, Chihuahua 26°56′N., 105°40′W. N.G–13

1885. Arrived by stage from Jiménez, late in July; also passed through on return trip from Batopilas in November or December. See Chihuahua (Estado) (*123a*).

Parras, Coahuila 25°25′N., 102°12′W. N.G–13

1880. Arrived April 21 or 22, by train from Saltillo; collected plants, April 22–30. Returned from a trip to San Pedro about June 8, leaving for Saltillo about June 28. During the two periods spent at Parras collected about 135 numbers of plants. See Saltillo (*2; 34d; 123a*).

1898. October 6–11; collected Nos. 423–54, and 789. See Coahuila (*123a*).

Paso de Progreso, Tamaulipas

1907. Not located on any map, but near Ciudad Victoria, *q.v.* Perhaps near the summit of the mountain pass on the Jaumave road, southwest of Ciudad Victoria some 20 km. A locality called Progreso is shown on this road, about halfway to the summit, on Hoja 42 of the *Atlas.*

Paso Robles Spring, California (?San Luis Obispo County)

1876. July 28. Not located; said by Palmer to be 30 miles north of Cambria, or presumably in Monterey County. Paso Robles, however, is in San Luis Obispo County, about 30 miles nearly east of Cambria. See San Luis Obispo (*34a*).

Pauls Valley, [Oklahoma] (Garvin County) GLO, 1879

1868. See Ft. Cobb.

Pawnee County, Nebraska GLO, 1922

1857–58. See Doniphan County, Kansas.

Peak's Island, Maine (Cumberland County)

1873. Palmer spent this summer as a member of a party employed by the Commission of Fish and Fisheries, working at Peak's Island. The spelling "Peak's" seems to have been in general use in Palmer's time. A USGS map of 1912 (North America, 1:1,000,000, sheet North K 19) uses the spelling "Peaks," and the USGS topographic sheet of 1916 (Maine, Cumberland County, Casco Bay Quadrangle, 1/62500) calls it "Peak Island." Palmer was paid at Portland, Maine, for the months of July to September, inclusive. He made at least one visit to Harpswell, Maine (*114b; 124b; 125b*).

Pecan Point, Arkansas (southeastern Mississippi County) GLO, 1914

1881. See Mississippi County. Palmer seems to have done some excavation here on more than one occasion. The relatively important "works" here are described and mapped by Thomas (*119*, p. 221). Thomas also states that the archaeological sites are located "nearly a mile northwest of the present landing," i.e. the steamboat landing on the Mississippi River (*88; 119*).

1882. July 5; see Mississippi County.

1882. October; Palmer describes digging here in this month; see Arkansas, and Mississippi County (*88*).

Pedernal

1853. See Río Pedernal.

Pemiscot Bayou, Arkansas (Mississippi County) GLO, 1886

1881. Also spelled "Pemisco," "Pemiscott," and (on the GLO map of 1886) "Pemiscol." Here were the Pemiscott Mounds mentioned by Thomas (*118*). See Mississippi County (*88*).

Pemiscot County, Missouri

?1882. Palmer reported mounds at Gayoso, according to Thomas (*118*).

Pennington Creek, [Oklahoma] (Johnston County) GLO, 1876

1868. Palmer collected plants here, probably at a stopping place along the stage road, June 25 and 26, and July 1 and 2; see Boggy Depot. The road from Cherokee Town to Boggy Depot crossed Pennington Creek in the Chickasaw Nation about 1½ miles southeast of the present village of Reagan (*120*).

Peñasco, San Luis Potosí   22°19′N., 100°56′W.   N.F–14

1878. Palmer visited a place of this name about September 1; it is probably the place about 20 km. north of the city of San Luis Potosí, *q.v.* (*114i; 123b*).

Peotillos, San Luis Potosí   22°30′N., 100°37′W.   N.F–14

1878. November 24; see San Luis Potosí (Estado).

1905. Arrived May 25, from San Luis Potosí; collected Nos. 608, 609, May 25–27. Called "Hacienda Peotillos" by Palmer and said by him to be 65 km. north of San Luis Potosí on the "Central R.R."; actually it is northeast of the city. He referred to this in 1878 as the "desolate" Hacienda de Peotillos, an adjective which seems rather strong unless he was referring solely to the surrounding country, which seems desolate indeed, dominated as it is by arborescent opuntias and other cacti, and desert shrubs including *Larrea* and *Adolphia.* The hacienda itself, by contrast, is an oasis. There is enough water to support a fine walled garden of pecans and other trees. The principal buildings, including a large tiled clock tower which still shows the scars of the revolution of 1910–14, date from 1863 (*123c*).

Petaluma, California   (southern Sonoma County)
GLO, 1928

1892. Visited June 27; collected Nos. 2,399–2,401, and 2,419, all from the vicinity of the railroad water tank. See California (*123a; 123c*).

Philadelphia, Pennsylvania   (Philadelphia County)

1876. Palmer is said to have visited the Centennial Exposition, probably on his return from Cambridge, Massachusetts, in October. See Davenport, Iowa.

Phillips County, Arkansas

1882. Palmer probably moved his base of operations (from Monroe County) to Helena about January 1; he visited Jonestown, Mississippi, January 3, undertook a trip from Helena up the St. Francis River (January 11), visited Marianna, Lee County (January

12–18), Forrest City, St. Francis County (January 20–22). Excessive and continued rains made his work impossible, and he returned to Washington, D. C. See Arkansas.

1883. Probably early November; see Little Rock.

Phoenix, Arizona (Maricopa County) GLO, 1933

1885. Arrived March 4 or 5 from the Pima Indian Agency, where he had packed and shipped to the Smithsonian Institution seventeen boxes of archaeological and ethnological materials, the accumulation of several weeks. On March 5, Palmer wrote of his plan to leave the following day for the Apache Agency, and doubtless he left Phoenix as planned, for he was at Maricopa Station on March 7 and left the same day for the Apache Reservation. According to his own notes, his plans changed abruptly. On reaching Bowie Station on the Southern Pacific he found himself short of funds and in poor health, and "resolved to return to Washington." The date of his arrival in Washington is unknown, but may have been about March 15 (*45*, item 24; *114b*).

Pike County, Indiana

1882. Probably September; see Indiana.

Pikes Peak, Colorado

1859–63. Specimens or letters so headed are not from the peak itself; as far as known Palmer never visited it. At the time of his residence in Colorado this name was given to the whole gold-mining area. In 1859, for example, he wrote from Kansas: "To morrow I start for the Gold mines of Pikes Peak," and in 1861 one of his letters is headed "Denver City, Pikes Peak, K[ansas] T[erritory]"; see Colorado.

Pikeville, Tennessee (Bledsoe County)

1882. April 11; see Tennessee.

Pila, San Luis Potosí 22°02′N., 100°52′W. N.F–14

1878. Safford has noted on a typed itinerary in the National Museum collection that Palmer made botanical collections here in August. This place is south-southeast of the city of San Luis Potosí, on the overgrazed desert plain. It is now somewhat south of the direct route to Álvarez, but Palmer wrote of his trip in 1878: "After he [Parry] left, I made three mountain trips, first to Alvarez, on horseback . . . stopping at Pila for a few days where I made a small collection & left it until my return. . . . Then went to San Miguelito Mts.—slow trip on burro . . ." (*114i*).

Pilar, Paraguay (Pilar) 26°51′S., 58°21′W. S.G–21

1853–54. East of the Río Paraguay, near the mouth of Río Neanibucú. Collections were made here, September 28–29, 1853; see Río Paraná. A second visit was made here, January 31, 1854, but probably no collecting was done. See Asunción (*52; 123a; 125c*).

Pilot Town, Florida (Duval County)

1874. Visited August 16; see Florida. Not located on any map, but stated by J. M. Hawks (*35*, p. 109) to have been a group of "two or three residences" near the mouth of the St. Johns River, opposite Mayport (*114i*).

Pima Indian Agency, Arizona (at Sacaton, Pinal County)

1885. Palmer arrived from Mesa before February 11 with "a nice collection from the old ruins of this section"; collected additional ethnological material; left for Phoenix about March 3. He gave as his post office address while here: Pima Indian Agency, via Casa Grande, Pinal County. The Pima Agency had been established at Sacaton for a number of years previous to Palmer's visit, but apparently he did not ever mention Sacaton in referring to the agency (*45*, item 23; *114b*).

Pima Villages, [Arizona] (Pinal County)

1869. August or September, while enroute from Yuma, *q.v.*, to Fort Whipple. This name evidently refers to the villages along the Gila River near present Sacaton.

Pine Bluff, Arkansas (Jefferson County) GLO, 1886

1882–83. See Jefferson County (*88*).

Pinecate Bay

1870. Shells were collected here, according to Stearns. See Bahía de Adair (*115*).

Pine Key, Florida

1874. Not located, but perhaps same as Big Pine Key, Monroe County (GLO, 1926); see Florida. Visited June 22, probably on a trip out from Key West; collected at least one alga (*20*).

Pine Mountain(s), California (San Luis Obispo County) GLO, 1900

1876. Visited July 22; said to be opposite [i.e. northeast of] San Simeon Bay. Gray lists 23 numbers from "Pine Mts.," perhaps this locality. Pine Mountain also appears on map sheet North I 10, in 35°41′N., 121°05′W. See San Luis Obispo (*34a*).

Pine Mountains, Utah (Washington County)

1877. Not located, but said to be "20 miles north of St. George," *q.v.* Palmer is said to have been here May 12, probably enroute to Mountain Meadows (*110*).

Piquete Ytati, Paraguay

1853. Not located, but said to be on the bank of the Río Paraguay, 102 miles by river above Asunción. Specimens were collected November 8. See Río Paraná (*52; 123a*).

Placerville, California (Eldorado County) GLO, 1928

1861. Late August. See San Francisco, and Hangtown.

1892. June 22; see Coloma.

Pleasant Hill, Missouri (Cass County) GLO, 1891

1864. Palmer was in charge of certain army patients here, during January and February. See Missouri (*125d*).

Pleasant Point, Maine (Washington County) CGS, 801

1872. On the mainland about 5 miles northwest of Eastport. Ethnological specimens were collected here (*114f*).

Pocatello, Idaho (Bannock County) GLO, 1939

1893. Arrived May 6; at first collected nothing because of the lateness of the season and his own illness; visited Market Lake (May 14–15), returning May 16; collected at Pocatello May 17–27 (Nos. 2–58); left for Shoshone by train May 31, and returned June 14; on June 15 collected Nos. 160–62, 586, 598; left for Blackfoot June 16, by rail and returned July 20 from Idaho Falls; collected in the vicinity of Pocatello, July 21–August 7 (Nos. 389–452 and 585); left for Blackfoot August 8 and returned August 16, leaving again August 18 for Shoshone and returning August 27; collected in the vicinity of Pocatello August 28–29 (Nos. 533–50). Packed and shipped equipment and left for Salt Lake City, Denver, and Washington, D. C., September 13. While at Pocatello made trips to "Big Canyon" (July 22), the Port Neuf River bottom "8 miles northwest," opposite Old Fort Hall (July 24), "Pocatello Canyon" (July 29), the garden of C. H. Smith on an island "2½ miles long" in the river at Pocatello (July 30) (*45*, item 128; *114i; 123a*).

Pocatello Canyon, Idaho (?Bannock County)

1893. Not located, but said to be the canyon of Pocatello Creek, 6 miles east of Pocatello. Collected Nos. 417–33, July 29 (*45*, item 128; *114i; 123a*).

Poinsett County, Arkansas

?1882. See Harrisburgh.

Point Habella, Arizona

1869, 1870. See Puerta Isabel, Sonora.

Point Isabella, Arizona

1869, 1870. See Puerta Isabel, Sonora.

Point Loma, California (San Diego County) GLO, 1928

1888. December 15; see San Diego.

Point Pedirnal

1853. See Río Pedernal.

Poplar Creek, Tennessee

1881. See Tennessee.

Port de San Josa, San Luis Potosí

1878. See San José.

Port Isabella

1869, 1870. See Puerta Isabel.

Portland, Maine (Cumberland County)

1873. See Peak's Island.

Portneuf River, Idaho (probably Bannock County)

GLO, 1939

1893. On July 24, Palmer visited the river bottom at a point 8 miles northwest of Pocatello and opposite Old Fort Hall; he collected a few plants. He also collected along the river on August 7 (*45*, item 128; *123a*).

Porto Albuquerque, Brazil (Mato Grosso)
19°27′S., 57°23′W. S.E–21

1853. The river port of Albuquerque, *q.v.* Specimens were collected here along the Río Paraguay, November 29. See Río Paraná (*123a*).

Portraro Ranch, Guerrero

1895. Probably Palmer's variant of Potrero; see El Marqués.

Posa de Guadalupe, San Luis Potosí

1878. Not located, but presumably the same as Presa de Guadalupe, *q.v.*

Posos, Rancho de, San Luis Potosí

1878. See Pozos, Rancho de.

Poston's Ranch, Arizona (Yavapai County)

1869. July 20; said to be 22 miles from Fort Whipple on the way to Bill Williams Mountain, *q.v.* Probably this is an error (the notes quoted here are transcribed from Palmer's originals) for Postle's (or Postal's) Ranch, which according to Barnes (*7*, p. 343) was 22 or 24 miles northeast of Prescott, on the old stage road from Ash Fork to Prescott. "Preston's Ranch," *q.v.*, is undoubtedly the same as Poston's (*114g*).

Potato Ranch, California (San Bernardino County)

1876. May 29. In the San Bernardino Mountains; see San Bernardino (*123b*).

Pozos, San Luis Potosí 22°06′N., 100°53′W. N.F–14

1878. Mentioned on a typewritten itinerary in the National Herbarium. A small town, on the desert plain southeast of the city of San Luis Potosí, on Palmer's road to Pila and Álvarez, *qq.v.*

Pozos, Rancho de, San Luis Potosí 22°48′N., 100°27′W.

1878. November 25; this is apparently the place (called "Rancho de Posos" by Palmer) where he camped the third night out of San Luis Potosí on the road to Tula; see San Luis Potosí (Estado). It appears in the *Atlas* (Hoja 42, S. Luis Potosí) as "Pozos de S. Ana," and on Sheet N.F–14 (San Luis Potosí) as "Pozas de Sta.Ana"(*114i*).

Prairie County, Arkansas

?1883. See Des Arc.

Presa de Guadalupe, San Luis Potosí 22°52′N., 100°08′W. N.F–14

1878. November 27; Palmer camped here, having left Santo Domingo the same day. Called by him "Posa de Guadalupe," but this is almost certainly an error in transcription; see San Luis Potosí (Estado) (*114i*).

Prescott, Arizona (Yavapai County) GLO, 1933

1876. Arrived from Wickenburg April 20 or 22; collected about 41 numbers of plants; left for Hardyville, *q.v.*, about May 4. While at Prescott botanized at Walnut Grove and perhaps at the Juniper Mountains, "30 miles west of Prescott." This latter locality is in doubt, for the itinerary in the Gray Herbarium collection gives the date August 23 (when Palmer was in northern Nevada). If April 23 was intended, Palmer must have made a special trip from Prescott to the Juniper Mountains; it seems more probable that he visited them in the course of his trip to Hardyville (*34a; 48; 114b; 114i*).

Preston's Ranch, Arizona

1869. Not located, but visited by Palmer July 20, enroute from Fort Whipple to Bill Williams Mountain. Probably same as Poston's Ranch, *q.v.* (*123a*).

Progreso, Yucatán 21°17′N., 89°40′W. N.F–16

1877. See Veracruz (Ciudad).

Pueblo Viejo, Veracruz 22°11′N., 97°51′W. N.F–14

1910. About 3 km. southeast of Tampico, on the coastal side of Laguna Pueblo Viejo; called "Old Town" by Palmer. Nos. 351–99 were collected here in February (Nos. 351–75 were duplicated by those of the collection made at Pánuco (April 20–25). Palmer's field book gives the dates of collection of Nos. 351–99 as February 10–25, but his journal shows that he spent most of this time in Tampico, visiting Pueblo Viejo on February 9, ?10, 12, 23, and 24; he seems to have collected from day to day, completing the sets of each number by repeated visits to the same locality. The field books also show that Nos. 400–50 were collected here (May 23–31), as well as Nos. 531–60 (June 1–2); the journal shows that Palmer made trips to Pueblo Viejo from Tampico on May 2, 3, 4, 16, 22, 23, and 26 (*123a; 123c*).

Puerta, Tamaulipas 22°21'N., 97°52'W. N.F–14

1910. A locality near the railroad about 15 km. north of Tampico; visited May 7, according to Palmer's journal. Also called La Puerta.

Puerta Isabel, Sonora 31°48'N., 114°40'W.

1869. The site of a shipyard at the head of the Gulf of California; called "Port Isabella" by Palmer. He probably made his first trip here by steamer from Yuma in August; his second visit was from October 6 (or somewhat before) to October 19. He shipped some of his previous collections from here in October, giving his address as "Mouth of the Colorado River." He collected here birds and invertebrates and probably plants; from the shipyard he went across the gulf to Baja California in a small boat with four men who were getting clams, the trip lasting several days. He notes that the shipyard was 6 miles up Isabella Slough, and continues "To the end of Gore & Montague Is., 10 miles, . . . and to the clamflats on lower California side 50 miles and 5 miles further on to where we anchored up the slough." He returned to Yuma, *q.v.* See also Colonia Lerdo, and Colorado River, mouth of (*45*, item 57; *114e; 114i; 123*a).

1870. Palmer was at the "Mouth of the Colorado" September 4, thus doubtless at Puerta Isabel, probably enroute to Adair Bay. See Colorado River, mouth of (*114e*).

"Point Habella, Arizona," referred to in a manuscript itinerary in the National Herbarium as having been visited in 1869, 1870, and 1885, is doubtless "Port Isabella," wrongly transcribed.

Puerto de San Jose, San Luis Potosí

1878. See San José.

Puerto Pedernal, Paraguay (Chaco) 23°46'S., 57°18'W. S.F–21

1853. See Río Pedernal.

Pulaski County, Arkansas

1882–83. See Little Rock, and Jefferson County.

Quaker Aspens, Arizona (Coconino County)

1869. July. Said to be 9 miles from Turkey Creek and 8 miles from Bill Williams Mountain, *q.v.* (*114g*).

Quebrada Honda, Durango 25°30'N., 106°36'W. N.G–13

1906. Nos. 211–27 collected here, May 20–21; this was apparently a stopping place on Palmer's return trip from San Ramón, *q.v.* Palmer gives the location as "60 km. northwest of Tepehuanes," which is approximately correct (*123c*).

Quemada, La, Zacatecas 22°28′N., 102°56′W. N.F–13

1878. This is apparently the place about 50 km. southwest of the city of Zacatecas, *q.v.*, near Villanueva. Palmer excavated ruins here, and described them at some length. He located the Hacienda de la Quemada as being 44 km. "south" of Zacatecas, near "Cierro de los Edificios," in "latitude 104–32–40, long. 22–18–46" (*34c; 34d*).

Quinta Carolina, Chihuahua

1908. April 10. Not located on a map. In the valley of the Río Sacramento, north of the city of Chihuahua. In 1908, this was a private estate, with a beautiful mansion surrounded by bald cypresses and other trees, about 10 km. (6 miles) north of the city. Palmer stated that "Quintas Carolina" was 3 miles east of the city. The stream valley is now (1951) heavily grazed and cultivated, and the mansion is somewhat dilapidated. See Chihuahua (Estado).

Rancheta Fresno, Chihuahua

1908. Visited May 4 from the city of Chihuahua. See Chihuahua (Estado).

Rancho Chichimequillas, Guanajuato

1898. See Chichimequillas.

Rancho de Guaymas, Sonora

1887. See Guaymas.

Rancho de Posos, San Luis Potosí

1878. See Pozos, Rancho de.

Rancho Lodiego, ?Sinaloa

1891. See Lodiego.

Rancho San José, Baja California

1890. Visited January 24; said by Palmer to be 9 miles north of La Paz, *q.v.*

Rápidos Castillo, Nicaragua 11°01′N., 84°24′W. N.C–16

1867. Called "Castillo Rapids" by Palmer, and shown under this name in Squier's *Nicaragua.*[39] See San Francisco, California.

[39] II (1852), map facing p. 217.

Rascón, San Luis Potosí 22°N., 99°16′W. N.F–14

1878. See Gallinas.

1905. A station on the railroad to Tampico, about 160 km. east of San Luis Potosí. Nos. 650–85 collected here June 19–22, and No. 766 on June 21 (*123c*).

Raton, New Mexico (Colfax County) GLO, 1886, 1936

1884. December; Palmer came by rail from Washington, D. C., to "Ratoon," over the pass to Las Vegas, down to "Nut" (a station on the railroad), and on to Yuma (*114g*).

Raton (or "Ratoon") Mountains, New Mexico

1865. Palmer crossed the pass here in June, enroute to Fort Whipple, *q.v.* (*114g*).

Raza Island, Baja California

1890. See Isla Rasa, Baja California.

Red Creek, Utah (northeastern Iron County) GLO, 1902

1877. See Paragonah.

Red Foot Lake, Tennessee

1882. See Reelfoot Lake.

Red River Station, "Colorado"

1869. April, enroute from Sheridan, Kansas, to Santa Fé, New Mexico. Not located, but possibly a stage station, in New Mexico rather than in Colorado, south of Raton Pass. The stage road crossed what was then called the Red River, near Red River Peak, a few miles southwest of present Raton (*114g*).

Redwoods, [California] (?Monterey County)

1876. Probably not a locality, but Palmer's way of referring to the redwood forests of the Santa Lucia Mountains, visited early in August. Fifteen collections from "Redwoods" are listed by Gray. See San Luis Obispo (*34a*).

Reed's Landing, Arkansas (Pulaski County)

1883. January 15; see Jefferson County. On the east side of the Arkansas River, 10–12 miles southeast of Little Rock, located on U. S. Geological Survey Map, Little Rock Sheet, Ark. (edition of September, 1893) (*88*).

Reelfoot Lake, Tennessee (Obion County)

1882. Probably arrived from Paris or Savannah, Tennessee, about the middle of May; he was at the lake (living at the Idlewild Hotel) on May 30, June 3, and June 6; on June 6 he had "almost finished his work" and sent to Washington a catalogue of ethnological specimens, Nos. 1–46 (Division of Ethnology, Cat. Nos. 57,430–57). He probably collected a few plants. Left for Ripley, probably about June 10. The name of the lake was erroneously given by Faxon as "Red Foot Lake." The following localities are cited by Thomas (*118*) as having been explored or reported by Palmer: Grassy Island (in Reelfoot Lake), Gun Point (east shore of lake), and Choctaw Creek (7 miles northwest of Gun Point) (*26; 114a; 114b; 114c*).

Refugio County, Texas

1879. December; see St. Marys.

República Argentina

1853–55. See Paraguay.

Riacho Novia, Paraguay (Chaco)

1853. Probably entering the Río Paraguay from the west, about 22°54′ south latitude. Palmer's journal, as quoted by Safford, records a stop here during the afternoon of November 15, a few hours above Concepción. See Río Paraná (*123b*). The locality is listed on Ladouce's *Mapa de la República del Paraguay* (1: 1,200,000, undated).

Riacho Soldoquhua, Paraguay (Concepción or Chaco)

1853. Enters the Río Paraguay a short distance below the Río Apa. Specimens were collected here, November 18; see Río Paraná (*123a; 125c*).

Richardson County, Nebraska GLO, 1922

1857–58. See Doniphan County, Kansas.

Riley's Mill (or Mills), [Oklahoma] (?Johnston County)

1868. Palmer collected plants here, in the Choctaw Nation, probably June 26; see Boggy Depot. Not located, but according to Miss Muriel H. Wright this mill may have been owned by James Riley, a prominent Choctaw and a signer of the Treaty of 1866, who was murdered about 1869. She suggests that the mill may have been near the crossing of the Boggy Depot road on Blue River, east of Tishomingo, Oklahoma, possibly on Sandy Creek (*120*).

Río Apa S.F–21

1853. Enters the Río Paraguay from the east, in latitude 22°05′ south, longitude 58°02′W., and forms the boundary between Paraguay and Brazil at that point. Specimens were collected near its mouth, November 19. Called "Appa River" by the members of the La Plata Expedition. See Río Paraná (*52; 123a; 125c*).

Río Bermejo, Argentina S.G–21

1854. Forms the boundary between Formosa and Chaco, Argentina; enters the Río Paraguay from the west, in latitude 26°54′ south. The *Water Witch* stopped briefly near the mouth, February 1, but apparently no specimens were collected. Called "Vermejo River" by the members of the La Plata Expedition (*52; 125c*).

Río Blanco, Jalisco 20°47′N., 103°24′W.

1886. Palmer made several trips here from Guadalajara, *q.v.*, and collected Nos. 1–73 (June 3–10), 145–213 (July 1–8), 301–50 (August 15), 501–611 (September 17–23), 643–89 (October 12–20), 729–64 and No. A (chiefly in September and October). In the U. S. National Herbarium are field notes for certain numbers, as follows; these bear the actual date of collection (indicated below in parentheses), which may not agree exactly with the inclusive dates as stated in the published account (*144*) of this year's collection: 12–14 (6–8 Je), 44 (9 Je), 188–213 (2–9 Jl), 301–305 (12–14 Au), 466 (12 S), 512 (12 Jl), 501–27, 535, 557, 588–93 (17–23 S), 645, 677, 682 (16–19 Oct).

Río Blanco was said by Watson to be "ten miles west by north of Guadalajara, a valley with a range of low mountains on the east called the Cerro de San Estevan"; actually the place is more nearly north by west from the greater part of the city of Guadalajara, or almost directly northwest of the center of the city (*123a; 144*).

Río Blanco does not appear on ordinary maps because it was never a settlement in the conventional sense. In Palmer's time it was a cotton mill, situated on the small rapid stream of the same name. The mill is no longer active, but the buildings are inhabited by a few people. The mill site and the upper part of the stream are on the plateau a few hundred meters from the edge of the barranca which angles off to the northeast to the great gorge of the Río Grande. The country on the plateau level is now mostly grassland, with scattered groves of oaks and occasional pines that suggest a former more extensive forest cover. One or two kilometers to the north and northeast (not east) lies the Sierra de San Estéban, which after Palmer's visit was to become a favorite collecting locality of C. G. Pringle. These mountains are dry and rocky and relatively bare of woody vegetation except for groves of oaks on the steep western faces. The country to the east falls off abruptly into the barranca; Río Blanco itself drops in an initial sheer fall of perhaps 15 m., followed by a succession of cataracts and rapids. Vegetation in the barranca is arid-tropical in aspect, dominated by species of such genera as *Agave, Ficus, Bursera, Psidium,* and *Ipomoea.*

Río Frio, Texas

1880. The printed itinerary distributed with Palmer's collections reads: "Between the Frio and the Nueces rivers, on the road to Laredo, Texas; January 27 to 28—1880." Palmer made at least eight collections here, while enroute by coach from San Antonio to Monterrey. One of the roads from San Antonio ran almost directly south, crossing the Frio near Tilden, McMullen County, then turning southwestward to cross the Nueces near Fort Ewell in southeastern La Salle County. The route is shown on some contemporary maps, e.g. Ross's New Connected County & Rail Road Map of Texas and Indian Territory, 16 miles to 1 inch (St. Louis, 1871) (*2; 142*).

Río Nazas, Coahuila

1898. Hitchcock (37, p. 370) cites a specimen from this locality (Palmer's No. 507). This was apparently collected during a visit to Torreón, *q.v.*, October 13–20.

Río Negro

1853. See Río Otuquis.

Río Nueces, Texas

1880. See Río Frio.

Río Otuquis S.E–21, S.F–21

1853. Enters the Río Paraguay from the north [i.e. from the west side], in latitude 20°10′ south; here forms the boundary for a short distance between Paraguay and Bolivia. A party from the *Water Witch,* including Palmer, ascended the river about "30 miles," November 24–27. Specimens were collected near the mouth, and at the highest point reached. Called "Rio Negro" by the members of the La Plata Expedition. See Río Paraná (*52; 123a; 125c*).

Río Paraná S.G–21, S.H–21

1853–55. The *Water Witch* began the ascent of the river August 31, 1853, visiting La Paz (September 14) and Corrientes (September 23–25). Entering the Río Paraguay she visited Villa del Pilar (September 28–29) and stopped at Asunción (October 1–November 7); resuming the ascent of the river she visited Piquete Ytati (November 8), Concepción (November 12–15), San Salvador (November 16), Río Apa (November 19), Pão de Azucar (November 20–21), Fuerte Olimpo (November 22), the Río Otuquis (Negro) (November 24–27), Forte do Coimbra (November 28), Porto Albuquerque (November 29), and Corumbá (November 30–December 3). On the return trip she touched at Albuquerque (December 4–7), Forte do Coimbra (a party, including Palmer, visiting Gruta do Inferno, December 9), San Salvador (December 14), Concepción (December 15–18), the Río Pedernal (December 18), and reached Asunción December 20. For the movements of the *Water Witch* and Palmer in 1854 and 1855, see Corrientes, and Montevideo (*42*).

Río Pedernal, Paraguay (Chaco)

1853. Enters the Río Paraguay from the west, in latitude 23°50′ south. Specimens were collected near its mouth, November 12, and also on the return trip from Corumbá, on December 18. The localities called "Point Pedirnal" and "Puerto Pedirnal," *q.v.*, by the members of the La Plata Expedition are thought to be at or near the mouth of this river. See Río Paraná (*52; 123a*).

Río Puerco, Arizona (probably Navajo County) GLO, 1933

1869. Palmer collected plants here June 26, and several birds June 27, "3 days from Navajo Springs." See Navajo Springs (*114e; 114i*).

Río de Sabinas, Coahuila 27°37′N., 100°47′W. N.G–14

1880. Plants were collected, probably along or near the river, at Juárez, *q.v.* Sometimes cited as "Juraz on the Sabinas River."

Río San Carlos, Arizona GLO, 1933

1867. See Camp Grant.

Río San Juan, Nicaragua N.C–16

1867. See San Francisco, California. The transisthmian route followed this river from San Carlos on Lake Nicaragua, to San Juan del Norte (Greytown) on the Atlantic. For a large scale map of the river see Squier's *Nicaragua*.[40]

Río San Pedro, Arizona GLO, 1933

1866–67. See Camp Grant.

Río San Romickeo, Arizona

1867. April 27; not located, but said to be a tributary of the Río San Pedro; see Camp Grant (*45*, item 10).

Río Tamesí, Tamaulipas N.F–14

1879. Palmer traveled from Tantoyuquita, at the head of navigation, to Tampico, February 1–3. See San Luis Potosí, and Tamaulipas (*45*, item 263; *114i*).

1910. Palmer collected along the river just above Tampico, near where it flows into the Río Pánuco from the northwest, January 3, 10, and 12. See Tamaulipas (*123a*).

Río del Tunal, Durango N.F–13, N.G–13

1896. Flows generally northeastward, 8 to 10 km. south and east of the city of Durango. Palmer collected Nos. 9 and 10, probably May 5, at a point said by him to be 5 miles from the city. Called "Tunal River" by Palmer (*123c*).

Río Verde, Arizona (eastern Yavapai County) GLO, 1897

1865. Appears on most maps as "Verde River." Plants were collected here, about 50 miles east of Fort Whipple, *q.v.*, by Coues or Palmer, August to October. See Camp Lincoln (*48*, Vols. 11, 14, 17, 20).

1885. See Mesa.

Río Verde, San Luis Potosí 21°56′N., 100°W. N.F–14

1878. Left the city of San Luis Potosi for Río Verde February 17, and returned about March 25. He visited Guascama ("the Hacienda of Don Baltasar Mayor de Parra, at Guascama, 5 leagues west of Angostura"), Valle de Maíz, and the Hacienda de Angostura (*24; 31; 34b; 34d*).

1904. Palmer came here by rail from San Luis Potosí; he collected

[40] *Ibid.*

Nos. 1–61 and 463–65 (June 2–8). Nos. 62–84 were collected at Laguna Media Luna ("Half Moon Lake") near Río Verde; the printed labels distributed with these collections from the United States National Herbarium bore the legend "Media Luna." Palmer made a second trip to Río Verde from San Luis Potosí, June 25–29 (*34a; 114i; 123a*).

1905. Arrived probably May 9, from San Luis Potosí. Collected Nos. 573–74 (May 11–13) (*123a; 123c*).

Río Yaqui, Sonora (mouth of) 27°37′N., 110°38′W. N.G–12

1869. Palmer left Guaymas by schooner November 21, reaching the mouth of the river the third day. For two weeks he was a guest at the ranch of Don José Maldonado, located some "ten miles" up river. He started his return trip on December 8, walking most of the way along the shore and collecting as he went, accompanied by a small boat offshore. He reached Guaymas December 16. Numerous specimens labeled as from the Yaqui River, numbered serially, are in the United States National Herbarium; he also collected shells here. The name has sometimes been reported in literature as the "Taqui River" (*18; 114i; 123a; 123c*).

Ripley, Tennessee (Lauderdale County)

1882. June ?15–26; probably left June 26 for Charleston, Missouri, *q.v.* See Tennessee (*114b*).

River Plata

The printed labels distributed with certain of the plants collected by Palmer on the *Water Witch* expedition bear the legend: "Exploration of the River Plata and adjacent countries during the year 1853–56." See Paraguay.

Rock Hill, South Carolina (York County)

1884. See South Carolina.

Rock Springs, California (San Bernardino County)

1876. About 25 numbers of plants collected here May 14–18, enroute from Hardyville, Arizona. In the Providence Mountains; shown on Bergland's (*126*) map in latitude 35°08′N., longitude 115° 16′W. See California, or San Bernardino (*34a; 123a*).

Rockwood, Tennessee (Roane County)

1883. ?June. Palmer reported various mounds near here, and another on the north side of the Tennessee River below Little Paint Rock Creek, according to Thomas (*118*). See Tennessee.

Rodriguez Creek, Florida [Monroe County]

1884. Collections from here are cited by Rathbun (*94*). Not located, but Rodriguez Key lies east of the south end of Key Largo, and separated from it by a narrow channel, as shown on U. S. Coast & Geodetic Survey Chart No. 1,249 (edition of 1921). See Florida.

Roman Mounds, Arkansas

?1883. Not located, but see Crittenden County.

Rosalia Bay, Baja California

1889. See Bahía de Santa Rosalía and Lagoon Head, Baja California.

Rosario, Coahuila 25°24′N., 102°12′W. N.G–13

1880. Called by Palmer "Hacienda Rosario"; visited June 8. This appears to be the Rosario located immediately south of Parras, *q.v.* (*123a*).

Roseville, California (San Diego County) GLO, 1907

1888. On Point Loma, west of San Diego, *q.v.* Palmer's field notes show that he collected No. 22 (or 269 of his principal series of this year) here in September (*114i*).

Ross Fork, Idaho (southern Bingham County) GLO, 1899

1893. Palmer stopped here enroute from Blackfoot to Pocatello, *q.v.*, August 16, to visit the Bannock and Shoshone Agency. The locality is about 12 miles north of Pocatello, and appears on modern maps as Fort Hall.

Rowan County, North Carolina

?1883. See North Carolina.

Rozell Mounds, Mississippi

1883. See Friar's Point, or Vicksburg.

Ruby Valley, Nevada (Elko County) GLO, 1894, 1930

1861. August; see San Francisco.

Rugby Tennessee (Morgan County)

1883. ?June. Palmer reported mounds and stone graves near here, according to Thomas (*118*); see Tennessee.

Rush, Texas

1879. October 2, according to a manuscript itinerary in the National Herbarium. Not located, but probably an error for Rusk, Cherokee County. Palmer was in adjoining Anderson County a few weeks after this date, and may have worked in Cherokee County as well. See Texas.

Russell Mounds, Arkansas

1883. Near Arkadelphia, *q.v.*

Russelville, Illinois (Lawrence County) GLO, 1885

1882. October 4. See Illinois. The usual spelling is "Russellville."

Ryhans, California

1892. See Tulare.

Sabinas Hidalgo, Nuevo León 26°30′N., 100°10′W. N.G–14

1880. February, enroute to Monterrey, *q.v.;* called Sabinas by Palmer (*45*, item 193).

Sabinas River, Coahuila

1880. See Río de Sabinas.

Sabine River, Texas

1879. Probably November; see Texas (*34d*).

Sabinito, San Luis Potosí 22°31′N., 99°22′W. N.F–14

1878. Palmer spent several days here, arriving from El Salto, *q.v.*, about December 12–15, and leaving for Ciudad del Maíz December 22; after an early start this latter day he noted that after noon he was traveling on "the new road" from San Luis to Tampico. His collections at Sabinito included 109 archaeological specimens, which were recorded as from "Savimto, Veracruz," a misinterpretation of "Savinito," the spelling always used by Palmer. There are two settlements called Sabinito in this part of San Luis Potosí, but the one visited by Palmer is undoubtedly the more southerly, about 15 km. west of Nuevo Morelos, Tamaulipas. See Venis Mecas, and Tamaulipas (*34d; 114i*).

Sacaton, Arizona (Pinal County) GLO, 1933

1867. Probably in August, enroute from Camp Grant to Yuma, *q.v.*

1885. See Pima Indian Agency.

Sacramento, California (Sacramento County) GLO, 1928
1892. See California.

St. Augustine, Florida (St. Johns County) GLO, 1911
1874. Palmer visited here April 17, enroute to Cedar Keys, and perhaps again in August. At least one plant was collected here, but the date unknown; see Florida (*34a; 114i*).

St. Charles, Arkansas (Arkansas County) GLO, 1886
1881. December 8; see Monroe County.

St. Charles Bay, Texas (Refugio County)
1879. Palmer collected shells here, probably in December; see Texas (*34d*).

St. Charles River, Arizona
1867. Same as Río San Carlos; see Camp Grant.

St. Francis County, Arkansas
1882. See Forrest City.

St. Francis River, Arkansas GLO, 1914
1882. See Phillips County.

St. George, Utah (Washington County) GLO, 1937
1870. Palmer left Salt Lake City by coach on May 31; he stopped two days at Fillmore, then "moved on to Beaver by the next change of coach (a spring buggy) staid over night and next morning took coach . . . to Cedarville." He also stayed a night at Cedarville, then went on to reach St. George on June 7. In Palmer's time the wagon road to St. George from the north followed approximately the route of the modern highway (Route US 91). I have not located his "Cedarville" on any map, but his account suggests that it must have been Cedar City, about halfway between Beaver and St. George. He left St. George for St. Thomas on June 17; for an account of this trip see p. 47 (*6; 45*, item 211; *114e; 123a*).

1875–76. Arrived October 15–20, 1875, from San Francisco. Collected plants and archaeological material; left January 5, 1876, for San Bernardino, California, via Salt Lake City (January 14–16) and ?San Diego. Palmer made several excursions while at St. George, collecting archaeological specimens near Kanab, Utah, and on the Muddy River, Nevada (*20; 34a; 34d; 114b; 114i*).

1876–77. Collected about 180 numbers of plants and probably some archaeological material. Arrived on December 28, 1876 (this according to the date on a letter to Putnam, but among Palmer's notes in Merwin item (45) No. 211 is a description of the Christmas ball in St. George on December 24), from Davenport, Iowa, and made his headquarters at St. George until June 22, 1877. Made trips to Johnson and Kanab, Utah (March, 1877), Beaver Dam, Arizona, and St. Thomas, Nevada (about April 12–25), Mokiak Pass and the Juniper Mountains, Arizona (about 27–May 4 and about June 1–4), Pine Mountains, Utah (May 12), Mountain Meadows (May ?14–22) and Mt. Trumbull, Arizona (June 7–15). Left June 22 for Red Creek (Paragonah), Utah (*20; 24; 34a; 34b; 34d; 45*, item 283; *110; 112; 114i; 123a*).

St. John, prairies of, [Florida]

1874. February. Said to extend from a point 26 miles a little north of west of St. Lucie, to the old road between Fort Capron and Tampa. See Fort Bassinger.

St. Johns River, Florida GLO, 1926

1874. Early February. At this time, according to Safford, Palmer's "limited time did not permit him to land and he made no attempt to collect"; see Tocoi, however. It is possible that he collected on the return trip to Jacksonville, which was made in April. See Florida (*123b*).

St. Louis, Missouri

1863. Palmer arrived with his company, from Fort Smith, Arkansas, December 17 (*125d*).

1864–65. See Missouri.

1868. Mid-January, enroute to Kansas City and Leavenworth; Palmer stopped for a talk with George Engelmann (*114b*).

1880. Possibly visited early in November; on October 15 and 28 Palmer wrote of a projected visit to Engelmann, and he may have stopped in St. Louis enroute from Texas to Cambridge, Massachusetts (*43a; 125b*).

1883. June 24, enroute from Carthage, Tennessee, via Nashville, perhaps on the way to Arkansas (*34a; 114b*).

St. Lucie, Florida (St. Lucie County) GLO, 1926

1874. Arrived by boat from Sand Point, February 14; went overland with a party to Fort Bassinger, thence by river to Lake Okeechobee, returning to St. Lucie March 17 and leaving for Jacksonville in a few days. See Florida (*9; 10; 123a*).

St. Marys, Texas (Refugio County)

1879. December 5; Palmer probably spent about the first ten days of December collecting archaeological material in Refugio and San Patricio counties. See Texas (*34d; 123a*).

St. Thomas, Nevada (Clark County) GLO, 1930

1870. Formerly west of the Muddy River near its junction with the Virgin; the site is now covered by the waters of Lake Mead. Palmer left St. George, Utah, June 17; his means of transportation was a threshing machine. The first night he camped probably in the Beaver Dam Mountains, passing the following day over a "plain covered with tree Yucca." The second night he camped where "Beaver Springs empties into the Virgin River" [i.e. near the present site of Littlefield, Arizona]. From this point his route lay along the Virgin River; he reached St. Thomas June 20, leaving again for Hardyville, Arizona, on June 25 (*114b; 123a; 123b*).

1877. Left St. George, Utah, probably about April 10; was in St. Thomas April 17–18; collected about 26 numbers of plants on Muddy River; returned via Beaver Dam (Littlefield), Arizona, reaching St. George about April 25 (*24; 34a; 110; 123a*).

St. Thomas, Virgin Islands, W. I. 18°21′N., 64°56′W. N.E–20

1855. According to Safford, Palmer stopped at this island while enroute from Montevideo to Washington, D. C., *q.v.* (*123b*).

St. Vrain River, Colorado (Weld County)

1861–62. A tributary of the South Platte, entering from the west about 40 miles north of Denver; usually, as on GLO, 1934, called St. Vrain Creek. Spelled "San Varain" by Palmer. He may have collected near its mouth on one of his trips up or down the Platte; see Colorado (*114b*).

Salinas, San Luis Potosí 22°38′N., 101°43′W. N.F–14

1878. Palmer stopped here April 9, enroute from San Luis Potosí to Zacatecas, *q.v.* (*45*, item 190).

Salinas Victoria, Nuevo León 25°57′N., 100°17′W. N.G–14

1880. February, enroute to Monterrey, *q.v.;* called Salinas by Palmer.

Saline Bayou, Arkansas

1883. Near Arkadelphia, *q.v.*

Saline County, Arkansas

1883. Palmer worked in the counties along the Arkansas River below Little Rock during much of the fall of 1882. He was in Woodson, Saline County, January 15, 1883, to take steamer to Reed's Landing. After return to Little Rock and a visit to the Thibault mounds 8 miles southeast (January 20) he was back in Benton, Salinc County, on January 27 and 28. Visited and worked at the Hughes mound and house sites 8 miles to the southwest. Descriptions and sketch of the site are given by Thomas (*119*, p. 246). From Benton Palmer went to Arkadelphia, *q.v.* (*88; 114b*).

1883. September 16. Bryant Station; Palmer came by train from Arkadelphia and apparently returned the next day (*88*).

Salt Lake City, Utah (Salt Lake County)

1861. August 14–17; see San Francisco.

1870. May ?25–31. Palmer arrived by train from Washington, D. C. He heard Brigham Young preach on May 30, and was also able to obtain from the Mormon leader a letter of introduction to aid him in his work in Utah; the letter is still preserved. He left Salt Lake City on the thirty-first, in cold and snow, his destination St. George, *q.v.* (*45*, item 211; *123a*).

1876. January 14; on this date Palmer wrote from Salt Lake City: "Arrived in this city after a very cold and tedious journey by coach . . . will start tomorrow Jan 16th [*sic*] for San Bernardino." See St. George (*114b*).

1877. Arrived August 13, from Spring Lake; went to "Touilla" (probably August 14 or soon thereafter). Left Salt Lake City for Davenport, Iowa, about the end of August (*24; 34d; 114i*).

1893. September; see Washington, D. C.

Salt Mountains, Nevada

1870. June 25; see Hardyville.

Salt Pond Key, Florida (Monroe County) CGS, 1251

1884. Rathbun cited collections made between Salt Pond Key and Stock Island (*94*). Salt Pond Key, two rocky islets, is immediately north of Key West.

Salt River, Arizona (eastern Maricopa County) GLO, 1933

1869. The records of the Division of Birds of the National Museum show that collections were made on the Salt River in this year. For possible dates see Yuma (*114e*).

Saltillo, Coahuila 25°26′N., 101°W. N.G–14

1880. Arrived from Monterrey March 20; left about March 22 for the Sierra Madre; spent April 1–20 at and near Saltillo, leaving April 20 for Parras, San Lorenzo, Coyote, San Pedro, and Acatita, returning via Parras and reaching Saltillo June 30. Left for Lirios about July 9; returning about July 14; left for the Sierra Madre about July 24; probably spent August 2–17 in and near Saltillo, leaving in time to reach Monclova about August 17 or 18. About 100 numbers of plants were collected in the vicinity of Saltillo, probably mostly during the periods April 1–15 and July 1–8, about 50 additional numbers were collected in "mountains 6 miles east of Saltillo," April 15–20 and July 17–20, and about 15 numbers were collected in "mountains west side of Saltillo," August 14–17. About 150 numbers were collected in the area designated by Palmer as the "Canon and elevated portion of Sierra Madre, 12–14 leagues south of Saltillo"; this was visited twice, March 22–30, and July 25–August 1 (*2; 24; 34a; 34b; 114i; 123a; 142*).

1898. Arrived from Washington, D. C., before April 19; collected Nos. 1–104 (April), 105–201 (May), 202–77 (June). On June 5, Palmer wrote that he had collected 200 species and "catalogued" 135. He visited San Luis Potosí and Guanajuato, probably returning early in September; collected Nos. 278–375 and 790–814 (September) and 376–418 (undated). Left early in October for Parras, Torreón, Mapimí, and Zacatecas, returning between November 4 and 11 and perhaps collecting Nos. 557–85 in November. On November 11 he wrote that he had been ill but was expecting to leave soon for Washington. See Coahuila (*114i; 123a*).

1902. Passed through early in August, enroute to San Luis Potosí, *q.v.* Returned from San Luis Potosí about November 10; collected Nos. 278–370 (November 10–20); visited Concepción del Oro, Zacatecas, probably leaving Saltillo November 20 or 21 and returning November 22. Left for Washington, D. C., probably soon after December 1 (*114i; 123a*).

1904. Arrived from San Luis Potosí about August 3; left for Concepción del Oro August 11; returned about August 15 and left at once for General Cepeda, returning probably August 18; visited

Chorro Grande, probably August 29–31, and San Lorenzo Cañon September 21–23; remained at Saltillo until November 5 or later, perhaps visiting Torreón October 23–26. Collected Nos. 331 (August 23), 432–48, 453, 455–62, and 473–76, either in Saltillo or at the Cerro del Pueblo west of the city. The dates of these collections are not well established, as those given by Palmer in various manuscript records do not agree with those on the field notes. The latest date shown is November 5 (*34a; 123a*).

1905. Arrived early in April from Washington, D. C.; collected Nos. 500–27 and 564–66 (April 9–11); visited San Lorenzo Cañon (April 16) and Agua Nueva (April 18); returned to Saltillo and collected a few numbers (April 21–28); left for San Luis Potosí before May 1, returning about June 28; visited San Lorenzo Cañon (July 9) and Chorro Grande (July 16–19); probably left for Washington, D. C., August 11 or 12. At Saltillo collected Nos. 563 (April 21), ?686–?90, probably 704–13 (July 28), probably 728–38 (July 25), probably 752–64 (August 10), 767–69 (August 11; see Chorro de Agua). The field notes in the Department of Agriculture collection and those at the Gray Herbarium are both incomplete, and the numbers as given above are provisional (*34a; 123a; 123c*).

Salto del Agua, San Luis Potosí 22°35′N., 99°24′W. N.F–14

1878. Palmer arrived at "Salto" December 11, having come by mule train from Tula, "22 leagues distant." He noted that the cascade here had a fall of 80 m., and that Sabinito ("along the Rio Salto, in the Huasteca") was but two leagues distant. This beautiful and renowned waterfall, on the river now called Naranjo, is known everywhere in this part of San Luis Potosí simply as El Salto, "The Waterfall." No modern road leads directly from El Salto to Sabinito, but the falls are accessible by a motor road on the east side of the river. Palmer probably left El Salto for Sabinito about December 12–15. See Sabinito, and Tamaulipas (*114i*).

Salton, California (?southern Riverside County)

1867. (?)August. A station on the stage route from Yuma to Los Angeles, *q.v.* (*123a*).

Salton Desert, California

1870. (?)September; see Los Angeles.

Saltzertown Mound, Mississippi

1883. See Washington, Mississippi.

San Antonio, Morelos

1878. Not located. Visited in June; said by Palmer to be an Indian town 1¼ miles from Cuernavaca (*45*, item 190).

San Antonio, Texas (Bexar County)

1879–80. Arrived from Longview about July 27, 1879, and left for Uvalde August 3 or 4. Was in San Antonio about September 19–27 and from December 25, 1879, when he arrived from Corpus Christi, to January 26, 1880, when he left by coach for Monterrey. On his return from Mexico he passed through San Antonio and stopped briefly, probably October 11–15, 1880. About 60 collections of plants were taken in 1879–80, probably most of them in September, 1879. See Guadalupe, and Texas (*34a; 34d; 142*).

San Antonio del Coyote, "Durango" [i.e. Coahuila]

1880. May 10; same as Coyote. Studley (*116*) refers to Coyote Cave as "near" San Antonio del Coyote. Palmer (*34d*) refers to San Antonio del Coyote as "5 leagues from the celebrated cave," and gives its position as latitude 25¼°, longitude about 103° (that is, considerably southeast of the actual position of Coyote). Any reference to Durango is apparently quite erroneous; the several caves in the Sierra de San Lorenzo, and the near-by places which Palmer visited on the Hacienda de Coyote, are all in Coahuila (*123a*).

San Benito Island, Baja California

1889. See Isla San Benito, Baja California.

San Bernardino, California (San Bernardino County)

GLO, 1928

1867. (?)August; see Los Angeles.

1870. (?)September; see Los Angeles.

1876. Arrived from Salt Lake City about February 1. On February 22 Palmer wrote Eaton: "Returned this morning from a long journey S.E. . . . in six days expect to leave for Arizona." According to a manuscript itinerary (*114i*) he was at the mouth of Williams Fork, Arizona, on February 14, and at Palm Springs, California, on February 16. There is a statement under item 80 of the Merwin Catalogue (*45*) that Palmer left San Bernardino on February 16, to visit the "Coahuillas Indians of the desert." The "long journey S.E." (see above) may have been to the Colorado River or to an Indian settlement, or both. Palmer left San Bernardino by coach for Ehrenberg,

Arizona, February 29, and returned May 25, having left Hardyville, Arizona, by coach, and traveled via Rock Springs (May 14–?18), the Mojave River, Stoddards (May 19–23), and Crafton (May 23). The type of the genus *Canbya* was collected May 18 on the Mojave Desert, doubtless on the upper Mojave River. In a letter to Engelmann, June 15, Palmer wrote of this trip: "Returning . . . from Arizona . . . passed the cactus you want on the Mojave River and on the desert . . . Coach being loaded with passengers could not stop—fifteen miles further and a station was come to [;] here I stayed several days collecting plants but could not find any cactus it being near the mountains." While at San Bernardino, Palmer undertook a trip to San Bernardino Mountain, via Mill Creek, passing Bridal Veil Falls and Potato Ranch (all May 29), and reaching the summit May 30. He was injured by a fall on the return journey, and went to Crafton (May 31) to recuperate. Left Crafton (June 8) on a trip to the upper Mojave River, reaching Stoddard's Ranch (June 10), Holcombs' [on the return trip?] (June 11) and Bear Flat Station (June 11), and returning to Crafton (June 14) and San Bernardino (June 15). On June 15 he said in his letter to Engelmann: "As soon as my injuries permitted took team and went over to the Mojave Desert and reached nearly the cactus field when in consequence of pain and heat (110 in shade) had to return . . . ." Palmer probably left San Bernardino for San Luis Obispo about June 20, traveling by rail to San Pedro, thence by steamer. Gray lists 3 numbers collected at San Bernardino in 1876 (*20; 24; 30; 34a; 34d; 45*, item 80; *114i; 123a*).

1887. May, enroute from Washington, D. C., to Guaymas. Palmer wrote: "On the cars while passing through the Indian nation was taken with a severe attack of fever and ague was so sick I had to go to San Bernardino and wait there several days" (*45*, item 62; *114i*).

1888. Palmer made his headquarters here while employed by the Department of Agriculture during this summer. Arrived May 26, from Washington, D. C.; left June 2 for Mt. Whitney, but finding that snow in the mountains made this trip impossible, collected about Kernville and returned to San Bernardino June 16; visited Los Angeles and San Diego, returning June 24; visited Victor, and probably Hesperia, June 25–27, and tried a second time to reach Mt. Whitney, returning to San Bernardino before July 29; left for San Diego July 30. Perhaps visited here September 7–8. See California (*45*, item 62; *114i; 123a*).

San Bernardino Mountain (San Bernardino County)
GLO, 1928
1876. See San Bernardino.

San Blas, [?Mexico]
1869. According to the records of the Division of Ethnology, U.S. National Museum, Palmer collected ethnological specimens (Nos. 9,405–47, 9,475–78), from "Indians near San Blas." I am unable to explain this reference, unless the collector secured these materials while he was at Guaymas or on the Yaqui River. The town of San Blas, Sinaloa, is about 200 km. farther south than he is known to have traveled in this year.

San Blas, Nayarit 21°32′N., 105°16′W. N.F–13
1892. January and April; see Nayarit.

San Carlos, Nicaragua 11°08′N., 84°48′W. N.C–16
1867. See Nicaragua, or San Francisco, California. This was the site of an old fort at the head of the Río San Juan, the outlet of Lake Nicaragua.

San Diego, California (San Diego County) GLO, 1928
1861–62. Palmer came here from San Francisco, *q.v.;* he worked here for the Geological Survey of California, probably from October, 1861, to mid-January, 1862. His work was chiefly the collection of marine invertebrates, under the direction of J. G. Cooper. He says "I boarded with P. O. Neill now of Old Town or North San Diego." See California (*45*, item 61; *114b; 123a*).

1875. Arrived about January 15, enroute from San Francisco to Guadalupe Island. He was in San Diego at least until January 26. He returned from Guadalupe Island late in May and was in San Diego until about June 20. Following this he made trips to Soledad and Jamul Valley, and a protracted trip to the Cuyamaca Mountains (July 4 to about August 7). A week later he left for Fort Yuma by stage, but stopped off to visit the "Tantillas Mountains" in Baja California, returning to San Diego probably not before September 18 or 19. He was in San Diego "packing his collections" about September 21 (*114g*), and visited Murphy's Canyon September 22. Left for San Francisco about October 7. About 135 plant collections were made here in 1875 (*20; 34a; 34d; 114b; 123a*).

1876. Gray lists a single collection (No. 304) from here (*34a*).

1888. Visited from San Bernardino, *q.v.*, about June 20–24 (*114i*).

1888–89. Arrived about August 1, 1888, from San Bernardino, "to rest"; made short trips to various points; collected chiefly lichens. Visited Santa Catalina Island (about August 16–?25), Coronados Islands (August 18), perhaps San Bernardino (September 7–8), Roseville (September), Coronado Beach (September), False Bay (September). Left for Yuma October 7 and returned October 12; collected at Point Loma lighthouse (December 15) and about the harbor (December 16). Left by steamer for San Quintín, Baja California, about January 20, 1889 (*23; 34a; 45*, item 62; *114i; 123a*).

1889. Arrived about February 26, from San Quintín; left March 1 on the steamer *Queen of the Bay* for Lagoon Head, Cedros Island, San Benito Island, and Guadalupe Island, returning to San Diego April 8; left for Yuma April 18, returning May 10; made a trip toward San Bernardino, May 14–about June 1; left for Ensenada and Colnett, Baja California, June 5, returning June 25; was probably hospitalized in San Diego or at least was unwell until late in October; left for San Francisco October 27.[41] See California (*114i; 123a; 125f*).

1895. Visited about May 1; see San Francisco.

1897. Arrived by steamer after leaving Guaymas October 21; left for Washington, D. C., October 29 (*123a*).

San Diego, San Luis Potosí

1878. December 29. Not located, but probably the same as San Dieguito, which he must have passed while enroute from San Nicolás to Buena Vista. See Ciudad del Maíz (*114i*).

San Diego Mission, California (San Diego County)

1875. See Murphy's Canyon.

San Dieguito, San Luis Potosí 22°02′N., 99°14′W. N.F–14

1878. See San Diego, San Luis Potosí, and Ciudad del Maíz.

1904. Nos. 84½–154 collected here (June 13–16). A station on the railroad to Tampico, about 175 km. east of San Luis Potosí (*34a; 123a*).

[41] A note in *Garden & Forest* Vol. III (January 15, 1890), 36, states that Dr. Edward Palmer sailed from San Diego on the twenty-fifth of December, 1889, for La Paz and Guaymas, and that T. S. Brandegee sailed on the same steamer. According to Palmer's own notes, (*123a*) he left San Francisco, q.v., on December 27; possibly his steamer touched at San Diego on the twenty-eighth or twenty-ninth instead of the twenty-fifth as stated in *Garden & Forest*.

1905. Collected Nos. 618–46 here (June 7–10); probably returned to San Luis Potosí about June 12 or 13 (*34a; 114b; 123c*).

Sand Point, Florida

1874. Same as Titusville, *q.v.*

San Felipe, California

1875. See San Felipe Canyon and Ranch.

San Felipe, Guanajuato 21°29'N., 101°13'W. N.F–14

1878. See Guanajuato (Estado). Now called Ciudad González.

San Felipe Canyon, California (San Diego County)

1875. July 27. Palmer's manuscript itinerary says "six miles east from Julian." A few collections were made here; Gray listed 3 collections from San Felipe, which seems to be the same locality; and Palmer mentions a single one from a point 13 miles east of San Felipe Canyon. San Felipe appears on the GLO map of 1876, in R 5 E, T 12 S, and this is apparently Palmer's locality. The canyon is now called Sentenac Canyon. See Julian (*34a; 123a*).

San Felipe Ranch, California (San Diego County)

1875. July 26. A few (probably about 18) collections were made here or at San Felipe Canyon, *q.v.* Palmer's manuscript itinerary says "To edge of desert by way of San Felipe ranch 16 miles east of Julian," but apparently what he meant was "to edge of desert 16 miles east of Julian (by way of San Felipe ranch)." Evidently he collected about the ranch and in the near-by canyon during a stay of two days, and made a quick trip (see above) to the edge of the desert farther east. See Julian (*34a; 123a*).

San Francisco, California (San Francisco County)

1861–62. Arrived August 26, 1861, traveling by stage from Denver via Julesburg, Colorado (August 7), Salt Lake City (August 14), Ruby Valley, Nevada, and Hangtown (now Placerville), California. On October 10 "joined the State Survey (Geological), and left for San Pedro . . . thence to La Player hear was the Custom house. . . ." Worked in the vicinity of San Diego, *q.v.*, and returned to San Francisco late in January, 1862. Left February 11 for New York, via Acapulco, *q.v.*, and Panama, on the steamer *Sonora* (*45*, item 61; *114b; 123a*).

1867. Palmer came here from Camp Grant, Arizona; his contract as acting assistant surgeon, U.S.A., was annulled here September 30. After visiting Sonoma, *q.v.*, he left October 25 on steamer *Moses Taylor* for New York, via Nicaragua. Landed at San Juan del Sur, Nicaragua, made the short crossing to La Virgen ("Virgin City") on Lake Nicaragua, went by lake steamer to San Carlos at the head of Río San Juan and then by river steamer down river to the Castillo rapids, by tramway around the rapids, and another steamer to Greytown. Here "after a short wait" he took a boat to New York (*45*, item 53; *114b; 125d*).

1870. Arrived in January by boat from Guaymas; left on the Pacific mail steamer for New York and Washington, via Panama, February 3. He touched at Cabo San Lucas, the fifth day out, and later at Manzanillo, Acapulco, and San José, Guatemala, reaching Panama the fifteenth day [February ?17]. He crossed by rail to Aspinwall and took steamer to New York, passing Cuba and Hispaniola the nineteenth day and reaching Sandy Hook the 26th day [February ?28] and New York the day after.

Palmer also came to San Francisco later this same year, probably from Los Angeles in October; from San Francisco he went directly to Washington, D. C., by way of Denver (October 22), arriving November 10 or 11 (*45*, item 53; *90; 114a; 123a*).

1875. Arrived January 3, from New Haven, enroute to San Diego and Guadalupe Island; left January 14. Returned from San Diego between October 7 and 10, and left for St. George, Utah, about October 12 (*20; 34d; 45*, item 57; *114b; 123a*).

1876. Arrived on or before August 11, after his trip from San Luis Obispo, *q.v.*, to the "Redwoods" of the Santa Lucia Mountains. Probably left about August 15 by train, reaching Wadsworth, Nevada on August 20, Camp Halleck, Nevada on August 26, and Davenport, Iowa, about September 10 (*24; 34a; 114b; 114i*).

1889. Arrived from San Diego about October 31; left by steamer for Guaymas, December 27 (*114i; 123a*).

1890. Arrived by rail from Holbrook, Arizona, probably about June 15; left for Guaymas by the steamer *Newbern*, August 25 (August 23 according to Rose); on the way to Guaymas he touched at Ensenada, San José del Cabo (August 31), and La Paz (September 3) (*97; 114i; 123a*).

1892. May to August; Palmer made his headquarters for all or a part of this time at the California Academy of Sciences. See California, and Vallejo (*114i; 123a*).

Edward Palmer as an Old Man
His best-known portrait, it was published originally (1911)
to accompany a biographical sketch by Safford
in Popular Science Monthly.

The hamlet of Sabinito, San Luis Potosí, in the lowlands near El Salto.

The hacienda of Otinapa, Durango, as it appeared fifty-five years after Palmer's visit.

1894. Arrived late in September from Washington, D. C. (probably left Chicago September 24, by train); left on the steamer *San Juan* for Acapulco, Guerrero, October 8 (*45*, item 61; *114i; 123a*).

1895. Arrived April 20, from Acapulco, perhaps on the *City of Sydney*. Visited San Diego about May 1; left for Washington, D. C., soon thereafter, probably from San Diego (*45*, item 57; *114i; 123a*).

San Francisco, México (Estado de)

1878. Not located; said to be a small village near San Juan de Teotihuacán, where Palmer obtained some artifacts. See México, D.F. (*34d*).

San Francisco Mountain(s), Arizona (Coconino County)
GLO, 1933

1866. Palmer accompanied troops here from Camp Lincoln, *q.v.*, early in March.

1869. Leaving Fort Wingate, New Mexico, with an army escort, on June 22, Palmer traveled by way of Navajo Springs and the valley of the Río Puerco (June 26–27) and the Little Colorado. They forded the latter on June 30 and sighted San Francisco Peaks the same day. The peak was climbed to the snow line on July 4, after which the party went on to Fort Whipple, *q.v.* (*114e; 123a*).

San Gorgonio Pass, California (Riverside County)
GLO, 1907

1870. (?)September; see Los Angeles.

San Jerommo, Colima

1891. February 1. Not located, but probably not far from the city of Colima. The name is almost certainly a corruption of "San Jerónimo" or "Gerónimo" (*114i*).

San Josa, San Luis Potosí

1878. See San José.

San José, Baja California

1890. See La Paz.

San José, Chihuahua 26°56′N., 107°38′W. N.G–13

1885. This is apparently the Hacienda San José at which Palmer collected, and which is stated by Watson (*143*) to lie on the Batopilas River 25 miles south of Batopilas; actually the river turns abruptly to the west about 15 km. south of Batopilas, and San José is above the bend, about 10 km. south of Batopilas. Palmer collected Nos. 24–70, 72–79, No. B, and duplicate and supplementary Nos. 26–30, 49½, 49¾, 49a, 49b, 49c, 50f (reported by Watson as 508), 51a, 63½, 63a, and 63b. The date of Palmer's visit is unknown, but was probably August or September (*143*).

San José, Guatemala 13°55′N., 90°50′W. N.D–15

1870. February. A note among the Palmer manuscripts indicates that his boat touched at "San José" between Acapulco and Panama; presumably this, the port of Guatemala City, is the place meant; see San Francisco, California (*123a*).

San José, (Puerto de), San Luis Potosí 22°34′N., 100°29′W. N.F–14

1878. November 25, enroute from Peotillos to Rancho de Pozos. Called "San Josa" or "Port de San Josa" by Palmer, and characterized by him as "a few miserable huts." This was the pass through the mountains at the place where the San Luis–Tampico railroad now reaches farthest north, and turns abruptly southeast. The place appears as "Puerto (S. José)" on sheet 13–II–(T) of the *Carta de la República Mexicana a 100,000*[a] (edition of 1903) (*114i*).

San José de Guaymas, Sonora 27°59′N., 110°53′W. N.G–12

1887, 1897. See Guaymas.

San José del Cabo, Baja California 23°03′N., 109°41′W. N.G–12

1890. August 31, enroute from San Francisco to Guaymas (*123a*).

San Juan del Sur, Nicaragua 11°15′N., 85°52′W. N.C–16

1867. See San Francisco, California. This was the Pacific terminus of the trans-Nicaragua route; see Nicaragua.

San Juan de Teotihuacán, México 19°42′N., 98°52′W.

1878. Probably same as Teotihuacán. See México, D.F.

San Lorenzo Cañon, Coahuila

1904. Not located on a map. This is the first great canyon in the range southeast of Saltillo, about 6 miles (10 km.) from the city as stated by Palmer. Nos. 385–431, and 468–71 were collected here, September 21–23. The sides of the canyon are extremely high, steep, and rocky, but it is possible (1951) to ascend the stream valley by a horse trail. The lower slopes are arid, with vegetation of *Agave, Opuntia, Lindleyella mespiloides, Berberis trifoliata, Amelanchier denticulata,* and a few plants of *Juniperus.* Grazing by goats is heavy. Conifers on the summit slopes are visible from far below, and it is stated locally that before the revolution of 1910–14 no cutting of timber was allowed in the canyon, the stream ran clear and cold throughout the year, and the pines extended down to the lower slopes and even onto the now treeless plain (*34a; 123a*).

1905. Perhaps collected Nos. 534–57 here, April 16; for discussion see Saltillo. Palmer made a second visit here on July 9, and collected (probably) Nos. 693–700, 741, 744–48, 751, and perhaps 552–57 (*34a; 123a; 123c*).

San Lorenzo de Coahuila

A locality cited by W. B. Hemsley (*36*, Vol. 3, p. 339). Undoubtedly the same as San Lorenzo de la Laguna, *q.v.*

San Lorenzo de (la) Laguna, Coahuila

1880. About 85 numbers of plants collected here, May 1–10. Not located on any modern map, but doubtless the same as the San Lorenzo of the Wislizenus map of 1848,[42] near the bend of the Río Nazas at the northwestern end of the Sierra de San Lorenzo, about 30 km. northeast of the modern city of Torreón. According to the printed itinerary distributed with Palmer's plants, San Lorenzo is "22 to 27 leagues southwest from Parras"; the direction from Parras is actually somewhat north of west. The following note by Palmer, although it occurs alone with a collection of miscellaneous memoranda, has the ring of authenticity: "San Lorenzo de Parras. In a carriage with Don Rafael Azuela for Has-de-la Laguna 22 to 27 leagues S.W. of Parras. Stop for night at Boqueilla Laguna de Parras."

According to a manuscript written about 1849, and now in the possession of Dr. Bulmaro Valdes Anaya, of Torreón, all the present Laguna District was originally part of the Hacienda de San Lorenzo de la Laguna; one of the ranchos on it was called Coyote, *q.v.* In 1849, the Laguna was rich and fertile from the waters of the Río Nazas, and supported great woods ("bosques") of mesquite, willow, and poplar,

[42] A. Wislizenus, "Memoir of a Tour to Northern Mexico, Connected with Col. Doniphan's Expedition in 1846 and 1847," 30 Cong., 1 sess., *Sen. Misc. Doc. No. 26* (Washington, 1848. 141 pp.).

in which lived abundant game. The district was even then known for the production of corn, cotton, wheat, and beans, but the Sierra de San Lorenzo was difficult of access and seldom visited.

The Sierra de San Lorenzo is a very dry range, with a rather thick desert-plant cover of *Agave lecheguilla, Larrea tridentata, Fouquieria splendens, Jatropha dioica,* and *Euphorbia antisyphilitica.* At the foot of the mountains is an abrupt transition to the great irrigated plain of the "Laguna," which extends all the way to Torreón. Palmer's chief reason for coming here was to collect archaeological material from certain well-known prehistoric burial caves, the first of which was discovered in 1838. He was interested in what he supposed to be the original "San Lorenzo Cave," and another which he called "Coyote Cave." The manuscript mentioned above describes a visit, in 1849, to two almost undisturbed burial caves in these mountains. By the time of Palmer's visit more than thirty years later, the caves had been exploited and relatively little of archaeological value remained. See Saltillo (*2; 34d; 123a; 142*).

San Luis, Cuba (Oriente) 20°12′N., 75°52′W. N.F–18

1902. February; see Cuba.

San Luis Obispo, California (San Luis Obispo County) GLO, 1928

1876. Arrived June 26 (or before), probably by rail from San Bernardino to San Pedro, thence by steamer. Visited Hollands Ranch and Clarks Creek (or Ferry), July 2–3, McGinnis Ranch, July 10, Cambria, July 17, and returned to San Luis Obispo, July 20. Visited Pine Mountain and San Simeon Bay (July 22–23), Santa Cruz (July 24), Paso Robles Spring (July 28), Jolon (July 31), and the Santa Lucia Mountains (August 2). Reached San Francisco on or before August 11. The date of his last visit to San Luis Obispo is in doubt; in a letter to Baird, dated from there as of July 20, he said: "Start tomorrow after plants &c to the high Coast Red Woods near Monteray." As there seems to have been no reason for him to have returned from Cambria (if he was there on July 17), only to have retraced his steps to San Simeon Bay on July 22 and 23, there is evidently some part of the sequence needing further elucidation. About 45 numbers of plants are listed by Gray from San Luis Obispo (*34a; 114b; 114i; 123a*).

San Luis Potosí (Ciudad) 22°09′N., 100°58′W. N.F–14

1878. See San Luis Potosí (Estado).

1898. Arrived from Saltillo, probably in mid-July. Collected Nos. 588–742, chiefly in the public markets (July 20–August 10). Apparently went from here to Guanajuato late in August (*114i; 123a*).

1902. Arrived August 4 or 5 from Washington, D. C., via Texarkana, Laredo, and Saltillo. Collected Nos. 1–25 (all tunas, or fruits of *Opuntia,* from the city market), and 26–44 (miscellaneous articles from the city market), August 18–20. Most of his time here in this year was spent in an unsuccessful attempt to can the fruits and juice of the opuntias which are abundant and economically important in this region. See Saucito. Visited Álvarez September 5–10, returning to the capital September 11; collected Nos. 87–100 and 453–54 (in the city market), September 12–16. Left for Mesa Verde and Álvarez September 24; spent September 28–October 3 at Álvarez; returned to San Luis Potosí; left for Canoas on October 15, returned October 22; left for Saltillo about November 8–10 (*114i; 123a; 123c; 125a*).

1904. For itineraries see San Luis Potosí (Estado). Palmer made the city his headquarters from late May to early August.

1905. For details of trips see San Luis Potosí (Estado). Palmer made the city his headquarters from about May 1 to about June 28. He collected a few plants about the capital, including probably Nos. 610–17 (May 24) and 647–49, and several unnumbered collections of cacti (*34a; 123a*).

San Luis Potosí (Estado) N.F–14

1878. A collection of more than 1,000 numbers, in about ten sets, was distributed as from the vicinity of San Luis Potosí, under the joint names of C. C. Parry and Edward Palmer; most of the numbers were cited by Hemsley, under an arrangement made with him by Parry (*36,* Vol. 1, p. iv). Parry's field book shows that he, personally, collected about 220 numbers between April 1 and July 22; after this he left San Luis Potosí about August 3, traveling to his home in Iowa by way of Saltillo and San Antonio. The remaining 800 numbers were collected by Palmer, who was at San Luis Potosí or in the vicinity during the following periods: January ?23–February 16, March ?25–April 9, April 26–May 7, and July ?26–November 23. During the three months after Parry's departure he made several trips to mountains in various parts of the state. A detailed itinerary of his travels for this year follows:

Palmer reached Veracruz from New York, by boat, December 21, 1877, and went at once to México, D. F., where Parry joined him

January 4, 1878. They left by coach for San Luis Potosí on January 19, and reached that city about January 23. Palmer left about February 16 for Río Verde, Hacienda de Angostura, Guascama, and Valle de Maíz, returning about March 25. He left April 9 for Zacatecas, returning April 26 (probably after visiting Aguascalientes enroute). He left May 7 for Mexico City, arriving May 10; he visited Chalco (May 19), Cuernavaca (May 29–June 4), Toluca (June 15), Texcoco, Teotihuacán, and San Juan de Teotihuacán. He left Mexico City July 23, stopped at Tula, Hidalgo, the same day, and reached San Luis Potosí before August 1.

After Parry's departure for San Antonio, Palmer visited Pila and Álvarez (probably mid- or late August), Peñasco (about September 1), San Miguel de Mesquite (September 15), Bledos (probably about September 25 to about October 1), and the Sierra San Miguelito (probably early October). He made at least one and probably two more trips to Álvarez from San Luis Potosí (probably in October and November). He visited, probably during the autumn months, but in unknown sequence, the following localities in San Luis Potosí: Santa María, Sierra de Santa María, San Rafael ("and surrounding mountains"), Morales (and "Morales Mountains"), Hoorez [i.e. Juárez] Mountains, "Escabrillos Mountains," Ladrillera, and Pozos.

On November 23, accompanied by a servant, Palmer left the city of San Luis Potosí for Tampico, which he reached February 3, 1879. His own story of the trip has been preserved in a series of transcribed notes; he says, in part: "My self & servant took passage on board freight train of 5 carts drawn by mules. . . . camped the second night at the desolate Hacienda Peotillo."

The third day, November 25, the train reached Puerto ("San Josa"), and "camped the 3rd night at Rancho de Posos." The fourth day the party reached the Ranchita de Santo Domingo, the residence of the owner of the mule train who, although he had contracted to take Palmer to Tula, now refused to do so. Palmer and his servant continued on muleback, leaving Santo Domingo November 27 and camping that evening at Presa de Guadalupe. Thus far their route was approximately the same as the one which the paved highway now follows. From San Luis Potosí it bears generally northeast across the desert plain. The arid, yucca-covered hills gradually close in, and no pass to the east is apparent from the present highway until, at a point about 120 km. from San Luis Potosí, the road swings abruptly to the right, turns to the southeast and crosses some low summits before entering a second interior desert basin beyond Presa de Guadalupe. Palmer's mule train may have taken a more direct but more arduous pass across from Pozos to Santo Domingo; the automobile route perforce swings somewhat farther to the north.

Palmer and his servant continued alone from Presa de Guadalupe, and reached Tula, Tamaulipas, on December 1. They made a trip to the Sierra Naola (December 3–6, visiting Naola, Boludo and Buey), and left Tula for Salto on December 9, reaching the latter place on December 11. They spent several days at Sabinito (about December ?15–22), then went on to Valle de Maíz (December 24). From here Palmer made a trip to the southeast, to San Nicolás (December 28), Gallinas (December 29), "San Diego" and Buenavista, Micos (January 1–3, 1879), and Minas Viejas (January 3–13). Returning to Valle de Maíz January 14, he made a trip to Custodio (January 17–25), then left Valle de Maíz January 27 with his servant, proceeding on horseback to the point of embarcation (Tantoyuquita) at the head of navigation on the Tamesí River, Tamaulipas. He reached Tantoyuquita on January 30, having passed the Boca de la Abra the day previous, and camping that same night out of the mountains. He embarked February 1 and reached Tampico at 3:00 P.M. on the third (*20; 34a; 34d; 45*, items 190, 263; *90; 113; 114a; 114i; 123a*).

1898. See San Luis Potosí (Ciudad).

1902. See San Luis Potosí. (Ciudad).

1904. Reached the city of San Luis Potosí about May 20–25; left for Río Verde, by rail, on June 2, returning June 8; visited San Dieguito June 13–16; returned to the capital; left by carriage for Santa María del Río, June 20, returning June 23 or 24; left for Río Verde June 25, returning June 29; collected No. 163 at the city, July 10; visited Álvarez July 13–23, returning July 24; left for Saltillo August 3 (*34a; 114i; 123a*).

1905. Reached the city of San Luis Potosí, from Saltillo, about April 28–30. Visited Zapatillo May 1–3; left for Río Verde May 9, returning about May 14; visited Álvarez, May 19–22; collected about the capital May 24; visited Peotillos May 25–27; visited San Dieguito June 7–10, returning to the city about June 12 or 13; visited Rascón June 19–22; returned to San Luis Potosí; went on to Saltillo about June 28 (*34a; 123a*).

San Maguel de Mezquitic, San Luis Potosí

1878. Same as Mezquitic, *q.v.*, or see San Luis Potosí (Estado).

San Miguel, Chihuahua 27°01′N., 107°38′W. N.G–13

1885. The Hacienda San Miguel, the residence of Alexander Shepherd, near Batopilas, where Palmer made his headquarters from August to October. See Batopilas, and Chihuahua (Estado).

San Miguel de Mesquite, San Luis Potosí

1878. Same as Mezquitic, *q.v.*, or see San Luis Potosí (Estado).

San Miguelito Mountains

1878. See Sierra San Miguelito.

San Nicolás de los Montes, San Luis Potosí 22°08′N., 99°26′W. N.F–14

1878. Visited December 28; see Ciudad del Maíz; called San Nicolas by Palmer (*114i*).

San Padro, Jalisco

1886. See San Pedro, Jalisco.

San Patricio County, Texas

1879. December; see St. Marys, and Sharpsburg.

San Pedro, California (Los Angeles County) GLO, 1928

1862. January. A few marine shells from here are cited by Philip P. Carpenter (*14*). Palmer came here from San Diego (*114b*).

1876. Probably arrived soon after June 15, by rail from San Bernardino, leaving at once by steamer for San Luis Obispo (*114i*).

San Pedro, Jalisco 20°38′N., 103°18′W.

1886. October. Southeast of Guadalajara and now essentially a suburb of that city. Now usually called "Tlaquepaque" (as on map sheet N.F–13), less often "San Pedro Tlaquepaque," and rarely "San Pedro." Palmer collected archaeological and ethnological material here, chiefly examples of the pottery for which this place has long been noted. See Jalisco (*45*, item 192).

San Pedro, "Mexico"

1886. Same as San Pedro, Jalisco, *q.v.* This locality is cited by E. Lewis Sturtevant as one from which he received, "in 1866," seventeen ears of corn collected by Palmer.[43]

[43] New York Agricultural Experiment Station *Annual Report No. 5* (Geneva, 1887), 64.

San Pedro de las Colonias, Coahuila 25°45′N., 102°59′W. N.G–13

1880. Known to Palmer as San Pedro. Visited May 20–21 (or more probably May 18–28); Palmer then went to Acatita, "26 leagues north," May 31, returning to Saltillo via San Pedro, Álamo de Parras (June 5), and Parras (June 8) (*34a; 34b; 34d; 40; 112 123a*).

1896. November 18, enroute from the city of Durango to Eagle Pass; Palmer planned to spend one or two days here (*114i; 123a*).

San Pedro Martin (Island), Baja California

1887, 1890. Names used in citing collections from Isla San Pedro Mártir, *q.v.*

San Pedro Martir, Baja California

1887, 1890. See Isla San Pedro Mártir, Baja California.

San Pedro Spring, Chihuahua

1908. May 28; see Madera.

San Quentin (or San Quentin Bay), Baja California

1889. See San Quintín.

San Quintín, Baja California 30°27′N., 115°56′W. N.H–11

1889. Arrived about January 22, from San Diego. Collected until about mid-February, and returned to San Diego. A note by Palmer reads: "I collected every day; I did not go very far from the harbor, as it was very hard to walk in the loose sand. . . . I crossed the harbor . . . climbing two of the volcanic peaks. . . . I soon exhausted the field . . . and had no means of reaching the interior." He collected Nos. 600–741 (numbers under 700 were collected in January, 700–40 in February, according to Vasey and Rose). Some gaps in the series may be explained by the loss of Palmer's original catalogue; this never reached Washington with the plants, and he made up a second one from memory. Nos. 601, 603, 609, 629, 636, 641, 651, 653, 656, 672, 679, 694, 702, 706, and 710 are not accounted for by Vasey and Rose (*132*) or by A. S. Hitchcock (*37*); Nos. 607, 657, and 695 are duplicated, and a supplementary No. 669a is included. The printed labels distributed with this collection bore the legend "San Quentin Bay"; the locality was called "San Quentin" by Palmer and by Vasey and Rose (*114i; 123a; 123d*).

San Rafael, San Luis Potosí

1878. Not located. Palmer collected here and in the "surrounding mountains"; his own pencilled notes imply that sixty-five collections were made in the mountains. See San Luis Potosí (Estado) (*114i*).

San Ramón, Durango

1906. Visited April 21–May 18, from Tepehuanes. Nos. 51–210, 531, 534, and 535 were collected. On May 26 Palmer wrote from Tepehuanes: "I returned two days ago from Paradise (San Ramone Mine) . . . the only way to get to that place is on horse back four long days ride each way." The field notes state that San Ramón lies "80 miles west of Durango"; actually it is probably almost due west of Tepehuanes, near the corner where Durango, Sinaloa, and Chihuahua adjoin; see Quebrada Honda, and Tepehuanes (*114i; 123c*).

Sansalito, California

1892. Same as Sausalito, *q.v.*

San Salvador, Paraguay (Concepción) 22°49′S., 57°51′W. S.F–21

1853. East of the Río Paraguay. Specimens were collected here November 16; a second visit was made December 14, on the return trip of the *Water Witch* from Corumbá. See Río Paraná (*52; 123a; 125c*).

San Simeon Bay, California (northwestern San Luis Obispo County) GLO, 1907

1876. About 20 collections made here, July 22 (and perhaps 23); see San Luis Obispo (*34a; 123a*).

Santa Águeda, Baja California 27°15′N., 112°23′W. N. G–12

1890. Visited March 3–6, on a horseback trip inland from Santa Rosalía, *q.v.* Nos. 211–64 were collected; the dates of collection are given as March 4 and 5 (*123a; 135*).

Santa Ana Pacneco, Guanajuato

1878. Not located, but mentioned in a manuscript itinerary in the National Herbarium. See Guanajuato (Estado).

Santa Anita, D.F. 19°24′N., 99°07′W.

1878. May 19; see México, D.F. Most of the vegetables for Mexico

City formerly came by canal from Xochimilco to Santa Anita. The latter place is now in the southeastern section of the city, by which it has been absorbed.

Santa Catalina Island, California (Los Angeles County) GLO, 1928

1888. Palmer's field notes show that Nos. 1–12 (or 248–59 of his series of this year) were collected August 16 on the "southeast side" of the island. Called "Catalina Island" by Palmer. In a letter to Watson dated August 26, Palmer indicates that he has returned from the island the previous day. See Islas Coronados, and San Diego (*34a; 114i*).

Santa Catarina, Nuevo León 25°41′N., 100°28′W. N.G–14

1880. Palmer made at least one visit here, in February, from Fabrica de la Fama. See Monterrey (*45*, item 193).

Santa Clara River, Utah (Washington County) GLO, 1937

1875. A visit to an archaeological site "on the east side of the Santa Clara River, about three miles from St. George," is reported. See St. George (*1*).

Santa Cruz, California (Santa Cruz County) GLO, 1928

1876. According to the manuscript itinerary in the Gray Herbarium collection, Palmer visited here July 24; Gray lists a single collection (No. 212). It seems unlikely that this date is correct if the dates of his visits to Paso Robles, Jolon, and the Santa Lucia Mountains are also correctly given. See San Luis Obispo (*34a*).

Santa Eulalia, Chihuahua 28°35′N., 105°53′W. N.H–13

1908. After looking for a good collecting ground about the city of Chihuahua, Palmer made a short visit here by rail, April 4. On a second trip from Chihuahua he arrived April 28, collected Nos. 126–39 (April 28–29), and returned to Chihuahua April 30. This place is now officially known as Aquiles Serdán (*123a; 123c*).

Santa Fé, New Mexico (Santa Fe County) GLO, 1936

1869. Arrived late on "Saturday" [i.e. Monday], April 12, by coach; see Sheridan, Kansas. Left by coach for Albuquerque, April 13; see Fort Wingate (*114g*).

Santa Lucia (Range or Mountains), California
(Monterey County) GLO, 1928

1876. August 2. It was probably in this range, somewhere north of Jolon, that Palmer made his collections in the "Redwoods." Gray lists a single collection from "St. Lucia Mts." and 15 from "Redwoods." See San Luis Obispo (*34a; 123a*).

Santa María, San Luis Potosí

1878. Probably Santa María del Río; mentioned in a typewritten itinerary in the National Herbarium.

Santa María del Río, San Luis Potosí 21°48′N., 100°43′W.
N.F–14

1904. Nos. 154½–162 were collected here, June 21–23, on a trip from San Luis Potosí. On August 2 Palmer wrote from the capital: "Hired a conveyance to go 15 leagues to Santa Maria Del Rio (there being no other way of reaching that place except horse back which was not to be thought of." Spelled "Santa Marie del Rio" on the printed labels distributed with this collection (*34a; 123a*).

Santa Rosa Hill, Chihuahua

1908. Palmer's variant of Cerro de Santa Rosa, *q.v.*

Santa Rosa Mountains, Guanajuato

1878. Mentioned in a manuscript itinerary in the National Herbarium. Presumably this refers to the mountains near the famous old mines of Santa Rosa, a few kilometers northeast of the city of Guanajuato (21°04′N., 101°12′W.).

Santa Rosalía, Baja California 27°19′N., 112°17′W. N.G–12

1890. Arrived February 23, by steamer from Guaymas; left on horseback for Santa Águeda on March 6; left for Guaymas by the steamer *Korragan,* March 16. Collected Nos. 177–210 (February 23–March 3), and 265–73 (March 15). The dates of collection of Nos. 177–210 are erroneously given by Vasey and Rose (*135*, p. 80) as February 20–March 3; the printed labels distributed with the collection bear the dates February 24–March 3, and the year 1889; the field notes are dated February 24 to March 3 (*114i; 123a; 135*).

According to Palmer's field notes, Nos. 197–210, inclusive, were collected in a range of mountains ("contiguous to Santa Rosalia") made up entirely of pure gypsum.

Santa Rosalía, Chihuahua 27°42′N., 105°10′W. N.G–13

1908. Visited from Chihuahua, June 13–15. Palmer was in search of certain cacti; collected Nos. 382–88; returned to Chihuahua, probably June 17 (or 16). Santa Rosalía is now usually called "Camargo" (*114b; 123a; 123c*).

Santiago de Cuba, Cuba (Oriente) 20°01′N., 75°49′W. N.F–18

1902. February; see Cuba.

Santiago Papasquiaro, Durango 25°03′N., 105°26′W. N.G–13

1896. On April 6, Palmer wrote that he had been invited to visit a mine owner, presumably the owner of Mina Tres Reyes, in the "pine mountains," and that he planned to make a collection of the spring flora that follows the melting snows. He left Durango about April 9, and spent April 11–15 at Santiago Papasquiaro, collecting Nos. 31–53. He spent April 16–19 at Mina Tres Reyes, said to be 13 miles west of Santiago Papasquiaro, at an elevation of 8,200 feet; here he collected Nos. 54–89. He made a second trip from Durango to Santiago Papasquiaro later in the season, and collected Nos. 392–472 and 967–73 (August 1–11) (*114i; 123c*).

Santo Domingo, San Luis Potosí 22°52′N., 100°17′W. N.F–14

1878. November 26, four days out of San Luis Potosí, enroute to Tula. Said by Palmer to be 50 leagues from San Luis and 26 from Tula. The driver of a mule train with whom he had traveled this far refused to take him farther, and he was forced to hire a mule and a jack for himself and his servant to ride; he left on November 27 for Tula. See San Luis Potosí (Estado) (*114i*).

San Varain River, Colorado

1861–62. Same as St. Vrain, *q.v.*

San Xavier, Arizona (Pima County) GLO, 1933

1869. Palmer is said to have visited the mission of San Xavier del Bac in October, on a trip out from Tucson (*123a*).

Sarassa (P.O.), Arkansas (Lincoln County) GLO, 1886

1883. On the south side of the Arkansas River, in R 6 W, T 7 S, a few miles up river from Heckatoo, *q.v.*

Saucito, San Luis Potosí 22°12′N., 101°01′W. Atlas, 42

1902. August 16. Palmer notes that he saw burro-loads of tunas (fruits of *Opuntia*) taken from here into the city of San Luis Potosí, a few kilometers to the southeast (*123a*).

Saus, Tamaulipas

1880. See El Sauz.

Sausalito, California (Marin County) GLO, 1928

1892. No. 2,392 was collected here, June 20. The printed label distributed with this collection bears the name "Sansalito." See California (*123a; 123c*).

Savanito

1878. A variant spelling of Sabinito, *q.v.*

Savannah, Tennessee (Hardin County)

1882. Early May; see Tennessee.

Savannah Farm, Tennessee (Polk County)

1882. ?April. According to Thomas (*118*), Palmer explored mounds, a cemetery and a village site here, on the north bank of the Hiawassee River about 5 miles above Conasauga Creek. The locality is said to be that mentioned by Thomas in an earlier paper.[44] Palmer's notes state merely that it is 15 miles east of Charleston. See Tennessee.

Savimto, "Veracruz"

1878. Palmer supposedly collected 109 archaeological specimens here; the name is a misspelling of Savinito. See Sabinito (*34d*).

Savinito or Savineto, San Luis Potosí

1878. Same as Sabinito, *q.v.*

Selsertown Mounds, Mississippi (Adams County)

1883. See Washington, Mississippi. This group of mounds (called "Saltzertown" by Palmer) was described at length by Thomas (*119*, pp. 263–67, Plate XIV). According to Thomas they are "about a mile northwest of the site of the old village of Selsertown, 7 miles a little west of north from Washington, and 2 miles northwest of the railroad

[44] *Magazine of American History*, Vol. XI (1884), 404.

station (Stanton)." Palmer's ideas about this group of mounds are discussed by Thomas.

1884. Early July. Palmer apparently planned to come here from Little Rock, *q.v.* The visit is mentioned by Thomas (*119*).

Seminole Agency, [Oklahoma] (Seminole County)
GLO, 1876

1868. The territory occupied by the Seminole Indians in nearly the same area as that of the present Seminole County, Oklahoma, between the main Canadian River and the north fork of that river. The road between Fort Gibson and Cherokee Town passed through the Seminole Nation. Palmer passed along this road in February, on his way to Fort Cobb, *q.v.*, and again on his return from the Indian Territory, *q.v.*, late in September. He also seems to have made a trip from Cherokee Town, *q.v.*, into this area, about July 18–20. His field notes mention collections made along the Little River (i.e. probably southwest of present Wewoka, Seminole County), and also in the hills "west" of the Canadian River, presumably along the road between Pauls Valley (or Cherokee Town) and the Seminole Agency (*45*, item 297; *120*).

Sequachee Valley, Tennessee

1882. April. Near Pikeville, Bledsoe County; see Tennessee.

Sevierville, Tennessee (Sevier County)

1881. August ?15–31. Palmer explored mounds opposite here, on the west bank of the Little Pigeon River, according to Thomas (*118*). See Tennessee.

Sharpsburg, Texas (San Patricio County)

1879. December; see Texas, and Corpus Christi.

Sheridan, Kansas (northern Sheridan County) GLO, 1884

1869. Palmer went by coach from here to Santa Fé, New Mexico, via Fort Wallace, Kansas, crossing the Smoky River and the Arkansas River, then via Iron Springs, Colorado, Red River Station, Colorado, and reaching Santa Fé April 12. Sheridan does not appear on modern maps; it lay in T 6 S, R 28 W. As of January 1, 1869, it was the western terminus of the Eastern Division of the Union Pacific Railway[45] (*114g*).

[45] Henry V. Poor, *Manual of the Railroads of the United States for 1869–70* (New York, 1869).

Shirley's New Store, [Oklahoma] (Grady County)

1868. February 20, according to Safford, who states that this was the trading post of Dr. John Shirley[46] on the Washita River (*123b*). According to Palmer it was 10 miles west of Line Creek, on the road to Fort Cobb, *q.v.* (i.e. near present Verden). In one place spelled "Sherby's" by Palmer (*123a*).

Shoals, Indiana (Martin County) GLO, 1886

1882. August; see Indiana.

Shoshone, Idaho (Lincoln County) GLO, 1939

1893. Arrived May 31, by train from Pocatello; hired a team to go to Blue Lakes, leaving June 1 and returning June 6; left for Pocatello June 14. Collected at Shoshone June 7–13, Nos. 122–59, 562, 572, 587. On a second visit from Pocatello, Palmer reached Shoshone (August 18) visited Blue Lakes (August 22–24) and collected along the Little Wood River. Nos. 506–18 and 532 were collected during this visit to Shoshone (August 19–20). He returned to Pocatello August 27 (*114i; 123a*).

Shoshone Falls, Idaho (Jerome County) GLO, 1939

1893. Arrived June 3, by team from Blue Lakes; collected Nos. 88–121, 565, and 568 (June 4–5). Left for Shoshone June 6. See Blue Lakes, and Shoshone.

Sienga, Durango

1896. Not located, but presumably Palmer's phonetic rendering of *ciénaga* (swamp); probably near the city of Durango. Reported as the locality of Palmer's No. 948,[47] but not mentioned in the field notes.

[46] Dr. John Shirley (?–1875) and his brother William Shirley were located at the Wichita Agency in the capacity of contractors or traders before the Civil War, and remained there after the Agency was taken over by the Confederate forces. John Shirley is known as the founder of Cherokee Town, where he had a store and other business interests from about 1869 until his death. William Shirley appears on the payrolls of the Wichita Agency for many years as interpreter and contractor for supplies, principally prairie hay. In 1874 his store—"Shirley's Store"—was north of the Washita near the Wichita Agency. Palmer may have met both brothers, and there may be some confusion in the several references to Shirley among his notes. Miss Muriel H. Wright, who supplied the above data on the Shirleys, informs me that apparently no formal biographical account of either of the brothers has ever been compiled.

[47] *Contributions from the United States National Herbarium,* Vol. XVII (1913), 291.

Sierra de Álamos, Sonora 27°N., 109°05'W. N.G-12

1890. Called Alamos Sierra by Palmer; see Álamos.

Sierra Madre south of Saltillo, Coahuila

1880. March 22-30, and July 25-August 1. This locality was so cited by Watson (*142*), who also referred to it as the "Sierra Madre 40 miles south of Saltillo." This distance from Saltillo is evidently Watson's equivalent of the distance given in Palmer's reference to the locality as "Canon and elevated portion of Sierra Madre, 12-14 leagues south of Saltillo." The metric equivalent of Watson's distance of 40 miles (64 km.) is occasionally seen in the literature.[48] About 150 numbers were collected by Palmer in this area.

I. M. Johnston, in a series of papers on the flora of Coahuila and adjoining areas, definitely cites these Palmer collections as from the vicinity of Carneros Pass, but this appears to be questionable.[49] As far as I can learn, neither Palmer nor Watson ever used the name "Carneros," and I take it that Johnston based his inference chiefly upon the distance and direction from Saltillo, as given by Palmer. Actually, however, Carneros Pass is no more than about 24 miles (38 km.) south of Saltillo. At 4,190 m. to the league, this is about 9 leagues instead of the 12 to 14 specified by Palmer. Furthermore, although Palmer was often inaccurate in citing distances and directions, he was keenly aware of the physiographic and vegetational features of the areas in which he had worked, and I do not think it likely that he would have referred to the country around Carneros as an "elevated portion of the Sierra Madre." Upon his arrival in Saltillo on March 20, 1880, he wrote to George Engelmann that he had already arranged to leave at once to spend eight days in "a mountain section containing pine and oak." It is scarcely credible that his informants in Saltillo should have arranged for him to visit "a mountain section" where pine and oak were presumed to be abundant—a section which he later thought of as a part of the great eastern mountain chain of Mexico—and then have sent him south across the desert

[48] *North American Flora,* Vol. XXV (1924), 344.

[49] "Plants of Coahuila, Eastern Chihuahua, and Adjoining Zacatecas and Durango," Part I, *Journal of the Arnold Arboretum,* Vol. XXIV (1943), 306-39; Part II, *Journal of the Arnold Arboretum,* Vol. XXIV (1943), 375-421; Part III, *Journal of the Arnold Arboretum,* Vol. XXV (1944), 43-83; Part IV, *Journal of the Arnold Arboretum,* Vol. XXV (1944), 431-53; Part V, *Journal of the Arnold Arboretum,* Vol. XXV (1944), 133-82.

to Agua Nueva (at the foot of the pass) where pines and oaks are few and hard to find, and where elevations are generally low.

The vegetation in the region of Carneros Pass is xerophytic. Near the pass the most conspicuous plant is the celebrated *Yucca carnerosana,* which occurs in relatively dense stands. Woodland plants are completely absent. High on the surrounding hills are thickets, apparently of oaks and perhaps of other low shrubs, but at the present time (1951) there is no evidence of coniferous forest anywhere in sight. Pringle visited the pass in 1889, and described his climb "through stubborn chaparral of dwarf oaks, *Ceanothus greggii,* etc.," to the summit of the mountains more than 4 miles west of the pass.[50] Here he found *Pseudotsuga* and *Cupressus,* along with several species of *Pinus* and *Juniperus,* but his description indicates the presence of many xerophytic species then as now, and suggests that the areas where conifers and associated species grew were few and far between, as well as difficult to reach.

Palmer, even as early as 1880, when he was only about fifty years old, was neither willing nor able to combine a day's collecting with a strenuous 10 or 20 mile hike in the mountains, as was Pringle's custom. It seems more likely that Palmer's collections of *Cupressus, Abies* (not otherwise known from Carneros Pass), *Pseudotsuga,* and *Pachystima* (not otherwise known from Mexico), came, as he wrote "from an elevated portion of the Sierra Madre," that is, from one of the principal ranges southeast (not south) of Saltillo, in areas where most of the above genera are still found in abundance, and where Palmer could have collected them easily. A particularly pertinent example is the *Pachystima,* which would be quite out of place, ecologically speaking, in even the most mesophytic oak-thickets near Carneros Pass, but which is abundant in the mountain forests east of Lirios.

I suggest, therefore, that Palmer's locality was "12 to 14 leagues" (about 60 km.) southeast, rather than south, of Saltillo, perhaps in the vicinity of San Antonio de Alanzanes. This area had been accessible to Josiah Gregg for a botanical excursion in 1848, and it was doubtless equally available to Palmer in 1880.

Sierra de la Miguelito, "Mexico"

A locality cited by Scudder (*112,* p. 96). Probably the same as Sierra San Miguelito, *q.v.*

[50] Davis, *Life and Work of Cyrus Guernsey Pringle,* 67.

Sierra Naola, Tamaulipas 23°05'N., 100°W. Atlas, 42

1878. A small range west and northwest of Tula, its western hills extending into San Luis Potosí. Palmer left Tula December 3 in an attempt to get information about the Indians of the Sierra Naola (always spelled "Nola" by him). He stopped at the settlement called Naola ("Nola"), then went on to the mountains, where "in the ravines found many plants in bloom." He visited El Boludo (San Luis Potosí) and Buey, whence "after collecting a few plants retraced my steps to Nola." He may have reached Naola this time on December 4, for he notes that he "spent one day in the mountains & along the road botanizing & collecting insects—At night arrived at Nola." On December 6 he returned to Tula. Collections from this trip to "Sierra Nola" have been cited by various workers, including Watson (*141*, p. 250) and Scudder (*113*) (*34b; 114i*).

Sierra (de) San Miguelito, San Luis Potosí 22°N., 101°07'W. N.F-14

1878. A small range about 15 km. south and a little west of the city of San Luis Potosí. Probably visited early in October, perhaps during the course of a trip to Bledos, *q.v.;* see also Pila. This is a relatively dry mountain range, and is now accessible by mule trail only. It is possible that at the time of Palmer's visit some protected areas supported an interesting vegetation, since the topography is steep and the highest points reach more than 2,500 m. in elevation. Palmer's own pencilled notes imply that he collected 198 plant specimens here. Insects from this locality are in the Museum of Comparative Zoology (*34b; 114i*).

Sierra de Santa María, San Luis Potosí

1878. October. Not located, but mentioned in a manuscript itinerary in the National Herbarium. Quite probably these may be mountains near Santa María del Río.

Silao, Guanajuato 20°56'N., 101°26'W. N.F-14

1898. August; see Guanajuato (Estado).

Silver City [?New Mexico]

A locality cited by Hemsley (*36*, Vol. 3, p. 378); no date is given, and probably some error is involved, as Palmer is not known to have visited this area.

Silver Reef, Utah (Washington County) GLO, 1893

1870. June. An incidental mention among Palmer's notes. This is the site of an old mine and mining camp near Leeds, and a little west of Toquerville; see St. George (*45*, item 282).

Sinaloa N.G–12, N.G–13, N.F–13

1891. Collected Nos. 1,413–1,809. See Culiacán, Imala, and Lodiego (*114; 123a; 123c*).

1897. See Topolobampo.

Sisson, California (Siskiyou County) GLO, 1907

1892. Palmer came here from San Francisco, via the San Francisco and Portland Railroad. Collected Nos. 2,433–2,573 (2,570 is duplicated), and 2,607–67 (this second series grasses), July 13–27. About 30 numbers were collected on a trip from Sisson to the timberline on Mt. Shasta, the remainder chiefly in the bottomlands near the Sacramento River about Sisson. The printed labels distributed with this collection bore the legend "Mount Shasta and vicinity." From Sisson Palmer went to Edgewood, *q.v.* The settlement of Sisson is now known as Mt. Shasta (*114i; 123a; 123c*).

Skull Valley, Arizona (Yavapai County) GLO, 1921

1865. Near Fort Whipple, *q.v.* Collections were made here in May and June by "Coues and Palmer"; since Palmer did not reach Fort Whipple until July 26, Coues, is doubtless responsible for the collections (*48*, Vols. 8, 19).

1869. See Fort Whipple.

Smith Mound, Arkansas

1883. Near Heckatoo, *q.v.*

Smith('s) Pauls, [Oklahoma]

1868. Palmer's name for the place now called Pauls Valley, Garvin County. See Fort Cobb.

Smoky River, Kansas

1869. See Sheridan, Kansas. Probably Smoky Hill River, perhaps crossed in the modern Logan County or Wallace County.

Smuggs Mound, Arkansas

1882–83. Same as Snuggs Mound, *q.v.*

Snake Plains, Idaho

1893. The printed labels distributed with Palmer's collections of this year bore the legend "Plants of the Snake Plains of Idaho." See Idaho.

Snuggs Mound, Arkansas (Jefferson County)

1882–83. Mentioned by Palmer as Smuggs Mound; said by Thomas (*119*, p. 242), to be 1 mile south of Garretson's Landing, *q.v.* (88).

Soledad, California (San Diego County) GLO, 1879

1875. On the coast about 15 miles north of San Diego, *q.v.* About 4 collections were made here, June 23 (*34a; 123a*).

Soledad, Coahuila 26°48′N., 101°40′W. N.G–14

1880. About 80 numbers were collected here, September 9–19. Said by Palmer to be "a section of low mountains with few oaks, 25 miles southwest from Monclova." See Monclova (*2; 142*).

Sonoma, California (Sonoma County) GLO, 1928

1867. Palmer came here from San Francisco in October to take the "grape cure," then thought efficacious in the treatment of malaria (*45*, item 62; *123a*).

Sonora N.H–11, N.H–12, N.G–12

1869. Palmer made two trips down the Colorado River to Puerta Isabel, *q.v.*, the first in August. For notes on the earlier visit see Fort Whipple. Palmer was at Puerta Isabel at least from October 6 to October 19, when he left for Yuma and Tucson. He left Tucson November 1 for Altar, Hermosillo, and Guaymas, reaching Guaymas early in November. He left for the Yaqui River, November 21, returning December 16, and leaving Guaymas for San Francisco, California, about the end of December. Collections of plants from "Sonora" are numbered at least to 29, which has been identified as *Karwinskia Humboldtiana* (*114b; 114i; 123a*).

1870. See Puerta Isabel.

1884–85. See Colonia Lerdo.

1887. Reached Guaymas May 31, from Washington, D. C., after a detour to San Bernardino, California. From Guaymas made three visits to Baja California (June 3–10, October 24–November 5, November 22–December ?25). Left for Washington January 12, 1888 (*34a; 114i; 123a; 145*).

1890–91. See Guaymas.

1897. See Guaymas.

South Carolina

1884. Probably May; Palmer collected ethnological specimens from mounds 17 miles west of Chester, Chester County, "near where Turkey Creek empties into Broad River," and also from an area 9 miles east of Rock Hill, York County (U.S. National Museum, Division of Ethnology, Catalogue Nos. 91,826–96). After this the collector returned to Washington, D. C. (*114c; 114f*).

Southerland Springs, Texas

1879. Same as Sutherland Springs, *q.v.*

Spencer, Tennessee (Van Buren County)

1882. April; see Tennessee.

Spring Brook, [Oklahoma] (Garvin or Pontotoc County)

1868. See Indian Territory. According to Palmer this was 12 miles from Cherokee Town, on the road to the Seminole Agency and Fort Gibson. This is presumably Spring Creek of USGS, Stonewall Quadrangle (*45*, item 297).

Spring Lake Villa (or Ville), Utah (Utah County)

1877. Not located on a map, but the same as Spring Lake of the GLO map of 1876, and of modern maps. Named by Eliza Johnson when her husband established a home there in 1861 (see footnote 18, p. 64). Palmer stated that the terminus of the U[tah] S[outhern] R.R. was 7 miles from Spring Lake Villa at the time of his visit, and the GLO map of 1876 indicates that the railroad ends about the same distance from Spring Lake. Palmer arrived July 24, after a four-day wagon trip from Beaver. He collected archaeological material and insects, and left for Salt Lake City about August 11. See Paragonah (*24; 34d; 45*, item 282; *113*).

Squaw Peak, Arizona (eastern Yavapai County) GLO, 1933

1865. Palmer collected here December 6, on "the most prominent feature in the low ranges of mountains which hem in the valley of the Rio Verde" (quoted from a letter to Engelmann, January 30, 1873). See Camp Lincoln (*24*).

Stephens Mounds, Arkansas

1883. Said by Palmer to be near Newport; apparently these are the Stevens Mounds referred to by Thomas (*119*, p. 225); see Independence County (*88; 119*).

Stock Island, Florida (Monroe County) CGS, 1251

1884. Rathbun (*94*) cites collections made between Salt Pond Key and Stock Island. The latter is the first key to the east, about a mile from Key West.

Stoddards, California (San Bernardino County)

1876. May 19–23; see San Bernardino (*45*, items 24, 62; *123a*). A stop on the stage route from Hardyville, also called "Stoddards Station."

Stoddards' Ranch, California (San Bernardino County)

1876. June 10, on a trip from Crafton to the Mojave Desert. Probably the same as Stoddards. See San Bernardino (*123b*).

Stone Mound, Arkansas

?1882. Near Harrisburgh, *q.v.*

Stoneville, Mississippi (Washington County) GLO, 1915

1883. March; see Vicksburg.

Stonewall Mine, California

1875. Same as Oriflamme Mine, *q.v.*

Stranger River, Kansas (Leavenworth County)

1858–59. Appears currently (GLO, 1925) as Stranger Creek. Usually written "Strainger" by Palmer. See Leavenworth, Kansas.

Sulphur Spring, Florida

1874. Visited in April. See Florida. Not located, but possibly the present Green Cove Springs, Clay County, of which Hawks (*35*) wrote: "The celebrated sulphur spring has been visited by thousands." The GLO map of 1876 also shows a Sulphur Spring (evidently a spring, not a settlement) about 15 miles southwest of Enterprise, *q.v.*, in T 19 S, R 28(?)E (*114i*).

Sumter County, Alabama

?1884. Palmer visited (perhaps in January) the "Cedar Hammock Group" of mounds, and collected a few ethnological specimens.

See Alabama. His description, according to Thomas (*118*) was the one published in the "Report on the Mound Explorations" (Thomas, *119*). The location of this group of mounds is given as Sect. 5, T 17 N, R 1 E of Stevens Meridian (*114f*).

Superstition Mountains, Arizona (northern Pinal County)
GLO, 1933

1885. Visited February 3, on a trip from Mesa, *q.v.* (*123a*).

Sutherland Springs, Texas (Wilson County)

1879. At least 105 collections of plants were made here, August 22–30; a few others are cited simply as from Wilson County. See Texas (*2; 142*).

Tacoi, Florida

1874. Same as Tocoi, *q.v.*

Talladega County, Alabama

1883 or 1884. Palmer reported mounds and an Indian cemetery near Talladega, according to Thomas (*118*); see Alabama.

Talley's (Ranch), California (San Diego County)

1875. Palmer's manuscript itinerary of his trip of this year says: "July 7–17, 1875. Talley's Ranch Stockton valley amid the Cuyamaca mountains five miles from Julian." He made about 110 or more collections during this ten-day period, some doubtless at or near the ranch and some in the mountains a short distance away. Some of the numbers marked "Talley's" in the list made by Gray are marked "Cuyamaca" in Palmer's own list, and vice versa, so it is probably impossible to determine the exact source of any given number. See Julian (*34a; 123a*). I am indebted to Mrs. Ethel B. Higgins and to Bertram B. Moore, both of San Diego, for the information that Talley's Ranch was in Section 21, T 13 S, R 4 E, and is shown on the Township plat as approved by the U.S. Surveyor General in 1876, and is also shown on the county map made by J. D. Schuyler in 1889.

Tamatán, Tamaulipas 23°43′N., 99°10′W. Atlas, 42

1907. About 2 km. southwest of Ciudad Victoria, *q.v.;* visited several times by mule car from the city (*123a*).

Tamaulipas N.G–14, N.F–14

1878–79. Palmer collected in the southwestern part of the state while enroute from San Luis Potosí, *q.v.*, to Tampico. He reached Tula December 1, 1878, having come on muleback from Santo Domingo; he made a trip to Sierra Naola (December 3-6), made some collections near Tula, then "left Tula Dec 9–for Salto 22 leagues distant–by mule pack train returning empty. . . . Started at noon & made 6 leagues." On December 10 the train made 10 leagues and "camped late by a fine stream of water [probably the Río Naranjo]. Could not put away my plants which were left till morning." On the eleventh the party reached El Salto, San Luis Potosí, about noon. Palmer then traveled in the state of San Luis Potosí until January 27, 1879, when he set out from Valle de Maíz, on horseback, with his servant. He seems to have crossed into Tamaulipas near Nuevo Morelos; he camped two nights in the mountains, reaching the Boca de la Abra the third day, December 29, and camping that night on the lowlands beyond. The following day he reached the steamboat landing, Tantoyuquita, at the head of navigation on the Río Tamesí, said to be 160 miles from Tampico. Here he found the boxes and bales he had previously sent from San Luis Potosí, and embarked with them on February 1, reaching Tampico at 3:00 P.M. on the third. He engaged passage to New York on the schooner *Comet*, and after a delay of two weeks she set sail on February 21 (*34a; 34d; 45*, item 263; *114i; 123a*).

1907. Reached Ciudad Victoria from Washington, D. C., about February 1; a copy of his diary, which begins February 4, is extant. Until April 11 he was at Ciudad Victoria, visiting Cañon Seco, Cañon del Novillo, Tamatán, and Paso de Progreso; left April 12 for Arguelles, Xicoténcatl, and Gomes Farías, returning by the same route April 23; stayed at Ciudad Victoria until June 18, revisiting Cañon Seco, Cañon del Novillo, Tamatán, and Paso de Progreso. Left for Washington, D. C., by rail, June 18 (*114i; 123a; 123c*).

1909–10. Reached Tampico from Washington, D. C., late in December, 1909; the city was his headquarters until mid-June, 1910. His movements are recorded in his field notes and in a copy of his diary. He visited the Río Tamesí January 3, 10, and 12; visited La Barra February 1–8; visited and collected at Pueblo Viejo February 10–25 (more or less regular trips from Tampico each day); visited Isla de Juana Ramírez March 8–9; probably visited Laguna de la Puerta March 23–24, La Barra April 2–3, and Arbol Grande April 17; left for Pánuco, Veracruz, April 20, returning April 25; visited Arbol Grande May 1, 13, 19, and 28, Pueblo Viejo on May 2–4, 16, 22, 23–31, and

June 1–2, La Puerta on May 7, Altamira on May 10, and La Barra on May 17, 18, and 20. Left Tampico for Washington, D. C. about June 15 (*114b; 123a; 123c*).

Tampa Bay, Florida (?Hillsborough County) GLO, 1926
1884. July 15; see Florida.

Tampico, Tamaulipas 22°13′N., 97°51′W. N.F–14

1879. Arrived February 3 from San Luis Potosí; for his route see San Luis Potosí and Tamaulipas. On this trip collected 130 numbers of plants, 137 archaeological specimens (28 from Tampico, 109 from "Savimto"), and some insects. Left Tampico for New York on the schooner *Comet*, February 21 (*34a; 34d; 45*, item 263; *125g*).

1909–10. Arrived probably late in December, 1909; the city was his headquarters until mid-June, 1910. He made many short trips out from Tampico (as far as 10 or 15 miles), as evidenced by a typed copy of his diary which is extant, but printed labels were not made for most of these localities, and the plants collected there were distributed as from Tampico. Dates of all collections made at Tampico and La Barra are uncertain except Nos. 1–181 and perhaps 251–304, because of Palmer's custom of entering collections from the same locality in the same field book, without accurate indication of date of collection. During the period May 1–22, when the field books show that Palmer collected Nos. 472–95 at Tampico, his diary shows that he visited Arbol Grande (May 1, 13, and 19), Pueblo Viejo (May 2–4, 16, and 22), La Puerta (May 7), Altamira (May 10), and La Barra (May 17, 18, and 20). At Tampico the following collections were made (dates as given in the field books): Nos. 1–181, 582–87 (January 1–31), 182–250 (March 10–April 19), 305–40, 575–80, 588, 589 (April 27–30), 472–95 (May 1–22), 496–510, 563–76 (June 3–6). Palmer left Tampico for New Orleans and Washington, about June 15 (*114b; 123a; 123c*).

Tantillas Mountains, Baja California

1875. Not located on any map, but the location fully discussed by Joseph Ewan (*25*). Palmer's own manuscript itinerary of his trip of this year says: "The canon [the "Big Canyon of the Tantillas Mountains"] is 5000 feet de[s]cent is 10 miles from Tresposes and nearly parallel with Larkens Station." Palmer also notes that "Tresposes" is 24 miles from "Lasjuantas," which in turn he says is 43 miles from Tecate Valley Station. If, as stated by Safford, Palmer traveled to the Tantillas Mountains by wagon from Campo, California, he probably left Campo on September 5 or 6; he was at "Lasjuantas" [i.e. probably Las Juntas, *q.v.*] on the seventh, at "Tresposes" [i.e. probably Tres Pozos, *q.v.*] on the eighth, and at the "Big Canyon" on the ninth and tenth. It seems, therefore, that Palmer's "Tres Pozos" is the place of that name which appears on some maps [e.g. on Sykes's map of the Colorado Delta Region[51]] at 32°22′ north latitude, 116°04′ west longitude, northwest of the highest parts of the Sierra de Juárez. The Tantillas (or Cantillas) Mountains are doubtless part of the Sierra de Juárez, as pointed out by Ewan. The "Big Canyon" is probably one of the gorges cut into the steep eastern slope, with the upper end of the gorge at about the 116th meridian and 32°15′ north latitude. While at the Tantillas Mountains Palmer made 60 to 75 collections, returning by an unknown route to San Diego, which he reached September 16 or 18. On his trip to the Tantillas Mountains he was accompanied by George W. Dunn of San Diego, who seems not to have been with him on his first trip out from San Diego in August, and Palmer may have returned to San Diego from Mountain Spring about August 20 before starting out again for Baja California (*34a; 80; 123a*).

Tantoyuquita, Tamaulipas 22°33′N., 98°33′W. N.F–14

1879. Palmer arrived here January 30, the day after passing the Boca de la Abra. The place was said to be the head of navigation on the Río Tamesí, 160 miles from Tampico. Two lines of steamers ran to Tampico, but Palmer was delayed two days while awaiting the loading of freight; he left February 1. See San Luis Potosí (Estado), and Tamaulipas (*45*, item 263; *114i*).

Taqui River

1869. See Río Yaqui.

Taylor's Bend, Tennessee (Jefferson County)

1881. September. A bend in the French Broad River, 9 (or 7) miles east of Dandridge; the mounds here are mentioned by Thomas (*119*, page 357); see Tennessee.

Taylor Mounds, Arkansas

1882. See Hollywood.

[51] Godfrey Sykes, *The Colorado Delta,* American Geographical Society *Special Publication No.* 19 (1937), map.

Tecate (Valley Station), ?Baja California

1875. August 16; at least two collections were made here. Palmer's manuscript itinerary of this year locates this place "20 miles further East from wild cat Lower California." In Palmer's time the stage route from San Diego to Fort Yuma passed into Baja California near Tiajuana, then back into California near Tecate, San Diego County, in the southeast corner of T 18 S, R 3 E; presumably his locality was near this, or just over the border into Mexico. See Immigration Association's Map of California (about 1885); also USGS, Cuyamaca Quadrangle (edition of 1903). See also Fort Yuma (*123a*).

Tejamen, Durango 24°48′N., 105°07′W. N.G–13

1906. Palmer made a trip here, probably from the city of Durango, collecting Nos. 466–530, 536–45, 564–69 (August 21–27), and returning to Durango about August 28 or 29 (*114i; 123c*).

Temosachic, Chihuahua 28°57′N., 107°50′W. N.H–13

1908. June 2–3; see Madera.

Tempe, Arizona (Maricopa County) GLO, 1933

1885. Apparently visited here January 29, from Mesa, *q.v.*, which was 8 miles to the east. Palmer notes that he spent a day here, and Safford notes that he collected "ethnological material." Palmer says of Tempe: "In olden times this used to be called Hayden's Ferry and comprised Charles T. Hayden's Mills and large store" (*45*, item 24; *123b*).

Temple, Arizona

1885. Cited in the Safford manuscripts, apparently in error for Tempe.

Ten-mile Creek, Florida (?St. Lucie County)

1874. February. Said to be 10 miles west of St. Lucie; see Fort Bassinger (*10*).

Tennessee

1881. As an assistant in the Bureau of Ethnology, Palmer investigated aboriginal mounds at Newport (about July 15–25), and Greeneville (July 29–August 8), visited Bakersville, North Carolina (about August 10), worked at Sevierville, Tennessee (August ?15–31), visited Dandridge (September 2), Jacksboro, Paint Rock Ferry, Kingston (September 26), Niles Ferry and Taylor's Bend (all in September). He was at Loudon about September 30, and probably spent some time in September at the junction of Poplar Creek and the Tennessee River, near the mouth of the Clinch River. Most of October was spent near Kingston, Roane County; early in November Palmer moved his headquarters to Arkansas, *q.v.* (*20; 26; 34a; 34d; 38; 114a; 114b; 114c*).

1882. Continuing the work of 1881, Palmer visited Niles Ferry, Monroe County (April 5), Pikeville, Bledsoe County (April 11; referred to by Palmer as being in "the Sequachee Valley, Bloodsoe Co."), Dayton, Rhea County (April 15), Chattanooga (April 17–?20), Spencer, Van Buren County (April), Georgetown, Meigs County (?April), Charleston, Bradley County (?April), and Savannah Farm, "15 miles east of Charlestown" (?April). About May 1 he left for Paris, Henry County, thence visited Savannah, Hardin County, and Reelfoot Lake, Obion County (May ?15–June ?10), and spent a few days at Ripley, Lauderdale County (June ?15–26), leaving June 26 for Charleston, Missouri (see references for 1881).

1883. First visited in February and March; see Memphis. Later Palmer was in Chattanooga (June 10), Carthage (June 18), Nashville (early June), Charleston (?June), vicinity of Rockwood (?June), vicinity of Cleveland (?June), Rugby (?June) and Jolley's Island (?June) (*114b; 114c; 114i*).

Tensas River, Louisiana GLO, 1930

1883. Palmer's variant of Tensas was "Tensaw"; see Louisiana.

Teotihuacán, México 19°42′N., 98°52′W. N.E–14

1878. See México, D.F.

Tepehuanes, Durango 25°20′N., 105°43′W. N.G–13

1906. Arrived from the city of Durango, probably March 24 or 25; collected Nos. 9–47 (March 25–April 16); left for San Ramón mine about April 17, returning May 24; visited Tobar May 28–31; collected Nos. 258–331, 532, 561–63 at Tepehuanes (June 4–25); returned to Durango June 26 (*114i; 123c*).

Tepic, Nayarit 21°31′N., 104°53′W. N.F–13

1892. Palmer made his headquarters here from January 3 or 4 until April 28, but most or all of his collections were made in January and February. His plants are numbered 1,813–2,040 (–?2,067), and the field notes indicate that all were collected at Tepic before February

6. He is known to have visited and collected elsewhere in Nayarit, however, some of the trips having been made as late as mid-February; see Nayarit, and Jalisco (Nayarit) (*45*, item 189; *114i; 123a; 123c*).

Tequila, Jalisco 20°54′N., 103°48′W. N.F–13

1886. Collected Nos. 351–424, August 25–September 5. Field notes for Nos. 362, 366, 367, 372, 404, all dated August 29 or 30, are in the U. S. National Herbarium. The locality was said by Watson to be "twenty miles northwest of Guadalajara, in a deep volcanic depression surrounded by more or less barren mountains." Actually, at Tequila the Río Grande passes through a barranca which, although precipitous, is readily accessible from the town. The barranca of Tequila was later a favorite collecting ground for Cyrus Guernsey Pringle, and it may well be that Palmer also collected within it. See Jalisco (*123a; 144*).

Tetso River, Arizona

1867. Not located, but said to have been visited by Palmer on April 27 of this year, and so doubtless near Camp Grant, from which place Palmer wrote on April 20: "Tomorrow leave . . . after the Indians into a very rough and almost unknown country." See Camp Grant (*24; 48*, Vol. 24, p. 366).

Texas

1879–80. Reached San Antonio from Longview about July 27, 1879 and made the city his general headquarters until the following January. Visited Uvalde, and Sutherland Springs (both in August), Laredo (August or September), Comfort (September), and Guadalupe (probably in September), returning to San Antonio about September 19. He visited Rusk (October 2), New Braunfels, Austin (early October), Bluffton, Georgetown, Palestine, and Neches (all October), Marshall and Longview (both early November), and Houston (November 8). From Houston he visited Brazoria, Orange and Liberty counties (all November), going thence to Victoria (November 28), Harwood and Cuero (both November), Goliad, St. Marys, Sharpsburg, Corpus Christi, and Lamar (all December), and returning to San Antonio late in December. He left San Antonio for Monterrey, January 26, 1880. Returning from Mexico the following autumn, he passed through Texas, visiting Eagle Pass (September 26–October 2), Uvalde (October 5–10), San Antonio and Fredericksburg (both October), and Palestine (October 28) (*2; 34a; 34d; 45*, items 193, 269; *123a; 142*).

Texcoco, México   19°31′N., 98°52′W.   N.E–14

1878. See México, D. F. Also spelled "Tezcoco."

Thibault Mounds, Arkansas   (Pulaski County)

1882–83. See Jefferson County. A locality about 8 miles southeast of Little Rock, described by Thomas (*119*, p. 245).

Tiajuana Valley, California   (San Diego County)

1875. Visited by Palmer August 14, and said by him to be "15 miles south of San Diego." See Fort Yuma (*123a*).

Tiburon Island

See Isla Tiburón.

Tierra Caliente

1878–79. Palmer sent archaeological material so labeled, to the Peabody Museum. The records indicate that this is a locality in the state of Mexico, but it seems probable that the term may refer simply to the lowlands of Veracruz, through which Palmer passed on his way to Mexico City in December, 1877 or may refer to similar areas in Tamaulipas, between Ciudad del Maíz and Tampico, visited in January, 1879 (*34d*).

Tigh(e)'s (Ranch or Station), California   (San Diego County)

1875. Palmer's manuscript itinerary says: "Tighe's Ranch 45 miles north east from San Diego, July 1–6." The actual dates of his visit were probably July 5–6, for he wrote a letter to Eaton from San Diego on July 4, just before leaving on his trip to the northeast. About 25 numbers of plants were collected here. See California (*20; 34a; 123a*). Tighe's (not Tigh's) Ranch was in Section 16, T 13 S, R 2 E, on the old San Diego–Julian road, about 8 miles east of Ramona. It is shown on the township plat as approved by the U. S. Surveyor General, Sept. 21, 1875. For this latter information I am indebted to Mrs. Ethel B. Higgins and to Bertram B. Moore, both of San Diego.

Tiller Mound, Arkansas

1882. November 22. Near Winchester, Drew County; described by Thomas (*119*, p. 240). The name is written "Filler" in the published version of Palmer's Arkansas notes. See Jefferson County (*88*).

Titusville, Florida (Brevard County) GLO, 1926

1874. Arrived early in February; collected at this time and also April 7–9, on the return from Lake Okeechobee. Also called Sand Point. See Florida, and Indian River (*20; 123a*).

Tobar, Durango

1906. See Tovar.

Tocoi, Florida (western St. Johns County) GLO, 1911

1874. On the St. Johns River, nearly west of St. Augustine. Collections were made here, perhaps on the trip from Jacksonville to Titusville, in February, but probably chiefly on the return trip, in April (specimens of *Asclepias* in the Missouri Botanical Garden are labeled "Tacoi . . . April 16"); see Florida (*48*, Vol. 15, p. 57).

Toka, or Tokaville, Utah

1876. Same as Toquerville, *q.v.*

Tolanan, Jalisco

1886. Said to be 6 miles east of Guadalajara; evidently this is a corruption of Tonalá; see Jalisco (*45*, item 192).

Toluca, México 19°18′N., 99°40′W. N.E–14

1878. About June 15; see México, D.F.

Tombigbee River, Alabama GLO, 1915

1884. January and March; see Alabama.

Tombstone, Arizona (Cochise County) GLO, 1933

1890. Palmer made a trip here from Fort Huachuca about April 25 or 27, but apparently collected nothing because of drought (*123a*).

Tonalá, Jalisco 20°38′N., 103°14′W. N.F–13

1886. See Tolanan, San Pedro, and Jalisco.

Tooele, Utah (Tooele County) GLO, 1937

1877. On August 14 Palmer wrote from Salt Lake City: "I go in the morning to Touilla head of Salt Lake as mounds are there." He probably collected no plants on this trip (*34d*).

Topolobampo, Sinaloa 25°36′N., 109°03′W. N.G–12

1897. Visited by steamer from Guaymas, September 15–25. Nos.

156, June 8 hung up in house to July 19 before dry, suculent leaves, grows in bunches among rocks hill sides.

157 July 16, fine showey shrub dry slopes in Mts & dry sandy spots wood openings in valley for 20 miles, as soon as daylight come it closes up bloom light straw color stamens same anthers yellow 2 to 4 ft.

158) Bulbous plant, Mt slopes, July 14 greenish near the eye black spines yellow ends stamens white anthers deep straw, pistil tinged purple.

159) July 10 moist raveins Mts petals tipped greenish yellow purplish blue body, white eye and stamens, Anthers black, buds underneath white

160.) July 10 paraciticalplant, succulant plant, fine straw colored tendrills, white bloom yellow anthers Golden City edge of Mts 14 miles from Denver. only [illegible] seen

Courtesy Smithsonian Institution

Palmer's field notes, as written by himself, 1861.

Edward Palmer in the field, near Culiacán, Sinaloa, in 1891.
The trees are Ipomoeas, the "tree morning-glories,"
which form an important element of the deciduous forests
of the Pacific slopes of Mexico.

177–?254, 269–71, and 273–75 were collected. Field notes are available for Nos. 177–230, 232, 247, 269 (*123a; 123c*).

Toquerville, Utah (Washington County) GLO, 1937

1870. June. An incidental mention in Palmer's notes (as "Tokaville"); see St. George (*45*, item 282).

1876. Palmer stopped overnight here, the day unknown; the place is cited as "Toka" in his notes (*45*, item 282).

Torin, Sonora 27°35′N., 110°16′W. N.G–12

1890. April 10–11, enroute from Álamos, *q.v.* to Guaymas (*123a*).

Toros (Station), California (Riverside County)

1870. A stage station, shown (as "Los Toros") on Bergland's (*126*) map in latitude 33°35′N., longitude 116°12′W. (?)September; see Los Angeles.

Torreón, Coahuila 25°33′N., 103°27′W. N.G–13

1898. Nos. 455–516, and 786–88 were collected here, October 13–20. See Coahuila.

1904. Notes written by Palmer imply that he visited Torreón, from Saltillo, October 23–26 (*123a*).

Touilla, Utah

1877. Same as Tooele, *q.v.*

Tovar, Durango 25°15′N., 105°47′W. N.G–13

1906. Probably arrived May 27, from Tepehuanes; collected Nos. 48–50, 228–57, and 533 (May 28–31). Spelled "Tobar" by Palmer and on many maps (*114i; 123c*).

Tracy, California (San Joaquin County) GLO, 1928

1892. August 22–23, enroute from San Francisco to Tulare County; Nos. 2,683–92 were collected in the bottom of the San Joaquin River near Tracy. See California (*123a; 123c*).

Treadwell, Arizona

The type-locality of *Tetraneuris arizonica* Greene, based upon Palmer's No. 259 of the 1877 collection, was so given by Greene.[52] The plant in question was collected at Mount Trumbull. See St. George, Utah.

[52] *Pittonia*, Vol. III (1898), 266.

Tres Pozos, Baja California 32°22′N., 116°04′W.

1875. Visited September 8, enroute to the Tantillas Mountains, *q.v.* Called "Tresposes" by Palmer, and said by him to be 24 miles from "Lasjuantas" [i. e. probably Las Juntas]. Probably not the Tres Pozos which appears on some maps (including sheet N.H–11 of the American Geographic Society's map) at 32°29′N., 116°12′W. (*123a*).

Trinidad, Guanajuato 21°02′N., 101°34′W. N.F–14

1898. August; see Guanajuato (Estado). This place is on the railroad between León and Silao (*123a*).

Trinidad, "New Mexico" (Las Animas County, Colorado) GLO, 1934

1865. June, enroute to Fort Whipple, Arizona, *q.v.* This was a new settlement at this time; Trinidad is not shown on the surveyor general's map of 1865 (Map of Public Surveys in Colorado Territory to accompany report of the Surveyor General, 13 miles=1 inch, 1865), but does appear on maps as early as 1869 (e.g. Indian Territory, &c., 1/1,200,000, U. S. Army Engineers, prepared by order of Maj. Gen. J. M. Schofield, compiled in 1869. Also Thayer's Sectional Map of Colorado, 12 miles=1 inch, 1871) (*114g*).

Troyville, Louisiana (Catahoula Parish) GLO, 1887

1883. Now called Jonesville; see Louisiana.

Tucson, Arizona (Pima County) GLO, 1933

1867. Early August, enroute from Camp Grant to Yuma, *q.v.* No. 245, *Jatropha cardiophylla,* was collected here August 10. The printed label distributed with this collection can be found among the illustrations in this volume. (*123*).

1869. Arrived late in October from Yuma, *q.v.* While at Tucson visited the mission of San Xavier del Bac, and Camp Bowie. Left by coach for Guaymas, *q.v.*, November 1 (*114b; 121; 123a; 123b*).

Tula, Hidalgo 20°03′N., 99°21′W. N.F–14

1878. The Peabody Museum received from Palmer a considerable collection supposedly from this place, but he probably never stopped here for any extended period. He passed through, enroute from Mexico City to San Luis Potosí, by stage, on July 23 and perhaps earlier in the year, but the Tula from which the archaeological material came was almost certainly Tula, Tamaulipas, *q.v.* (*34d; 114i*).

Tula, Tamaulipas 23°N., 99°43′W. N.F–14

1878. Palmer left San Luis Potosí, with his servant, on November 23. Traveling by mule train they went via Hacienda Peotillo, Puerto San José, Rancho de Pozos, and the Ranchita de Santo Domingo, reached on November 26. From here he went on muleback, going by way of Presa de Guadalupe, and reaching Tula December 1. He left Tula for the Sierra Naola on December 3, returning December 6, and leaving again on December 9 for El Salto (December 11), Savinito (December ?12–22), and Valle de Maíz. Archaeological material from this trip was probably collected from the Indians of the Sierra Naola, from the vicinity of Tula, and about Savinito (*24; 34d; 90; 113; 114i; 141*).

Tulare, California (Tulare County) GLO, 1928

1892. Arrived about August 24; collected Nos. 2,693–2,732, chiefly in the direction of Tulare Lake, *q.v.*, which at that time had "receded 22 miles from its original water line," and near the "Bayou 5 miles South of Tulare city." The dates of the collection, according to the field notes, were August 25–30. Palmer went from Tulare to Visalia on September 2, returning about September 5; on September 6 he visited "what was once an Island in the Lake Tulare by Harrisons Route 22 miles West of South to Ryhans as the ancient Island is now known"; here he collected Nos. 2,749–69. He left Tulare for Palm Springs September 10. See California, and Tulare Lake (*114i; 123a; 123c*).

Tularc City, California

1892. Same as Tulare, *q.v.*

Tulare Lake, California (Kings County) GLO, 1907

1892. The printed labels distributed with Palmer's collections from Tulare and vicinity read: "Between Tulare and Tulare Lake." The earlier series (Nos. 2,693–2,732) was collected in August, chiefly within a radius of 3–5 miles from Tulare. The second series (Nos. 2,749–69) was collected between Tulare and Ryhans, the latter formerly an island in Tulare Lake but at the time of Palmer's visit (September 6, 1892) 1½ or 2 miles from the lake. See also Tulare (*123a; 123c*).

Tunal River, Durango

1896. See Río del Tunal.

Turkey Creek, Arizona (Yavapai County)

1869. July. Said to be 15 miles from Hell Canyon on the road to Bill Williams Mountain, *q.v.* (*114g*).

Tuscaloosa, Alabama (Tuscaloosa County) GLO, 1915

?1884. January 13; see Alabama.

Tyson('s) Well, Arizona (Yuma County) GLO, 1912

1869. August and September. A station on the stage road between Prescott and Ehrenberg, 21–25 miles east of Ehrenberg. See Fort Whipple (*7; 123a*).

Union Pass, Arizona (Mohave County) GLO, 1921

1876. May 6 or 7, enroute from Prescott to Hardyville. In the Black Mountains about 25 miles west of Kingman (*123a*).

Uriba, [Arizona]

1869. Same as Oraibi, *q.v.*

Uruguay

1853–55. See Montevideo, and Paraguay.

Utah GLO, 1876, 1893, 1902, 1908, 1937

1870. See Salt Lake City, St. George, and St. Thomas.
1875. See St. George.
1876. See St. George, and Wales.
1877. See St. George, and Paragonah.

Uvalde, Texas (Uvalde County)

1879, 1880. Arrived about August 3 or 4, 1879, from San Antonio, having left San Antonio August 1 or thereafter. The date of his visit to Uvalde, as given in the printed itinerary distributed with his plant-collections ("last week of July"), is evidently erroneous. He collected about 60 numbers of plants here, either in 1879 or during his second visit, October 5–10, 1880, while enroute from Eagle Pass to San Antonio (*2; 34d; 123a; 142*).

Vallecillo, Nuevo León 26°40′N., 99°58′W. N.G–14

1880. February, enroute to Monterrey, *q.v.* (*45*, item 193).

Vallecito, California (San Diego County)

1867. ?August. A station on the stage route from Yuma, said to be 117 miles on the way to Los Angeles, *q.v.* It appears on the Immigration Association map of California (*ca.* 1885), in R 6 E, T 14 S (*123a*).

Valle de Maíz, San Luis Potosí 22°24′N., 99°37′W.

1878–79. A name often used by Palmer in referring to the place now called Ciudad del Maíz, *q.v.* In Palmer's time most maps listed this town as "El Maíz."

Vallejo, California (Solano County) GLO, 1928

1892. Visited July 6, from San Francisco; Nos. 2,423–32 were collected. See California (*114i; 123a; 123c*).

Valley of Mexico

1878. At least a few plants collected there in this year; see México, D.F. (*31*).

Venis Mecas [Mexico]

?1879. Not located; stated by Scudder (*113*) to be in San Luis Potosí and to have been visited by Palmer on January 6 [year not stated]. The collections to which Scudder referred, now in the Museum of Comparative Zoology, are dated January 6, 1878. At this time Palmer and Parry were in Mexico, and Safford, quoting from Palmer's journal, says that on January 6 he visited "the market south of the palace" in the capital. If the date as given above be correct, Venis Mecas must lie in the vicinity of Mexico City. Among Palmer's notes at the Peabody Museum, however, is a reference to "Venis Meices," located "a few miles from Savinito." Apparently both "Venis Mecas" and "Venis Meices" are corruptions of Minas Viejas (San Luis Potosí), where Palmer worked from January 3 to January 13, 1879 (not 1878) (*34d; 114i*).

Veracruz (Ciudad) 19°12′N., 96°08′W. N.E–14

1877. Arrived December 21, on the steamer *City of New York*, having touched at Havana, Progreso, and Campeche; left December 22 by rail for Mexico City, planning to visit "an Indian settlement" on the way; had breakfast at Boca del Monte on December 23, and reached Mexico City at 7:30 in the evening. See San Luis Potosí (*34d; 114i*).

Parry left New Orleans December 22, 1877, reached Veracruz December 28, left for Mexico City January 2 or 3, 1878.

Veracruz (Estado) N.F–14, N.E–14

1877–79. See Savimto, Tampico, and Veracruz (Ciudad).

1910. See Isla de Juana Ramírez, Pánuco, Puebla Viejo; see also Tampico, and Tamaulipas.

Vermejo, Río (or River)

1854. See Río Bermejo.

Vicksburg, Mississippi (Warren County) GLO, 1915

1883. About March 15–19; from here Palmer visited Greenville, and from there visited the Rozell Mounds ("6 miles east of Friar's Point"), and other mounds 1½ miles east of Stoneville. Thomas (*119*, pp. 259–60) describes and figures these Stoneville mounds, locating them 9 miles from "Granville." From Vicksburg, Palmer returned to Memphis, *q.v.* (*114c*).

Victor, California (San Bernardino County) GLO, 1900

1888. Now Victorville (GLO, 1928). Palmer collected Nos. 223½–230 at "Victor," June 25–27. See San Bernardino (*133*).

Victoria, Ciudad, Tamaulipas 23°44′N., 99°08′W. N.F–14

1907. Arrived from Washington, D. C., about February 1; collected Nos. 1–267, 563–71, 575–79 (February 1–April 9, according to the field notes). Visited Cañon Seco (called also by Palmer "Canon de Salamanca"), February 13 and 23, March 21, and April 5; visited Cañon del Novillo February 16, March 22 and 23; visited Tamatán March 18 and 20 and April 4, and Paso de Progreso March 30 and April 6. Left Ciudad Victoria for Gomes Farías April 12, and returned April 23; collected Nos. 360–561, 572–74, 580, 581, 584 (May 1–June 13, according to the field notes); visited Paso de Progreso May 16 and 29, and June 6; visited Tamatán May 17 and 18, Cañon de Salamanca May 23, and Cañon del Novillo May 24; left by train for Washington, D. C., June 18 (*114i; 123a; 123c*).

Victoria, Texas (Victoria County)

1879. November 28–30; on the twenty-eighth Palmer wrote: "I go from hear in a day or two for Corpus Christi." On December 3 he was in Goliad, on December 5 at St. Marys, and December 11–20 at Corpus Christi and Lamar. His route in reaching Victoria is unknown; he visited Harwood and Cuero in November, however, and may have come this way from Houston, stopping to make archaeological collections in De Witt County (*2; 34b; 34d; 113; 123a*).

Victorville, California (San Bernardino County)
GLO, 1928
1888. Same as Victor, *q.v.*

Viesca, Coahuila 25°21′N., 102°48′W. N.G–13
1880. June 5, enroute from San Pedro to Parras. Known to Palmer as Almo de Parras; this is apparently his variant of Álamo de Parras, which appears on a map of northeastern Mexico prepared in 1846 by U. S. Army engineers[53] (*123a*).

Villa Concepción, Paraguay
1853. Same as Concepción, *q.v.*

Villa del Pilar, Paraguay 26°51′S., 58°18′W. S.G–21
1853, 1854. Same as Pilar, *q.v.*

Villaldama, Nuevo León 26°30′N., 100°26′W. N.G–14
1880. February, enroute to Monterrey, *q.v.* (45, item 193).

Villa Salvador, Paraguay
1853. Same as San Salvador, *q.v.*

Villa Santiago, Guanajuato
1898. August. Not located, but perhaps Palmer's variant of Valle de Santiago, which appears on sheet N.F–14 of the American Geographic Society's map. See Guanajuato (Estado) (*123a*).

Vincennes, Indiana (Knox County) GLO, 1886
1882. August–September. See Indiana.

Virgin City, Nicaragua
1867. See San Francisco, California. This is evidently Palmer's version of La Virgen, *q.v.*, a settlement on Lake Nicaragua where the transisthmian route crossed from San Juan del Sur. In E. G. Squier's *Nicaragua*, "Virgin Bay" is shown in the lake in this area.[54] Palmer apparently did not visit Nicaragua in 1862, although some of his notes mention such a visit.

[53] George W. Hughes, *Memoir Descriptive of the March of a Division of the United States Army under the Command of Brigadier General John E. Wool, from San Antonio de Bexar, in Texas, to Saltillo, in Mexico,* 31 Cong., 1 sess., *Sen. Doc.* 32 (Washington, 1850).

[54] I, map facing p. 2.

Virgin River, Arizona–Nevada GLO, Nevada, 1941; Arizona, 1933

1870. June; see St. Thomas, Nevada.
1877. April; see Beaver Dam.

Visalia, California (Tulare County) GLO, 1928

1892. Arrived from Tulare, *q.v.*, probably September 2; on September 4 visited the "hog wallows," said to be 21 miles to the northeast, and also collected Nos. 2,733–48 in a swampy bottom 10 miles east of Visalia. Returned to Tulare, probably September 5 (*114i; 123a; 123c*).

Wadsworth, Nevada (southeastern Washoe County) GLO, 1941

1876. Collected about 24 numbers here August 20, enroute from San Francisco to Camp Halleck and Davenport (*34a*).

Waldestein Mounds, Arkansas

1882–83. Near Linwood Station, *q.v.;* see also Long Lake.

Wales, Utah (Sanpete County) GLO, 1937

?1876. An incidental mention among Palmer's notes, as "New Wales," with citation of the year as 1876 and the note that this place was 12 miles south of Fountain Green, *q.v.* (*45*, item 282).

Wallace Wells, Arizona

1885. Not located, but said to have been visited March 8. See Phoenix (*123a*).

Wallen, Arizona (Pinal County)

1867. Camp, or Fort, Wallen, was 10–15 miles west of Tombstone, and may have been the locality at which Palmer collected his No. 205 on August 4, after leaving Camp Grant. This number is said to have come from "ravines in mountains on the Wallen road, near Davidson's Springs." See Yuma and Camp Wallen (*7; 24; 48*, Vol. 20, p. 780).

Walnut Creek, ?Nebraska (?Jefferson County) GLO, 1890

1862. Field notes of this year indicate that some specimens came from "Walnut Creek on the platt[e] road to Denver." This is presumably the Walnut Creek shown on Stansbury's map of his routes of 1849 and 1850;[55] the place was near the junction of Sandy Creek and Little Blue River (*114b*).

Walnut Grove, Arizona (Yavapai County) GLO, 1921

1876. April 24 or 28 (or both). On Hassayampa Creek about 20 miles south of Prescott, *q.v.* About 24 numbers were collected here (*34a; 45*, item 24).

Walnut Lake (Station), Arkansas (Desha County) GLO, 1886

?1882. In R 5 W, T 10 S. Palmer mentions digging, without success, in a mound on the bank of Walnut Lake, near the station on the Little Rock, Mississippi River and Texas R. R.; this may be the mound alluded to by Thomas (*119*, p. 237; see also *88*).

Warners Ranch, California (San Diego County)

1867. ?August. On the stage route between Vallecito and San Bernardino; see Agua Caliente valley, and Los Angeles. This locality appears on Johnson's 1861 map of "California . . . New Mexico and Utah" (1 inch equals about 48 miles). The same place appears as "Warners" on the Immigration Association's map of California (*ca.* 1885), in R 3 E, T 11 S, and in the same township, as "Warner" on the GLO map of 1907. Agua Caliente of earlier maps (in R 3 E, T 10 S) is Warner Springs of GLO, 1907.

Jonathan Trumbull (later Juan José) Warner (1807–95) emigrated to California in 1831. He moved to San Diego in 1843, became a Mexican citizen, and was granted 26,000 acres, the territory known as Agua Caliente or Warner's Ranch. One of the principal stage routes from Yuma to Los Angeles and on north to the gold fields was by way of Indian Wells, Vallecito, and Warner's Ranch.[56]

1875. At least one collection made here, July 24; said to be the site of hot springs; see Julian.

1889. May; see California.

Warner Springs, California

1875. See Julian, and Warners Ranch.

[55] Capt. Howard Stansbury, *Map of a reconnoissance* [*sic*] *between Fort Leavenworth on the Missouri River and the Great Salt Lake* (Corps of Topographical Engineers, scale, 1/1,000,000). Title varies, as in 32 Cong., Special sess., *Sen. Ex. Doc.* 3, II.

[56] H. D. Barrows, "Memorial Sketch of Col. J. J. Warner," *Annual Publications of the Historical Society of Southern California,* Vol. III (1895), 23–29.

Wasatch Mountains, Utah

1877. July; see Beaver.

Washington, D. C.

1852–53. Palmer arrived from Cleveland, probably early in December, 1852, enlisted in the United States Navy, left in January, 1853 as a member of the crew of the *Water Witch.* See Paraguay (*123a; 123b; 125c*).

1855. Was in Washington June 13, having just returned from Montevideo. Went within a few weeks to Cleveland, Ohio, returning in September; on September 19 was planning to leave for New York "next Monday morning" [i.e. the twenty-fourth], enroute to England. At this time he left at the Smithsonian Institution some grasshoppers collected at Cleveland (*114a*).

1862. March 7–14; see Fort Leavenworth (*123a*).

1864. April 20, on a quick trip from Kansas City in an attempt to make arrangements to join an expedition to Minnesota; probably left to return to Kansas City the following day (*114a; 125d*).

1867–68. From about November 1, 1867, to January 16, 1868; he came here from Camp Grant, via San Francisco, and left for Leavenworth, Kansas, and the Indian Territory (*24; 114b*).

1868–69. Arrived from Indian Territory, via Leavenworth, about November 1, 1868; left for New Mexico and Arizona March 14, 1869. The first part of his journey was by rail to Sheridan, Kansas (*114g; 123e*).

1870. Probably reached Washington in February, from San Francisco; left May 15, by train for Salt Lake City (*24; 123a*).

1870–71. Arrived November 10 or 11, 1870, from San Francisco; left for Woods Hole, Massachusetts, as assistant to Professor S. F. Baird of the Commission of Fish and Fisheries, mid-June, 1871 (*24; 34a; 90*).

1871–72. Probably returned from Woods Hole in October, 1871; left for Eastport, Maine, still as assistant to Professor Baird, June 1872 (*20; 24; 125b*).

1872–73. Palmer seems to have worked in Washington, probably for the Smithsonian Institution, from November, 1872, when he returned from Eastport, until he left for Portland, Maine, as assistant to Professor Baird, late in June, 1873 (*20; 24; 34b; 90; 125b*).

1881. Palmer was here for a few days, about June 20–30, enroute from Cambridge, Massachusetts, to North Carolina (*123a; 125b*).

1882. Arrived about February 10, from Arkansas; left to continue work with the Bureau of Ethnology, about April 1, going first to Tennessee, *q.v.*, and returning to Washington early in July, probably from Charleston, Missouri. Left for Indiana, *q.v.*, August 10 (*20; 34a; 34b; 34d; 114c*).

1883. December 4, probably between trips to Arkansas and Alabama (*125b*).

1884. Arrived May 26, from Georgia and South Carolina; the length of his stay is unknown; see Little Rock, where he was on June 30. After spending a part of the summer at Key West, Florida, he left for Washington, probably October 5. About December 15 he left for Arizona (*34a; 114b; 125b*).

1885. Arrived from Arizona some time before April 13 (perhaps about March 15; see Phoenix); left for Chihuahua by rail, via El Paso, about July 10 (*34a; 45*, item 24; *114a; 123a*).

1885–86. Arrived from Chihuahua and El Paso, probably mid-December, 1885; left May 16, 1886, for Guadalajara (*34a; 114b; 123a; 125f*).

1886–87. Arrived December 8, 1886, from Guadalajara; left May 14, 1887, by train, for Guaymas, Sonora (*20; 34a; 123a; 125f*).

1888. Arrived late in January, by rail from Guaymas, via Hermosillo, Nogales, Benson, El Paso, and Eustis, Florida. Was employed by the United States Department of Agriculture to collect plants in California, and left for San Bernardino about May 20 (*20; 34a; 114i; 123a; 125f*).

1891. Arrived from Guaymas April 20; left for Guaymas, via the "Ratoon Mts." and Nogales, July 18 (*34a; 49; 123a; 123d*).

1892. Arrived from California, *q.v.*, probably soon after October 1, and was in Washington the rest of the year (*114i; 123a; 123d*).

1893–94. Left for Pocatello, Idaho, about May 1, 1893; returned about September 20, via Salt Lake City (September ?9–13), Denver (September 14–16), and Kansas City. Probably was in Washington until September 21, 1894, when he left for San Francisco (*114a; 114b; 114i; 123a; 125f*).

1895–96. Arrived May 7, 1895, probably from San Francisco; probably was continuously in or near Washington until about March 15, 1896, when he left for the city of Durango (*114i; 123a*).

(?)1896–97. Arrived from Durango either late in 1896 or early in 1897; was authorized to furnish the Department of Agriculture a report on the timber trees of Mexico; left for Mazatlán, probably with J. N. Rose, about May 26, 1897; reached El Paso, Texas, about June 1; proceeded to Mazatlán with Rose, via Nogales and Guaymas. See Colima (*114a; 114b; 114i; 123a*).

1897–98. Arrived November 3, 1897, from San Diego; left a little after April 1, 1898, for Saltillo (*114b; 114i; 123a*).

1898–1901. Arrived from Saltillo, probably in December, 1898, and made no more long trips until 1902. Visited Mammoth Cave, Kentucky, in May 1899. Was appointed a "laborer" in the Botanical Division of the Department of Agriculture, at a nominal wage, to enable him to arrange and rewrite his notes on economic plants (appointments dated July 1, 1899 to June 30, 1901, October 26, 1901 to January 15, 1902 (*114b; 114i; 123a; 123d; 125f*).

1902. Left for Cuba, with C. L. Pollard and William Palmer, probably early in January; he was in Washington on March 21, and probably returned early in March; left by train for San Luis Potosí, probably late in July; returned, from Saltillo, December 11 (*114b; 114i*).

1903–1904. There are no records concerning Palmer for the year 1903, but he was probably in Washington. He was appointed "expert" in the Bureau of Plant Industry, January 16, 1904 to May 15, 1904; about May 15 he left for San Luis Potosí. He returned, via Saltillo, probably in mid-November or late in the same month, and was in Washington until he left for Saltillo the next spring (*123a; 123d*).

1905–1906. Left for Saltillo late in March or early in April, 1905. Returned about September 1, and was made an "expert" in the Bureau of Plant Industry, September 1, 1905 to January 31, 1906. Left for Durango, March 5, 1906 (*114b; 123a; 123d*).

1906–1907. Arrived from Durango, probably in September, 1906; left for Ciudad Victoria, Tamaulipas, by train, January 23, 1907 (*114b; 123a*).

1907–1908. Arrived from Ciudad Victoria, by train, June 22, 1907. Was appointed "expert" in the Bureau of Plant Industry, October 30, 1907, to January 31, 1908. Left for Chihuahua March 27, 1908 (*123a; 123d; 125f*).

1908–1909. Arrived from Chihuahua about July 1, 1908, and was probably continuously in Washington until his departure for Tampico, late in December, 1909 (*114b; 123a*).

1910–11. Arrived from Tampico, via New Orleans, probably late in June, 1910, and was in Washington until his death, April 10, 1911 (*102; 103; 104; 114b; 123a; 125f*).

Washington, Mississippi (Adams County) GLO, 1915

1883. Late February or early March. Came from Memphis, *q.v.*, to visit the "Saltzertown" (i.e. Selsertown, *q.v.*) Mound (said to be 6 miles from Washington and 2 miles from the Stanton R.R. Station); probably went from here to Natchez (*114c*).

Washita River, Louisiana GLO, 1887

1883. See Louisiana.

Washita River, [Oklahoma] GLO, 1876

1868. The "False Washita" mentioned on the labels distributed with Palmer's plant specimens. He traveled up the river from Cherokee Town to the vicinity of Fort Cobb in February, and made the return trip early in June. See Indian Territory, and Fort Cobb.

Wellfleet, Massachusetts (Barnstable County)

1871. See Woods Hole.

West Columbia, Texas (Brazoria County)

1879. November 10; see Houston.

West Point, Arkansas (White County) GLO, 1886

1883. October; see White County. According to Palmer this had been a famous river settlement (on the Little Red River), but at the time of his visit was nearly deserted because the railroad had taken away the river traffic. He opened some mounds here; Thomas (*118*) mentions a mound 3 miles northeast, on the north side of the river, reported by Palmer. Also called by Palmer "West Port" (*88*).

Westport, Missouri (Jackson County) GLO, 1878

1865. See Missouri.

White County, Arkansas

1883. Palmer came to Hot Springs, Garland County, before September 30, probably from Arkadelphia; he was troubled by rheumatism and visited the springs for relief; on October 1 and 2 he went by train to Judsonia, via Malvern; on October 5 he went from Judsonia to West Point, 4 miles, by horse. He was at West Point on the sixth and possibly made a longer stay there; his whereabouts between this date and October 27, when he was in Lonoke County, are unknown (*88; 118*).

White County, Georgia

1884. In early May, Palmer visited a mound on the property of Captain James Nichols, in the Nacoochee Valley. See Georgia (*114c*).

White Water, California (Riverside County) GLO, 1928

1870. (?)September; at this time a stage station on the Ehrenberg–San Bernardino route. A few collections probably made here; Wheeler (*146*) notes that *Lepidospartum squamatum* var. *Palmeri,* supposed to have been collected in the "desert of the Colorado, Arizona," is endemic about White Water. See Los Angeles.

Wichita Agency, [Oklahoma] (Caddo County) GLO, 1876

1868. This agency was in Eureka Valley south of the Washita River, in R 10 W, near the Kiowa-Comanche Agency and Fort Cobb. Palmer was lodged here for a time, in May, after his dismissal from the Kiowa-Comanche Agency; see Fort Cobb (*114b; 124a; 125b*).

Wickenburg, Arizona (northwestern Maricopa County) GLO, 1933

1876. Arrived late at night, April 8, after leaving Ehrenberg at 5:00 in the afternoon, and traveling with "a good moon." Palmer notes that he collected plants on April 10; on the eleventh there was a frost and his money was stolen! He left about April 20 for Prescott. Gray lists 56 numbers of plants from "Wickenburg, etc." (*34a; 45,* item 24; *114b; 114i; 123a*).

Wildcat Station, Baja California

1875. August 15; at least one collection made here. See Fort Yuma (*123a*). Said by Palmer to be 8 miles beyond the point where the San Diego–Yuma road crossed the boundary at Tiajuana, and described by Orcutt as "two or three leagues" east of the crossing, "eastward to the further end of the [Tiajuana] valley," on the "San Diego and Fort Yuma stage road of former days."[57]

Williams River (or Fork), Arizona (between Yuma and Mohave Counties) GLO, 1933

1870. In Palmer's day often called "Bill Williams Fork." Arrived July 6, after a ride of 70 miles muleback, having left Fort Mohave July 4 with the mail carrier; stayed at Murray's Ranch; visited ranch of Ogdale & Kearney enroute to the copper mines 12 miles up Wil-

[57] *West American Scientist,* Vol. II (1886), 37.

liams Fork (July 7); probably on July 8 visited the mines with Mr. Hubbard the manager; collected there "a good many specimens," including large amounts of fruits of *Cereus giganteus,* the primary objective of this trip; returned to Ogdale & Kearney's ranch and "one-night" became sick and remained "several days"; returned to Murray's and left with mail carrier for Camp Colorado, *q.v.*, probably about July 20. See Hardyville (*45*, item 15).

1876. About 24 numbers were collected here March 11–12, at "Williams Fork, its junction with the Colorado." For a possible visit earlier in the same year, see San Bernardino; see also Ehrenberg (*34a; 45*, item 24; *114i*).

Willow Creek, Arizona

1867. April 28; not located, but a tributary of the Río San Pedro; see Camp Grant (*45*, item 10).

Willow Grove, Arizona

1876. See Camp Willow Grove.

Willow Spring(s), Arizona (extreme southern Navajo County) GLO, 1879, 1883

1890. About 10 miles northeast of the northeast corner of Gila County. Said to be in the White Mountains, about 75 miles south of Holbrook. Palmer arrived from Holbrook June 9, enroute to Fort Apache; stopping by chance at Willow Springs, at the ranch of an old acquaintance, he stayed until June 20, collecting Nos. 479–574; he left for Fort Apache on June 21, returning to collect Nos. 614–26 at Willow Springs on July 5 and 6, and leaving for Holbrook about July 7. The dates of the first visit to Willow Springs are erroneously given by Rose (*98*), as June 10–25 (*123a; 123c*).

Wilmington, California (Los Angeles County) GLO, 1928

1867. September 21, according to a typed itinerary in the National Herbarium. See Los Angeles.

Wilson County, Texas

1879. See Sutherland Springs.

Winchester (Station), Arkansas (extreme northeastern Drew County) GLO, 1886

1882. November 22; see Jefferson County, Hollywood, Tiller Mound (*88; 119*).

Woodruff County, Arkansas

?1883. Mayberry Mounds, 3 miles east of Cotton Plant, reported by Palmer, according to Thomas (*118*).

Woods Hole, Massachusetts (Barnstable County)

1871. July to September, inclusive. Palmer spent the summer as assistant to S. F. Baird, the commissioner of fish and fisheries; most of his time was spent in collecting invertebrates at Woods Hole; he also collected a few plants and birds, and made at least one visit to Wellfleet, Massachusetts (*24; 90; 114b; 114e; 114i; 125b; 137*).

Woodson, Arkansas (Saline County) GLO, 1886

1883. See Jefferson County, and Saline County.

Xicoténcatl, Tamaulipas 23°N., 98°56′W. N.F–14

1907. Arrived April 12, by stage from Arguelles; left for Gomes Farías, in a hired wagon, April 13, returning April 21; returned by stage to Arguelles, April 22 (*123a*).

Yadkin River, North Carolina

1883. See North Carolina.

Yaqui River, Sonora

1869. See Río Yaqui.

Yellow Hill Council House, North Carolina (Swain County)

1881. About July 10. Yellow Hill was one of five principal Cherokee villages in this area, situated on Oconaluftee ("Lufty") Creek. It is now the site of the Cherokee Agency, and is officially called Cherokee.[58] See North Carolina.

Yerbabuena, Chihuahua 26°58′N., 106°31′W. Atlas, 31

1885. Said by Safford to lie on the eastern slope of the Sierra Madre, at an elevation of 7,000 feet. Nos. 298–313 were collected here, probably in November on Palmer's return trip from Norogachic to Parral. Yerbabuena (of which no more than a stone ruin remained at the time of my visit in 1951), is about 20 km. west of the Río Balleza crossing at Terrero, on the road which ultimately goes to Guachóchic. The place is in the oak zone, at an elevation of about 2,000 m., near

[58] For synonymy see F. W. Hodge, *Handbook of American Indians North of Mexico, Bureau of American Ethnology Bulletin No. 30, Part 2* (Washington, 1910).

the head of a deep dry precipitous canyon which runs from there generally east toward Balleza. See Chihuahua (Estado) (*123b; 143*).

Ymala, Sinaloa

1891. Same as Imala, *q.v.*

Yuma, Arizona (Yuma County) GLO, 1933

1867. Palmer left Camp Grant about August 1; he made collections in the vicinity of Tucson on August 10; he visited Wallen, *q.v.*, Sacaton, Maricopa Wells, and Gila City. A note in the Division of Mammals collection states that he arrived by coach in Yuma on September 12 and proceeded to San Francisco; if the date is correctly given as September (not August) 12, his whereabouts for the previous month are unknown. See Los Angeles (*114g; 114i; 123a*).

1869. Palmer left Fort Whipple August 19, crossed to Ehrenberg, descended the Colorado River to Yuma and to Puerta Isabel. He returned to Yuma, went up the Gila River past Gila Bend to the Pima villages, visited Camp McDowell and Fort Whipple and then stayed and collected at Camp Date Creek until September 16, when he repeated his earlier trip to Ehrenberg, Yuma, and Puerta Isabel, then returned to Yuma and went to Tucson by coach. See Fort Whipple (*114a; 114b; 123a; 123b*).

1870. Palmer was "steaming down the Colorado River," probably from the Mohave Indian Reservation near Camp Colorado, with six boxes of specimens collected from the Mohave Indians, on August 9; he was in Yuma August 13, and at Puerta Isabel September 4. He returned to Yuma and Ehrenberg, thence crossing the desert to Los Angeles, *q.v.* (*24; 90; 114a; 114e*).

1884–85. Arrived, presumably directly from Las Vegas, New Mexico, in December, 1884. Left December 21 for Colonia Lerdo, *q.v.*, returning after January 1, 1885, and going on to Mesa, *q.v.*, between January 12 and January 20 (*114b; 114g; 123a*).

1888. Left San Diego for Yuma October 7, enroute for Colonia Lerdo; in Yuma he was unable to obtain suitable assistance for the trip, and so returned to San Diego October 12 (*114i; 123a*).

1889. Arrived April 21, from San Diego, via Los Angeles; left for Colonia Lerdo, *q.v.*, by wagon, April 23, accompanied by A. B. Alexander and C. H. Gilbert of the United States Fish Commission. He was back in Yuma by May 6, and left for San Diego May 7 or 8 (*34a; 37; 114g; 114i; 130; 131; 134*).

Zacatecas (Ciudad) 22°45′N., 102°35′W. N.F–13

1878. Palmer left San Luis Potosí "April 9—1878 for Zacatecas by coach at 4 a.m.—fare 12." He had supper and lodging at Salinas. The following day he stopped at Cano [Carro] Quicksilver Mine, "where they changed mules," made a second stop at Ojo Calientes, then after passing several "dreary dry looking settlements" he sighted a "fine lagoon 5 miles of Zacatecas," then Guadalupe. He reached the city of Zacatecas at 5:00 P.M., April 10. He spent almost two weeks there, but seems to have collected no plants and, as he wrote later, he found hardly enough archaeological material to pay him for the trip. His return trip to San Luis Potosí was begun April 23; his return route is unknown, although he may have gone by way of Aguascalientes; he reached San Luis Potosí April 26. See Quemada (*34d; 45*, item 190; *123a*).

1898. Nos. 743–85 were collected here, October 24–November 2, on a trip from Saltillo. On November 11, Palmer wrote from Saltillo that he had been taken with pneumonia soon after his arrival at Zacatecas, and had been forced to return to Saltillo as soon as he could travel. See Coahuila (*114i; 123a*).

Zacatecas (Estado) N.G–14, N.F–13, N.F–14

1878. See Zacatecas (Ciudad).
1898. See Zacatecas (Ciudad).
1902. See Concepción del Oro.
1904. See Concepción del Oro.

Zapatilla, San Luis Potosí 22°11′N., 100°49′W.

1905. Nos. 567–72 were collected here, May 1–3. Said to be a ranch 12 miles east of San Luis Potosí, i.e. about 3 km. north of Juárez, as shown on *Carta de la República Mexicana a 100,100*[a], hoja 13–II–(Z) (edition of 1903) (*123a; 123c*).

Zapoteca, [Mexico]

Not located; several specimens of insects in the Harvard Museum of Comparative Zoology are labeled "Zapoteca, Mex. Apr.," according to Nathan Banks.

APPENDIX I

Chronology of Palmer's Plant Collections, and Locations of Known Sets of Field Notes

Minor collections, of a few specimens only, are omitted from the following table (e.g. those from Kansas, 1863; New England, 1871–73; North Carolina and Tennessee, 1881–84). These are mentioned in the appropriate places in the geographical index to this work.

The number of separate collections distributed by Palmer can be stated with considerable exactitude for most years after 1870. When the number of sets is known precisely it is usually large, often more than ten. It is probable that all the collections made after 1900 (with the possible exception of the Cuban collection of 1902) included about ten sets, but the actual number is unknown for any year except 1910.

The collections of 1888, when Palmer collected in California for the Department of Agriculture, and 1897, when he spent a part of his time on other work and was also ill for a long period, appear to have been represented by small numbers of sets.

Field notes for the following years are represented by typed copies, deposited in the library of the University of Michigan: 1861, 1868, 1885 (grasses only), 1890–92 (PEI set only), 1893, 1894–95, 1896, 1897 (incomplete), 1898 (incomplete, Nos. 588–703, 705–85, 804–805 missing), 1902 (incomplete), 1905 (incomplete), 1906, 1907, 1908, 1910.

Numbers in italics refer to items in References and Sources.

Date	*Region*	*Number of Collections*	*Number of Sets*
1853	Argentina; Brazil; Paraguay	150?	1
1854–55	Argentina	200?	1
1861–62	Colorado (a few from Nebraska; Kansas)	165	1
1865	Arizona (with E. Coues)	600 approx.	1
1867	Arizona	250 approx.	1
1868	Indian Territory	484	2
1869	New Mexico; Arizona; Sonora; Baja California	400 at least	9 (1869–1870)
1870	Utah; Arizona; Sonora; California	200 [est. only]	
1874	Florida; Bahamas	105 algae	2 at least
		672 vasc. pl.	6 at least
1875	Guadalupe Island	119	11
1875	California; Baja California	462	12
1876	Utah; Arizona; California	660	10 est.
1877	Utah; Arizona	502	18
1878	San Luis Potosí (with Parry)	1,010	10
1878–79	San Luis Potosí; Tamaulipas	130	7 at least
1879–80	Texas; Coahuila; Nuevo León	1,441	15
		147	15 est.

Total Number of Specimens (Est.)	*Field Notes*
150	Accompany specimens in United States National Herbarium; for key to localities see *42*, p. 67.
200	Accompany specimens in United States National Herbarium; many notes are with specimens to which they do not pertain.
165	In Smithsonian Institution. See *114b*, Accession 291 (1863).
600	None known.
250 approx.	None known.
800 approx.	In Torrey Collection, New York Botanical Garden, together with Torrey's key to the field numbers and his assigned numbers.
4,000 est.	None known.
	None known.
200 approx.	None known. For list of collections with original field numbers see *34a, Miscellaneous Plant Lists,* Vol. I.
3,000	
1,200 approx.	Guadalupe Island notes in abridged form in enumeration by Watson. See *139*.
4,725	California and Baja California notes not known. For list of collections with original field numbers see *34a, Miscellaneous Plant Lists,* Vol. II.
5,000 est.	None known. For list of collections see *34a, Miscellaneous Plant Lists,* Vol. III.
8,000	None known. See *34a, Miscellaneous Plant Lists,* Vol. III.
10,100	None known. See *34a, Miscellaneous Plant Lists,* Vol. I; nearly all are cited in Hemsley, see *36*.
700 approx.	Same as 1878 collection.
16,000	
1,600 est.	Apparently none prepared except for the key to localities; collection listed by Watson, see *142* and *142b*.

Date	*Region*	*Number of Collections*	*Number of Sets*
1885	Chihuahua	455	12
1886	Jalisco	770	14 major 5 minor
1887	Sonora; Baja California	560 approx.	14
1888	California	310	3?
1889	San Quintín	142	7 at least
	Baja California, Sonora	308	7?
1890–92	Nos. 1–1,412; Baja California; Sonora; Arizona; Colima	1,422 approx.	Unknown
	Nos. 1,413–2,040; Sinaloa; Colima; Nayarit	628	39[1]
	Nos. 2,041–2,780; Nayarit?; California	540 approx.	Unknown

[1] Sets 1–11 contained more than 100 numbers each.

[2] Because of F. V. Coville's dual position as botanist of the Department of Agriculture and curator of the National Herbarium, his official correspondence and manuscript material pertaining to the work of collectors engaged during his

Total Number of Specimens (Est.)	*Field Notes*
4,500 approx.	Notes for grasses (74 numbers) at United States National Herbarium. Numerical list of entire collection published at Gray Herbarium. Watson enumerated the collection systematically, see *143*.
11,000 approx.	Notes for approximately 134 numbers are in the United States National Herbarium. For lists of the numbers represented see pp. 93–94 of this book Abridged versions of numbers and of the notes were published by Watson, see *144*.
5,000 approx.	None known. Watson published an enumeration of the collection, see *145*.
500 ?	California. Field notes for Nos. 1–277 are in the United States National Herbarium. Nos. 18–247, except 31, 107, and 151 were enumerated by Vasey and Rose, see *133*, with Palmer's notes given almost verbatim. For lichens see *Contributions from the United States National Herbarium*, (1893) I, 291–92.
800 approx.	San Quintín. None known. Vasey and Rose enumerated the collection, plus a few specimens from Lagoon Head, see *132*.
1,800 ?	Baja California and Sonora. Nos. 651–958 are in the United States National Herbarium. Vasey and Rose enumerated the collection, with abridged versions of Palmer's notes, see *134*.
8,500 ? 4,000 approx. 3,400 ?	Field notes for Nos. 1–2,780 are preserved, partly at the United States National Herbarium, partly by the Division of Plant Exploration and Introduction; for complete record see p. 102.[2] Reports were published, with abridged versions of the collector's notes, as follows: Vasey and Rose, Nos. 1–273, see *135*. By Rose, Nos. 276–751, 812, see *97*, *98*; Nos. 818–85, see *99*; Nos. 752–815, 886–1,410, 1,810–12, see *100*.

term of office are now physically divided; a part of the material may be found at the National Herbarium, and a part at Beltsville, Maryland, in the files of the Division of Plant Exploration and Introduction. The present division of Palmer's manuscript field notes seems to have been the result of chance, for all the collec-

Date	*Region*	*Number of Collections*	*Number of Sets*
1893	Idaho	550	21[3]
1894–95	Guerrero	635	12
1896	Durango	974	10 approx.
1897	Colima; Sonora; Sinaloa	279	Unknown
1898	Coahuila; San Luis Potosí; Durango; Zacatecas	814	10 approx.
1899	Kentucky	60 ?	3 ?
1902	Cuba (with Pollard & Wm. Palmer)	400 approx.	1 ?
	San Luis Potosí; Coahuila; Zacatecas	475 approx.	10 approx.
1904	San Luis Potosí; Coahuila; Zacatecas (Nos. 1–476)	476	Unknown
1905	Coahuila; San Luis Potosí (Nos. 500–769)	270	Unknown
1906	Durango	569	Unknown

tions, to which the notes pertain, are in the National Herbarium, and not now in the custody of the Department of Agriculture although some of them were made originally for that agency.

It should be noted that in later years Palmer was in the habit of keeping his field notes on newspaper stock, sometimes full size and sometimes folded into

Total Number of Specimens (Est.)	*Field Notes*
3,000 approx.	Palmer's journal and field notes at the United States National Herbarium.
5,000 approx.	A set of field notes in the Division of Plant Exploration and Introduction. Fernald enumerated a part of the collection, see *27*, and the grasses were reported upon by Lamson-Scribner, see *107*.
8,000 approx.	Nearly complete sets of field notes are at the Gray Herbarium and in the Division of Plant Exploration and Introduction.
500 ?	Nearly complete set of field notes in the Division of Plant Exploration and Introduction.
6,000 ?	Largest known set of field notes at the United States National Herbarium; this includes most of Nos. 9–813, except 588–785. For complete record see p. 111. Another set, of approximately the same completeness, is at the Gray Herbarium.
215	None known; probably none prepared.
400 ?	Cuba. None known.
3,500 ?	Mexico. Incomplete series of field notes at the Gray Herbarium, and a nearly complete set in Washington, partly at the United States National Herbarium and partly in the Division of Plant Exploration and Introduction.
Unknown	Nos. 1–476. An incomplete series of field notes at the Gray Herbarium.
Unknown	Nos. 500–769 (continued from 1904). Original notes in nine books, in Division of Plant Exploration and Introduction; two books pertain to tunas from the market of San Luis Potosí. For a list of numbers represented by notes see page 115.
Unknown	Field notes in Division of Plant Exploration and Introduction.

booklets. He often made more than one copy of the notes, and perhaps (this is not certainly known) made a copy for each set of the plants which he distributed. For some years two or more sets of notes are known to be extant, and no doubt there are others which we have not seen.

[3] Sets 1–11 contained 58 or more specimens each.

Date	*Region*	*Number of Collections*	*Number of Sets*
1907	Tamaulipas	584	5 or more
1908	Chihuahua	457	10 approx.
1910	Tamaulipas; Vera Cruz	598	9

Total Number of Specimens (Est.)	*Field Notes*
2,500 ?	Copy of diary, and original field books in Division of Plant Exploration and Introduction.
3,500 ?	Original diary and field books in Division of Plant Exploration and Introduction.
4,400 approx.	Copy of diary, and original field books, in Division of Plant Exploration and Introduction.

APPENDIX II

Annotated List of Herbaria Known to Have Significant Holdings of Specimens Collected by Palmer

This list is divided into two parts. The first part (arranged in approximate order of importance) gives those institutions which have holdings of major importance. The second part (arranged alphabetically) lists institutions which have minor holdings. The sets of different years as listed below are those which have come to my attention, and do not necessarily represent the total holding of any institution; nor does the mention of a given year necessarily mean that the institution in question has a complete or even large set of that year. When I have been able to learn the exact numbers of specimens in the sets of the different years, I have given the numbers in the general chronological account.

1. *Major Holdings*

United States National Herbarium, Washington, D. C. Contains collections made by Palmer while in the employ of the Department of Agriculture and other government agencies. This is the most nearly complete series of Palmer's plants, lacking scarcely any years except 1865–67. It contains many duplicates, especially for the period 1878–92 (from the herbarium of John Donnell Smith), and some (e.g. 1892) from the Biltmore Herbarium. This is the principal (and sometimes sole) repository for collections of 1853–55, 1860–62, 1869–70, 1897, 1899 (Kentucky), 1902 (Cuba), and contains the best set of the collections of 1888–93, and for some later years.

Gray Herbarium, Harvard University, Cambridge, Mass. A nearly complete series beginning with the Florida collection of 1874. Because Gray and Watson performed the principal service of identification for Palmer from 1874 until 1887, the best sets for these years (except 1878) are to be found at the Gray Herbarium. Here also is the best set for 1894–95, and perhaps for some later years.

Missouri Botanical Garden, St. Louis, Missouri. Contains a partial series of 1863, and almost the only series of 1865–67, these having been submitted to Engelmann for determination. Also contains sets of numerous years from 1875 on, including some duplicates from the private herbaria of Redfield and Engelmann.

New York Botanical Garden, Bronx Park, New York, N. Y. Weak in collections of years before 1874, but contains best set of plants of 1868 and occasional specimens (from Torrey herbarium) from this early period. Has nearly complete representation of years from 1874 to 1910, including many duplicates from herbaria of Britton, Brown, Canby, Crooke, LeRoy, Morong.

Royal Botanic Garden, Kew, Richmond, Surrey, England. Contains the first set of the collection of 1878 (sent to Hemsley for determination), and a large series from that time until 1910.

British Museum (Natural History), London, England. Has a large series beginning with the Guadalupe Island collection of 1875.

Conservatoire et Jardin Botaniques, Geneva, Switzerland. Has a large series beginning with the Guadalupe Island collection of 1875; includes duplicates from the herbaria of De Candolle and Boissier.

Chicago Natural History Museum, Chicago, Ill. Contains a set of the California collection of 1875 (from Rothrock), and numerous series of later years, especially from 1893 to 1910. A set of the plants of 1869–70 went to Chicago but the recipient is unknown.

California Academy of Sciences, San Francisco, Calif. Contains certain collections especially of later years. A set of the plants of 1869–70 went to California but the recipient is unknown.

Yale University, New Haven, Connecticut. Contains large series of the years 1869–87, from the herbarium of Eaton, with some duplicates from the herbarium of Brewer.

Komarov Botanical Institute, Leningrad, U.S.S.R. Contains sets of plants of the years 1875–91, bought during the period when Maximowicz was in charge of the herbarium.

Philadelphia College of Pharmacy, Philadelphia, Pa. Contains sets of 1875–80, from the herbarium of Martindale.

Academy of Natural Sciences, Philadelphia, Pa. Contains certain series, e.g. for years 1878–79, 1885. A set of the plants of 1869–70 was sent to Philadelphia but the recipient is unknown.

Iowa State College, Ames, Iowa. Contains sets of 1878, 1879–80, and 1885, from Parry's herbarium, and a set of 1892.

Botanisches Museum, Berlin-Dahlem, Germany. Formerly contained sets of various years beginning with 1875.[1]

Museum National d'Histoire Naturelle, Paris, France. Contains sets of certain years, including 1879–80 (from the herbarium of Cosson).

2. *Minor Holdings*

Arnold Arboretum, Harvard University, Jamaica Plain, Mass. Small sets of 1878, 1880, purchased by Sargent.

Brown University, Providence, R. I. Set of 1875 (Guadalupe Island), purchased by Olney.

Buffalo Museum of Science, Buffalo, N. Y. Set of 1875 (California), purchased by Clinton.

California, University of, Berkeley, Calif. Sets of 1890–91 (from Brandegee's herbarium), 1893, and perhaps others.

Calcutta, Botanic Garden, Calcutta, India. Set of 1892.

Copenhagen, Botanical Museum and Herbarium, Copenhagen, Denmark. Set of 1902 (Mexico).

Hitchcock, A. S. Purchased a small set of the California plants of 1892. These are presumably at Kansas State College, Manhattan, Kans.

Michigan, University of, Ann Arbor, Mich. Set of 1893 (from herbarium of A. J. Pieters) and miscellaneous duplicates, 1878–1910.

[1] See I. Urban, *Geschichte des Koeniglichen Botanischen Museums* (Berlin, 1916), 380.

Moffatt, W. S. Purchased a set of the California plants of 1892.

Nebraska, University of, Lincoln, Nebraska. Contains one of the two largest duplicate sets of the California collection of 1892, from the herbarium of Bessey. Bessey purchased Sets 1 and 2, but his manner of disposition of the extra set is unknown.

Notre Dame, University of, Notre Dame, Indiana. A set of 1888–89, from the herbarium of Greene, and perhaps other series from the same source.

Pomona College, Claremont, Calif. Set of the California plants of 1892, from the herbarium of Jones.

Vermont, University of, Burlington, Vermont. Set of 1879–80, purchased by Pringle.

Vienna, University of, Vienna, Austria. Set of 1879–80.

Wyoming, University of, Laramie, Wyo. Set of 1893.

APPENDIX III

Botanical Field Notes, Colorado, 1861

The original field notes made by Palmer in Colorado are filed at the Smithsonian Institution, under Accession 291. Editorial comments are in square brackets; otherwise the notes are an exact copy of the original, which is in Palmer's hand.

1861

6 miles up in the mountains & 14 from Denver City, Col. Teritory

No. 1. Larkspur, bronzey blue petal, dark purple calax bronzey mouth yellowish white striped blueish purple. Grown upon rich hill slopes June 11–1861

No. 2) Only grows upon ra[n]ge of mts blooms from May to June

No 2) Same as (No 2), but pink, rare very.

3) May 27 green calax white bloom orange anthers exposed sumit of hills poor soil, large tufts.

4) May 27 bulbus plant, rich soil warm shady opening in mountain & richest spot of the valley for 14 to 20 miles from mountains, but not on the river botoms.

5) May 29, dark orange, indifferent as to soil. grows on mountain ridges, richer the soil the larger the bloom

6) same as no 5 except being yellow by age & lighter orange in the young bloom cented like wallflower

7) same as 5 & 6 except being dark bluish red

8) same as 5, 6 & 7 except being dark yellow

9) May 27 light purple tinge, high exposed hills poor soil in bunches

10) May 10 very dark blackish purple anthers base yellow rim of

eye red then yellow then white petels purple shaded lighter towards the ends[.] grow in rich shady spots by rivers or marshes.

No. 11) dull whitish, green middle of petals[,] brown anthers and calax May 22, rich swamps or by streams

No 12) Yellow with black stripes lower lip peach color [(]also underneath the under petals [)], woods in mountains & valleys extending to the higher ridges for over 100 miles from Mts. blooms from May to June

13) hill slopes in poor soil yellow blo[om] July 10

14) July 10 Yellow in bunches among rocks poor dryish spots among mountains

15) May 29 Lavender, color petals, green center, stamens white edges, climbing plant rich soil among trees & shrubs

16) May 27 Greenish brown calex with shaded purple tube hairy with icey appearance, petals light blue, base & throat shaded purple with darker stripes of the same[;] pistils buff anthers white blue middle[;] in bunches among trees or rocks partially shaded

17) White bloom, swamps.

18) May 27 rich South slopes among woods openings in mountains & river bottoms for 20 miles from mountains rich purple, middle white, which turns purple by age

19) Mountain swamps

20) May 20 yellow row of cristals around middle lobe giving an icey appearance[,] with a purplish cast over young buds[.] yellow bloom in bunches

20) from Cotton wood creek Kansas to first range of mountains[.] moist shadey spots in woods, large bunches

21) May 21 Moist localities.

22) " 27 warm hill sides all over mts & wood openings along river bottoms for 20 miles from mts yellow bloom, Laburnium cented. to be found to the Arkansas Divide.

23) bloom first of March to [space left here] large bunches pure white, hiacinth cented, yellow anthers, large bunches suculent white roots, poor soil, hilley spots in mountains and exposed plains from first range of mts. to 100 or 150 miles along the valley

24th May 27. warm hill sides yellow bloom petals underneath purple striped

25) Moist shady spots in Mts May 27

26). May 27. hill slopes in mts & wood openings along rivers for 50 miles from mts bloom white, lobe tipped pink

27) moist localities Mts.
28 white bloom in bunches, moist spots mts
29) May to August, bloom blue purple buds warm shady localities in mts.
30) May 27 white tipped blue, hill sides poor soil
31) May 27 wood openings in mts and 14 miles along the river Platt, good soil white bloom tinged yellow.
32) May 27 warm hill slopes in Mts and exposed valleys 100 to 150 miles. yellow bloom curious bladder seed pods
33) May 27 Warm rich, Mts., slopes white bloom pink stripes lower lobe tipped pink (it extends a few miles along the wood openings of the valleys
34) June 22 mts in open spots in large bunches, light purple, white stripes up[p]er lip[;] two ft. high
35) June 2nd white, smell like honeycomb, shadey woods by streams Mts
36) May 27 white, rich shadey spots, Mts
37) " white inside brick red outside brown anthers exposed hills Mts
38) dark red, icey appearance, center or base of bloom green, upon all the Mt. ridges, Slopes and for 8 miles in the valley near rivers
39) May to July highest Mt. peaks light purple yellow anthers slightly cented
40) May 29 barren hills, white, when pink old
41) Shaded hill sides, Mts. whitey pink shaded May 18
42) June, Mts, by streams
43) " 18 strong offensive smell, white shaded le[a]d color anthers green, shade in large bunches by brooks, Mts.
44) June 18 sides of streams rich swamps purple buds, which gradually become blue, branches droops, Mts.
45) moist spots, Mts, and in the valley for several miles, white, greenish yellow stamens, pistil green
46) June 18 moist rich spots white shaded blue Mts
47) swamps, Mts, June 18
48) buds green, bloom greenish yellow swamps June 24, Mts.
49) swamps Mts, and valley for miles
50) June 18 white with slatey stripes anthers same, large bushey, 2 ft. shade, Mts
51) June 18 white, golden[,] anthers brown, stamens white. [One line

left blank before next words]. virgin thistle, Mts, and dry hills for 50 miles along valley smell like decayed meat

52) June 18 Mt slopes & 50 miles on the open plains, white, yellow anthers green pistils, cent like green peas, by age turns purple.

53) June 8 shadey spots, Mts. light purple shaded blue, buds purple slightly scented.

54) large patches exposed, Mt. tops June

55) [June] dry spots but shady, Mts, creamy white greenish white buds, 3 ft high

56) June 8 shaded rocks, Mts peaks, white shaded pink, in large patches

No 57) June 8 fulsome cent petals white, stamens calax & anthers greenish yellow shadey spots, Mts.

58. June 9 shade from Mts. to Mo. river

59) " 8, cream color stamens sulphur colour anthers petals bronz blue white underside calax same, petals turn down, shady, Mts.

60) June, Moist shadey localities Mts

61) " 8 greenish yellow anthers Mts shade

62) " shady locality, Mts. rocks, closes up at night open at sun rise, golden yellow

63) June 8 shady raveins, Mts, white shaded light purple.

64) June 8 yellow anthers, petals rich pink, shady wood openings Mts

65) moist localities Mts

66) June 10, pink shade edge of lip, lower lip spotted purple savery scented, petals white ground[;] wood openings Mts slopes and wood openings large patches in 50 miles along streams from Mts

67) June 27 Side of creeks nearly toutching water. Mts. 2 to 3 ft very showey purple bloom[,] anthers brownish, pistils white shaded purple.

68) June 18 warm hill side rich pink, striped, white uper lip

69) June 22 Lavender color bloom middle petals white, shaded Lavender greenish white stamens, yellow anthers, moist spots in Mts.

70) June 26 lilac bloom few purple stripes thick bunches, 2 ft. bottoms in Mts

71) June 14th end of petal sky blue, shady purple throat with dark purple stripes lower part of lower petal white purple striped in bunches on hill sides Mts and on plains 100 miles from Mts

72) June 24 yellow pistils, white stamens, black anthers, peuce color petals, Mts hillsides in bunches

73) small white bloom swamp Ju 24
74) June 22, calax shaded and tipped green petals white, tipped green[,] spotted purplish black[,] stamens & anthers greenish yellow wood openings, Mts, two to four feet
75) shady spots sandy soil Mts
76) June 24 green calax brown petel shaded green inside, pisti[l] yellowish white stamens, yellow anthers, Mts in damp localities & maney miles in valley
77) June 22 bloom blue, brown mark around the white eye, white stamens, yellow anthers, marshes, Mts.
78) June 22, Sulphur color wood openings, Mts
79) June 22 anthers and end of pistils black stamens and petals cherry color the center straw color, base green, dark brown dots, damp shady spots, Mts.
80) red pulpy, shady raveins Mts
81) Golden yellow buds white bloom, tube shade delecate pink, exposed hill sides, fine showey, Mts June 24
82) June 22 gold colored buds, stems of unopen blooms white, but when open pink, petals white shaded delace [*sic*] pink, hill side.
83) June 24, lilac bloom purple veins stamen blue, white anthers. hill sides Mts, and along river bottoms for 20 miles down the valley in abundance
84) June 24, large bunches 2 to 3 ft Mts slopes, bloom white delicately shaded purple light blue veins, pistil redish
85) June 18 hill sides poor soil Mts and for 50 miles in wood openings along rivers in the valley
86 + 87 [&] 88 Mt slopes June
89) June 24th Mt slopes, in clusters
90) swamps Mts, mottled red & white
91) compact bunches, Mts, fine, June 18
92) moist raveins, Mts, and valley 50 m
93) May 25th Mts slopes
94) Mts raveins showey clusters bloom
95) June 18 edge of rivers, Mts, brown calax, petals pink white eye
96) Lilac bloom purple stripes, white pistil, anthers yellow, strong weedy smell, 3 ft in thick bunch raveins, Mts
97) Mts moist spots bloom greenish brown
98) shady spots, Mts, bloom purple blue
99) July 20 bloom creamy white, darker end of tube with green shade. Mts

100) Mts raveins, small purple bloom
101) Mts raveins, 20 miles from mts in shady raveins among bushes, showey.
102) Mts slopes
103) " moist raveins July 1st (5 ft
104) June 29, Mts wood openings, bloom yellow, brown black middle
105) as above, but larger bunches
106) found upon mts. slopes and valley
107) June 24, creeksides Mts, sweet cented, bloom sea green, orange anthers.
108) June 24 bloom light puce white throat purple stripes, pistil yellow, white stamens, black anthers Mts slopes
109) rocky ledges Mts.
110) June 22 lower part of lobe white then mottled lavender, bloom Lavender shady raveins Mts
111) white tinged blue Mts raveins
112) bloom yellow, orange anthers, shady rocks in Mts.
113) by rivers & swamps, Mts.
114) July 1 edge of woods raveins Mts
115) June 22 among shady rocks Mts bloom white calax green stamens white anthers yellow 3 to five ft.
116) trailing bushy shrub, Mts ridges June 23 white bloom & pistils, yellow eye[,] calax shaded same, greenish [word illegible]
117) June 22 calax white pink shade. bloom inside pink with white stripes. dark shade among underbrush, Mts
118) June 22, Mts northern shady mountain slopes.
119) June 8 branching upright shrub shade, cent like unripe fruit, Mts seed ripe July 20th
120) June 2 Swamps & marshes, Mts large oblong berries black
121) June 8, upright bush 5 to 7 ft Mts, raveins and bluffy spots for 200 miles from Mts
122) May 29, strawcolor bloom, low branching shrub, strong acid smell
123) May 29, grown upon N. hillsides in irreguler beds bloom white, calax green, eye when old buff, when young lightly shaded, Mts.
124) May 29 bloom creamy white green pistil, dark red anthers green calax, 4 to 6 ft upright compact bush
125) May 29 bloom white anthers light yellow w[h]en young, but when old brown, rose cented lo[o]se growing shrub among rocks in raveins, Mts.

126) May 29 rich moist spots Mts bloom and ripen close to snow
127) creaping shrub close compact commonly called Larb[;] yoused as tobacco and for rheumatism, white tipped pink black anthers May 27, Mts
128) May to June hard irreguler bulb bloom white pink striped, delacate pink anthers
129) May 29 lo[o]se growing shrub moist raveins, 6 to 10 ft, Mts
130, May 29, yellow bloom red stamens, green pistils clove cented lo[o]se growing shrub 3 to 5 ft fruit ripen July 19 Mts, and 14 miles down the valley in wood openings
131 June 16 dry nowls to 16 miles from Mts but not in Mts.E. side compact bush 3 to 4 ft.
132) May to June pink tube & petals tipped white, green anthers fruit clear orange ripe July 19 irreguler growing shrub among rock 3 to 5 ft
133, April 21, warm shady hill sides ripen July 19th is clear bright red, fine acid flavor, Dwarf branching shrub
134) grown in thick patches rich soil Mts, slopes, bloom May 20
135) May 28 green bloom white anthers thin lankey growing shrub 8 to 10 ft no whare but in Mts.
136. May 28, white bloom, anthers yellow, fruit yellowish white alderberry, moist raveins Mts
137) May 29th Moist raveins Mts
138 " 27 "
139) July 19 [?; second digit illegible] hill slopes, Mts, white buds, peuce blooms pistils & stamens anthers yellow.
[Nos. 140–48, inclusive, omitted]
149 June 18 white bloom, orange eye yellow anthers, river sides Mts, and 20 miles down valley (Kennecanic
150) Nine bark Spirea bloom white anthers white tipped brown slightly sweet cented Mts raveins 3 to 5 ft.
151) Dark pink tipped dirty white snow white fruit, Mts underbrush and maney miles in valley
152) July 20 shady raveins, Mts.
153) " color merone or bronze, pistils ends black stamens yellow, shade Mts
154) Mt creeks bottoms bloom May 27.
155) July 18 hill sides among rocks white petals, yellow anthers & stamens, straw color eye which change to light peach by age, fine compact shrub 4 ft.

156. June 8 hung up in house to July 19 before dry, suculent leaves, grows in bunches among rocks hill sides.

157 July 16, fine showey shrub dry slopes in Mts & dry sandy spots wood openings in valley for 20 miles, as soon as daylight come it closes up bloom light straw color stamens same anthers yellow 2 to 4 ft.

158) Bulbous plant, Mt slopes, July 14[?; second digit illegible] greenish near the eye black spines yellow ends stamens white anthers deep straw, pistil tinged purple.

159) July 10 moist raveins Mts petals tipped greenish yellow purplish blue body, white eye and stamens, anthers black, buds underneath white

160) July 10 paracitical plant, suculant plant, fine straw colored tendrills, white bloom yellow anthers Golden City edge of mts 14 miles from Denver. only spot seen

Entrance of Mts

161 June 16th Golden gate dry nowls calax green outer rim inner purplish tinge bloom white internal organs greenish yellow

162) [June 16th] moist raveins near brush, branching out in large patches, calax green, bloom white shaded slightly purple.

163 slopes of ridges seed pod brick red calax greenish red, eye yellow blooms white anthers brick red stamens white pistil same but end tinged yellow.

164) dryish nowls, bunches, rich purple eye and lower part of upper lip tinged slate with white stripes.

165. slopes of ridges, 2½ ft, purplish white bloom, tube darker, end of petals underside dotted dark purplish green anthers yellowish brown.

Abbreviations to these notes are ft– for feet Mts for mountains and in mentioning colour of blooms, generaly say, yellow white or blue & withou[t] saying bloom so and so—

APPENDIX IV

Botanical Field Notes, Indian Territory, 1868

The original notes kept by Palmer in Indian Territory are filed among the Torrey papers at the New York Botanical Garden, together with Torrey's manuscript list of the collection. The numbers assigned by Torrey bear no relation to those assigned by Palmer, and two or more of the field numbers are often combined by Torrey. The notes themselves do not include any identifications, whereas in Torrey's list, as far as he completed it, most of the numbers are named at least to the genus. In the following enumeration, therefore, the field notes are preceded by what is essentially an index to them, namely a list of Torrey's numbers, with the generic names assigned by him. Palmer's field numbers, corresponding to those used below in the field-notes, are given in parentheses.

1. *Enumeration According to the Numbers Assigned by Torrey*

1. Delphinium (s.n.); 2. Clematis (231); 3. Anemone (13); 4. Thalictrum (120); 5. Nelumbo (125); 6. Menispermum (127); 7. Cocculus (413); 8. Argemone (153); 9. Argemone (183); 10. Corydalis (75); 11. Nasturtium (23); 12. Sisymbrium (12, 47); 13. Cheiranthus (48); 14. Streptanthus (216); 15. Vesicaria (s.n.); 16. Draba (76); 17. Nasturtium (62); 18. Polanisia (147); 19. Cleomella (396); 20. Lechea (347); 21. Hypericum (311); 22. Hypericum (349); 23. Ascyrum (14); 24. Ionidium (102); 25. Viola (s.n., Kioway Agency); 26. Viola (18); 27. Paronychia (200, 270); 28. Mollugo (213, 238); 29. Arenaria (377); 30. Cerastium (74); 31. Silene (s.n., Washita R.); 32. Silene (324); 33. Talinum (193); 34. Talinum (194); 35.

Sida (s. n.); 36 (see also 256). Sassafras (385); 37. Callirhoe (58); 38. Callirhoe (s. n.); 39. Callirhoe (169, 296); 40. Aesculus (3); 41. Negundo (s. n., Washita R.); 42. Geranium (s. n.); 43. Linum (93); 44. Linum (301); 45. Linum (435); 45a. Oxalis (81); 45b. Oxalis (16); 46. Ptelea (337); 47. Vitis (477); 48. Vitis (481); 49. Vitis (104, 456); 50. Vitis (429); 51. Vitis (403); 52. Celastrus (179); 53. Euonymus (124); 54. Ceanothus (246); 55. Rhus (8); 56. Rhus (341); 57. Rhus (66); 58. Rhus (118, 155); 59. Rhus (180, 223); 60. Prunus (34); 61. Prunus (35); 62. Prunus (479); 63. Prunus (480); 64. Prunus (457, 458, 459, 460); 65. Gillenia (s. n., Riley's Mill); 66. Crataegus (410); 67. Rubus (469); 68. Rubus (46); 69. Rubus (189); 70. Rosa (274); 71. Rosa (s. n.); 72. Psoralea (207); 73. Psoralea (297); 74. Polygala (359); 75. Polygala (282); 76. Polygala (224); 77. Cassia (445); 78. Glycyrrhiza (121); 79. Astragalus (6); 80. Astragalus (90); 81. Astragalus (21); 82. Astragalus (406); 83. Dalea (299); 84. Dalea (437); 85. Petalostemum (278); 86. Petalostemum (463); 87. Petalostemum (465); 88. Petalostemum (380); 89. Petalostemum (s.n., Cherokee Town); 90. Lespedeza (461); 91. Lespedeza (370); 92. Lespedeza (s. n., July 28, Sept. 1); 93. Desmodium (484); 94. Desmodium (483); 95. Desmodium (483bis); 96. Desmodium (432); 97. Desmodium (440); 98. Desmodium (484); 99. Amorpha (248); 100. Amorpha (137, 352); 101. Psoralea (247); 102. Psoralea (412); 103. Psoralea (105); 104. Stylosanthes (432); 105. Lathyrus (5); 106. Vicia (17); 107. Hosackia (257, 307); 108. Cassia (376); 109. Clitoria (411); 110. Rhynchosia (255); 111. Sophora (77); 112. Galactia (472); 113. Crotalaria (266); 114. Tephrosia (163); 115. Tephrosia (321); 116. Indigofera (166); 117. Cercis (33); 118. Phaseolus (s. n., Cherokee Town); 119. Baptisia (63); 120. Baptisia (387, 416); 121. Schrankia (210); 122. Acacia (245); 122a. Acacia (s. n.); 123. Desmanthus (340); 124. Desmanthus (310); 125. Neptunia (303); 126. Gaura (315); 127. Oenothera (262); 128. Oenothera (322); 129. Oenothera (72); 130. Oenothera (98); 131. Oenothera (393); 132. Oenothera (157); 133. Oenothera (112); 134. Oenothera (156); 135. Gaura (86); 136. Stenosiphon (388); 137 Gaura (203); 137a. Gaura (263); 138. Ludwigia (353); 139. Lythrum (281, 413); 139a. Ammania (s. n.); 140. Cucurbita (191); 141. Sicydium (150); 142. Mentzelia (344); 143. Passiflora (254, 474); 144. Passiflora (442); 145. Opuntia (217); 146. Eryngium (s. n., Cherokee Town); 147. Eryngium (360); 148. Cynosciadium (96); 148a. Leptocaulis (175); 149. Discopleura (305);

150. Cicuta (415); 151. Sanicula (272); 152. Sanicula (s.n.); 153. Cynosciadium (272); 154. Cornus (117); 155. Cornus (426); 156. Sambucus (182); 157. Lonicera (64); 158. Symphoricarpos (328); 159. Galium (178); 160. Galium (185); 161. Cephalanthus (267); 162. Diodia (336); 163. Houstonia (399); [164–186, inclusive, not named by Torrey].

187. Erythraea (402); 188. Sabatia (391, 462); 189. Sabatia (276); 190. Bignonia (408); 191. Phlox (251); 192. Gilia (367); 193. Ellisia (87); 194. Nama (144); 195. Nemophila (113, 165); 196. Fraxinus (196); 197. Bumelia (476); 198. Evolvulus (84, 209); 199. Convolvulus (398); 200. Convolvulus (109); 201. Convolvulus (28); 202. Cuscuta (395); 203. Heliotropium (436); 204. Lithospermum (45); 205. Lithospermum (24); 206. Onosmodium (136); 207. Solanum (183); 207a. Solanum (292, 331); 208. Solanum (103, 285, 290); 209. Solanum (451); 210. Solanum (237); 211. Datura (259); 212. Physalis (305); 213. Physalis (271); 214. Solanum (269); 214a. Solanum (288); 215. Physalis (111); 216. Ilysanthes (239); 217. Conobea (444); 218. Scrophularia (100); 219. Mimulus (379); 220. Veronica (59); 221. Buchnera (318); 222. Polypremum (312); 223. Herpestes (286); 224. Linaria (106, 159); 225. Penstemon (68, 158); 226. Penstemon (108, 192); 227. Gerardia (471); 228. Gerardia (466); 229. Gerardia (467); 230. Justicia (239, 417); 231. Ruellia (168); 232. Monarda (218); 233. Monarda (369); 234. Monarda (330); 234a. Monarda (362, 363); 235. Monarda (144); 236. Salvia (454); 237. Calamintha (345); 238. Hedeoma (176, 414); 238a. Hedeoma (94); 239. Pycnanthemum (430); 240. Teucrium (329); 241. Scutellaria (358); 242. Verbena (339); 243. Verbena (351); 244. Verbena (420); 245, 246. Verbena (21, 167, 438); 247. Verbena (260, 390); 248. Phryma (308); 249. Lippia (213); 250. Plantago (409); 251. Plantago (240); 252. Plantago (s.n.); 253. Plantago (139, 226); 254. Phoradendron (419); 255. Juglans (51); 256 (see also 36). Sassafras (385); 257. Quercus (11); 258. Quercus (56); 259. Quercus (55, 57); 260. Quercus (or Castanea) (54); 260a. Castanea (38, 41); 261. Populus (126); 262. Salix (50); 263. Morus (65, 225); 264. Morus (43); 265. Parietaria (131); 266. Ulmus (30); 267. Ulmus (31); 268. Ulmus (372); 269. Celtis (15); 270. Comandra (22); 271. Phytolacca (214); 272. Oxybaphus (s.n., Cherokee Town); 273. Oxybaphus (110); 274. Chenopodium (199); 275. Chenopodium (141); 275a. Chenopodium (s.n.); 276. Chenopodium (198); 277. Montelia (122); 278. Amaranthus (s.n.); 279. Froelichia (152); 280.

Froelichia (s.n., Canadian R.); 281. Iresine (s.n.); 282. Gossypianthus (s.n., Cherokee Town); 283. Polygonum (s.n.); 284. Polygonum (434); 285. Polygonum (s.n.); 286. Polygonum (450); 287. Polygonum (s.n., "Cherok."); 288. Polygonum (314); 289. Polygonum (418); 290. Polygonum (s.n.); 291. Rumex (71); 292. Rumex (177); 293. Eriogonum (364); 294. Euphorbia (s.n., Cherokee Town); 294a. Euphorbia (s.n.); 295. Euphorbia (447); 296. Euphorbia (275); 297. Euphorbia (405); 298. Euphorbia (73); 299. Euphorbia (s.n.); 300. Euphorbia (383); 301. Euphorbia (37); 302. Euphorbia (313); 303. Euphorbia (123, 394); 304. Euphorbia (397); 305. Cnidoscolus (99); 306. Croton (151); 307. Gynamblosis (s.n.); 308. Croton (133); 308a. Croton (146); 309. Pilonophytum (327); 310. Acalypha (275, 446); 311. Aphora (338); 312. Tragia (145); 313. Stillingia (148); 314. Phyllanthus (346); 315. Juniperus (1); 316. Pinus (seedlings) (384); 316a. Lemna (190); 317. Juncus (241); 318. Juncus (374); 319. Juncus (374); 320. Juncus (374); 321. Arisaema (128); 322. Smilax (69, 130); 322. Smilax (s.n.); 323. Spiranthes (407); 324. Cooperia (478); 325. Polygonatum (129); 326. Androstephium (89); 327. Allium (88); 328. Allium (114); 329. Commelina (91); 330. Nemastylis (302); 331. Sagittaria (286); 332. Yucca (173); 333. Yucca (252); [334–343, inclusive, not listed by Torrey]; 344. Heteranthera (265); 345. Sparganium (348); 345a. Potamogeton (s.n.); 346. Sisyrinchium (283); 347. Cyperus (211); 348. Cyperus (s.n.); 349. Cyperus (241); 350. Cyperus (132); 351. Cyperus (241); 352. Cyperus (374).

2. *Field Notes*

Editorial comments and additions are in square brackets; otherwise the notes follow Palmer's originals as closely as possible. Numbers in square brackets, following notes on individual specimens, are the Torrey serial numbers listed above. For a fuller account of Torrey's handling of the collection of 1868, see above, page 38.

Plants collected by Dr. Edward Palmer Surgeon to the Indians of the Leased District or that section between old Fort Cobb and Fort Arbuckle some where [i.e. were] collected in the Chickasaw & Chocktaw Indian nations the manner of their arrangement needs explanation those on sheets are not all marked of some species offten only one is marked off others all [six words crossed off by Palmer] others numbered notes with the corresponding numbers are inclosed some species on sheets are not marked at all so also some seeds rolled up in paper these where collected Sep 10 next day was afflicted with Congestive feaver thus they where not marked. Many seeds rooled up and marked with the date collected sufficient of the plant accompany to determine to what species they belong to, some are numbered they where in seed when the corresponding numbered species on sheets where collected.

It is wished that what ever markings or numbers accompany the plants that the same be retained as insects that feed upon them have been collected the insects being numbered or marked the same so in future the name of the plant may be had

[Another page] Several specimens of native fruits was collected and sent to the Agricultural Department as specimens off the same fruit trees, bushes or vines, are included in the plants sent you, if you need them all good if not and the Department applies to you sending the numbers of the fruit which corresponds to the plant number please forward them if you wish the plant specimens in your collection please loan them to the said Department for figuering.

EDWARD PALMER M.D.

Plants collected by Dr. E Palmer Kiowa Agency 17 miles S.E. of old Fort Cobb and on the Washata river those marked K. A are Kiowa Agency

No. 1 Ceder thinly scattered on the red sandstone bluffs which surrounds the agency March 14 they are 50 feet high & 5 feet circumference [315]

2 April 1 mosses damp localities among oaks

3 April 10 Grown among underbrush at the Agency and Washata river corn color center of petals Cherry grows from 4 to 8 feet [40]

4 holes of the red sandstone bluffs Kiowa Agency April 8th

5 large flowering pea petals majenta, whiteish middle changes to shade of white dark stripes of the same buds are soft fleshy white April 8 grows among red sand stone bluffs [105]

6 grassey openings among trees on hills Kiowa Agency April 10th light purple (white eye with dark purple stripes [79]

7 bushes 8 feet underbrush of the Kiowa Agency on Washtaw river Ap 8

8 a Dwarf shrub among broken rocks Kiowa Agency April 8 [55]

9 hills of Kiowa Agency April 10
10 ″ ″
11 ″ ″ 8 [257]
12 ″ ″ ″ [12 p.p.]
13 prairies among grass white by age bluish in large number together Mar 20 [3]
14 foot hill of Kiowa Agency April 8
15 Washata River April 2nd [269]
16 praries among grass in masses bloom young are pink by age majenta April 2 [45b]
17 trailing plant lilac white eye grows on grassey openings among hills & praria Ap 6 [106]
18 grows on rich low spots among sunflowers in praria openings violet color and white eye Ap 6 [26]
19 among broken rocks Kiowa Agency April 8
20 in bunches praria, in grass buds are creamy white petals purplish white orange anthers April 6th [also a detached scrap of paper, marked in ink perhaps by Torrey "20 Palmer," and in pencil by Palmer "purplish white midle of lower lobe darker part which encloses the anthers black."]
21 close tufts hills Kiowa Agency pink eye greenish yellow April 6th [81] [245–6, p.p.]
22 grows in patches somewhat seperate among underbrush in hills K.A Ap 6 [270]
23 rich low spots on praria Ap 8 K.A. [11]
24 prarias grows solitary, Ap 8. K.A Ap 6 [205]
25 grows on praria among grass in colonies showey blue K.A March 20
26 peculiar fern grows in the hollows of the sand stone rocks of K. A whare it is damp forming large dense green masses April 8
27 tops of red sanstone bluffs K.A. Ap 8
28 hollows of hills Kio.Ag. Ap [201]
29 low Damp spots woods K.A Ap 7
30 Swamp ellm. K.A April 26 [266]
31 Slipery ″ ″ [267]
32 banks of Washata River April 2
33 K.A Mar 25 pink white eye [117]
34 Dwarf plum bushes from 2 to 4 feet Ap 2 Among hills of K.A. and ridges of Washata river [60]
35 plum 5 to 8 feet K.A. Mar 25 [61]

36 Ap 21 grassey hilley locallities Washata river
37 Ap 21 Washata river grassey bottoms rich loom [301]
38 Ap 21 out skirts of woods Washata river two feet high [260a, p.p.]
39 grass plain Washata river Ap 21 in large close patches
40 Ap 21 grows in large tufts Grassey plains
41 irregular tree 8 feet K.A. Ap 21 [260a, p.p.]
42 Ap 22 K.A. & Wichata river
43 Ap 20 Mullberry 7 feet K.A under brush—[264]
44 Ap 21 among grassey hills Witchata river
45 high sandy bluffs grassey openings among oaks K.A Ap 21—color orange [204]
46 K.A. April 26 flower white grows in shadey nooks among rocks [68]
47 K.A. Ap 27 grassey openings among hills and oaks [12, p.p.]
48 Wall flower among broaken hills K.A. Ap 21—cented as the cultivated ones [13]
49 K A Ap 20 broken sand hills in patches thinly scattered
50 K.A. Ap 21 swamps 8 to 12 feet [262]
51 low bottoms K.A. Ap 26 [255]
52 K.A Ap 26 among grassey openings, on hills with oak it is found singly of a violet color
53 K.A. Ap 26 solitary among hills
54 K.A Ap 26 large irregular tree [260]
55 " " [259, p.p.]
56 " straight tree [258]
57 " " [259, p.p.]
58 malvea grows among grass rich spots near Washata river April 27 fine crimson white eye [37]
59 K.A. [crossed out] Ap 27 hills [crossed out] bottom of Washata river rich soil white bloom [220]
60 Ap 27 rich soil 2nd bottoms Washata
61 " " suculent leaves clear white bloom
62 Ap 27 rich soil 2nd bottom Witchata river scattered solitarily [17]
63 grassey plains strong grower fine showey light yellow [119]
64 fine showey honey suckle grows in irregular mass without climbing cented like Hyacinth [crossed out] Jessamine of a Lemon color & red shade base of tube K.A. Ap 28 [157]
65 K.A. Ap 30 Under brush 6 feet [263, p.p.]
66 K A Ap 30 among underbrush a small bush a few inches high [57]

67 K A May 2 swamps white change pink
68 K A. May 2 solitary grassey openings among timbered hills Delacate purplish, white shade, darker stripes [225, p.p.]
69 May 6 K A A rough thorney bush [crossed out] climbing plant abundant in all the woods rendering it difficult to travel [322, p.p.]
70 Dock grows low lands K A Ap 10 [291]
71 K.A. May 2 rich open spots among hills in tufts
72 fine bushey Onothera yellow May 1 KA openings among hills [129]
73 grassey hills and rich 2nd bottoms of Washata river April 20 [298]
74 low rich soil base of hills and 2nd river bottoms May 1 [30]
75 small plant rich bottom soil damp, base of hills and 2nd bottoms of rivers April 20 [10]
76 K A Ap 21 shadey hills [16]
77 small plant thinly scattering among grass undulating hills along rivers white bloom Washata [111]
78 rockey shadey hill sides K.A. Ap 20
79 plains along Washata Ap 21
80 Ap 21 showey anual very abundant grassey plains
81 Oxalis rich damp soil grassey 2nd bottoms and base of hills Ap 30 [45a]
82 in large compact masses plains May 4
83 rich low spots plains scattering May 3
84 light purple white bars May 3 grows on grassey hills, Washata river [198, p.p.]
85 very abundant grassey hills along the Washata river May 3
86 thick patches edges of woods rich soil along Washata river May 4 white bloom, but changes to pink and crimson as morning dawns [135]
87 in thick underbrush, damp white shaded slightly violet K A May 2 [193]
88 grassey hills Washata river April 1 yellowish white [327]
89 grassey hills Washata April 1 slightly cented as hiocinth, violet color [326]
90 light purple upper petal white eye, lower petal Darker purple Ap 25 shady woods K. A [80]
91 blue grassey plains and shady hills among grass May 1st Washata river [329]
92 Larkspur grassey plains Washata river May 4th

93 grassey hills Washata river May 4 [43]
94 " " violet color slightly mint cented May 4 [238a]
95 grassey plains of the Washata river roots eaten by Indians May 4
96 grassey hills Washata river fennel cented May 4 [148]
97 grassey hills of Washata river brown & golden yellow May 4
98 grassey hills Washata river bright yellow changes redish May 4 [130]
99 hills openings, among trees roots 3 feet long & 6½ inches in circumference cented as fine as the tuber rose the root equals to bloom while the leaf sting severely the l[e?]ast toutch fine white Washata river May 4th [305]
100 brown outside inside green lower lip turn down woods Washata river May 1st [218]
101 grassey hills Washata river suculent leaves, White May 4
102 Panzey grassey hills Washata river May 4th red lower lobe white & green center [24]
103 grassey 2nd bottoms of Washata river May 4 purple [208, p.p.]
104 grape among underbrush Washata river May 4th not great climbers [49, p.p.]
105 2nd bottoms and hills of Washata river May 4 among grass lilac color [103]
106 violet color, May 4 grassey hills of Washata river [224, p.p.]
107 2nd bottoms of Washata river May 4 several stems together, red bloom
108 finenely shaded violet darker edges of petals Dark purple stripes among thinly scattering trees hills of Washata river May 4 [226, p.p.]
109 edges of woods Washata river May 4th White [200]
110 crimson shadey openings Woods Washata river May 5th [273]
111 brown & yellow shadey opening among trees Washata May 5 [215]
112 grassey hills among trees Washata river opens by night May 5 [133]
113 grassey openings among hills Washata river May 6th royal purple [195, p.p.]
114 onions hills of Washata river May 1st [328]

Plants collected near old Ft Cobb by Dr. E. Palmer

115 its root is used raw and eaten for pain in stomach or when

powdered—alls in an infusion it is much used for Collic in horses grows in shady opening among trees on hills Disagreeable smell trailing plant black color May 20

116 the root is red and is much used in Diarrhea. made into a Decoction and drank grows upon grassey openings

117 an irregular growing shrub 5 to 10 feet grows base of wooded hills edges of woods, yellowish white bloom May 19 [154]

118 poisoned Ivy shruby in several stems 4½ feet foot hills Washata river May 21 [58, p.p.]

119 sandy hills annual not higher than three feet hills of the Washata —May 20

120 grows in close damp woods among underbrush near streams May 20 [4]

121 grows in sandy grassey openings among cotton woods near streams May 20th petals white [78]

122 shady wood Washata river May 20 [277]

123 shade edges of woods Washata May 20 [303, p.p.]

124 burning bush shrub upright grower rather compact 8 ft Dark brown [53]

125 Lilley from Lake near old Ft Cobb comanches call it Currates is eaten the roots being boiled eaten raw by Indians when boiled taste as Irish potatoes [5]

126 cotton wood seed May 20th [261]

127 Sasparilla grows in rich moist shady woods in thick masses its roots growing thick together and running a great distance May 20th bloom white is much used as a decoction for clenzeing the blood [6]

128 grows near streams in thick damp woods May 20 bloom straw color [321]

129 solomons seal bloom greenish yellow tipped green grows in rich wet shady woods May 20 [325]

130 a rough thorney climber in great masses among underbrush May 20 [322, p.p.]

131 Damp shady woods May 20 [265]

132 small grass grows in beds a little apart sand hills May 20 [350]

133 sand hills used to make tea a fine aromatic smell its tea tast like sage tea somewhat [308]

134 grassey openings wooded hills May 20

135 grassey openings wooded hills May 20 yellowish white

136 grass plains several stems white tipped green May 22 [206]

137 loose growing shrub in large bunches praria openings and edge of woods black—May 22 [100, p.p.]
138 upright plant in patches thinly scattered over grassey plains, white May 22
139 in patches, but little grass upon the ground old deserted ant hills May 24 [253, p. p.]
140 Malvia small very light purple bloom wood openings May 22
141 pigg weed light rich soil woodey openings & roadsides May 22 [275]
142 milk weed orange bloom grows in bunches grassey openings among woods May 22
143 bunches edges of woods May 22
144 purplish white mint cent grassey opening among hills May 20 [194, 235]
145 tufted plant, nettle sting May 22 openings among hills [312]
146 grassey hills May 22 [308a]
147 grassey hills stinking plant May 22 [18]
148 large bunches plains yellow [313]
149 sweet cented grass
150 climbing plant among underbrush white, May 22 [141]
151 grassey hills May 22, thinly scattered [306]
152 thinly scattered grassey hills May 22 [279]
153 virgin thistle grows on sand woody opening white May 22 [8]
154 large bushey plant sandy wood openings white sweet cented as tuber rose its root is as sweet as the bloom after it is dried—is very milkey [on a detached paper: "154 the root of this plant made into a decoction drank or applied externally generates milk in female breasts."]
155 climbing Ivy May 22 [58, p.p.]
156 yellow close by day May 20 grassey hills [134]
157 annual. Lemon color close by day May 20 wood openings [132]
158 very light purple lower lobe darker redish stripes yellow anthers [crossed out] pistil in bunches and many scattering near by May 20 [225, p.p.]
159 violet center of petal shaded white grows thinly scattered among grass wood opening on hills [224, p.p.]
160. thinly scattered in grass by openings on wooded hills, pink, white organs May 20
161 grassey openings wooded hills dark cherry color May 20
162 scattering in great numbers among grass wooded hills May 22

163 grows in large bunches edges of woods its roots when made into a Dection and poored into a fish hole brings them to the top and are easily caught May 20 upper petal whit upper surface cream under lower lobe white side, petals pink shady white center [114]
164 showey small annual brown [crossed out] lemon eye bloom between pink and light purple thinly scattering among grass wood opening on hills May 20
165 among grass in bottoms near woods, violet, eye softy purpy [i.e. purply ?] white color May 20 [195, p.p.]
166 edges of woods base of hills trailer, cherry light white base of upper petal and center of lower petal May 22 [116]
167 pink white eye grassey hills thinly scattering May 22 [245–6, p.p.]
168 tufts oak hills light purple darker striped tube whiteish May 22 [231]
169 trailing 2nd river bottoms among grass Crimson its roots are steeped in hot water and applied to wounds the roots is also pulverized and applied to cut & wounds it is also called buzzard weed or root from its smell [39, p.p.]
170 [number 170 written over as 210] root of this plant is pounded and by the Caddo Indians is carried with their bullets which are greased the dust adhereing and being Carried into the wound turns it yellow causeing the animal to be come insensable
171 Osage Tobacco used to smoke and as a decoction for Ague
172 used in a Decoction for sore throats
173 Adams needle Bears grass soap plant Spanish Bayonet the Delawares make ropes out of the leaves greenish yellow bloom [332]

A burr oak 2 feet 8 inches ¾ through contained 178 annular rings

174 in soil (rockey shady hills, May 22
175 a small annual cent of fennel May 26 [148a]
176 annual mint oder [238, p.p.]
177 low sandy spots hills in thick patches May 26 [292]
178 in thick Dense woods May 26 [159]
179 thick woods large shrub very scraggley greenis white bloom May 26 [52]
180 Black shumack the laves when red in the fall are dried by the Creek Indians tied in bunches and smoked as required grows on wooded rockey hills May 26th [59, p.p.]
181 grows in praria openings surrounded with woods white May 26

the milkey juice is used by the Indians to rub over brands of animals the hair falling out leaves the skin clear of any markings and when the hair grows out no trace of the former brand is left

182 grows along water cources, white, 8 feet May 26 [156]
183 among grass river 2nd bottoms purple May 26 [9] [207]
184 barren shady rocks May 27
185 Dark woods May 26 [160]
186 side of shady water courses May 26
187 rich 2nd river bottoms May 26
188 scattering in great numbers on rich compact Loam 2nd river bottoms May 26
189 edges of woods, scarce May 26 [69]
190 Lake near Witchata agency May 26 [316a]
191 Gord very common vine immence root bloom yellow greenish markins [140]
192 the root of this plant made into a Decoction is used as a cure for sore eyes [226, p.p.]
193 large showey bright pink—organs white anthers yellow sand hills May 28 [33]
194 small bloom pink allso its organs but anthers yellow and style white sand hills it with 193 blooms out as the day receeds May 28 [34]
195 praria along the Washata river 2nd bottoms May 29
196 edges of woods among grass small white bloom May 29 ["Fraxinus 196"]
197 2nd river bottoms near woods May 28
198 Pigg weed old road sides old fields & wood openings all over the country May 28 [276]
199 light sandy grassey hills May 28 [274]
200 in bunches wooded sand hills [27, p.p.]
201 edges of woods 2nd river bottoms rich loam May 28th
202 wooded sand hills Lilac bloom May 29
203 three feet sandy prarie near rivers, white at night change as day advance to pink then red May 29 [137]
204 large bunches near woods 2nd river bottoms May 29th
205 (yellow & black number but little apart old wood fields or light grassey opening near woods May 29th
206 praria sand hills scattered in numbers near each other May 29 pinkish white
207 a decoction made from the root and taken internally cures pain

in stomach small trailing shrub sand noles praria red petals organs white then green and then black May 28 [72]

208 sandy Praria near woods May 29

209 sandy praria violet color white eye May 29 [198, p.p.]

210 Sensative plant bright pink trailer sandy loam near water and sand plain May 29 used by Caddoes to put on arrows [121]

211 sand plains near river May 29 [347]

212 & 213 [28] foot of sand hills grassey openings among trees May 29

213 small plant runns into thick masses small white blooms white yellow eye when first bloom, change yellow by age, rich moist 2nd bottoms May 29 [249] [28, p.p.]

214 pinkish white bloom powdered root rubbed up with lard used for Itch leaves powdered and applied to wounds removes inflamation [270]

215 low ground by rivers or raveins center of bloom white rest pinkish May 31

216 grows on denuded sand hills among grass bloom black or mottled white or half white or purple with black base May 31 [14]

217 Cactus very scarce on sand rock May 31 yellow base red stamens yellow anthers white allso white middle [145]

218 sage smell sandy praria May 31 leaves around the blooms purplish white bloom greenish white purple dotts [232]

219 May 31 sand praria

220 wood openings May 31

221 sandy praria (rolling May 31

222 low wet raveins in praria May 31 white base of lower petal purple striped

223 White shumac the young shoots stripped of their bark are much eaten by the Indians when the leaves are red they are rubbed up by the Comanches into Rennecanic slightly greased and universally used to smoke upon many it produce great irretation of the mucus membrane [59, p.p.]

224 among shady woods, white June 6 [76]

225 Mullberry fine showey Dwarf tree 5 to 10 feet June 3rd [263, p.p.]

226 grassey sand hills with timber June 5th [253, p.p.]

227 Among grassey hills June 5

228 " "

229 " "

230 edges of shady woods June 5

231 Clematis moderate climber among under brush brownish red June 5th [2]
232 2nd bottoms in bunches June 5
233 2nd river bottoms Washata river June 5th
234 Damp spots, 2nd bottoms of Washata river June 5th
235 sandy hills slopes Washata river June 5
236 moist shady spots, June 5 Washata river
237 2 river bottoms Washata river June 5 yellow [210]
238 grassey 2nd bottoms of the Washata river June 5th white blooms [28 p.p.]

thus ends the collections on the Washata river and vacinity by E. Palmer M.D.

Plants collected at the Cherokee town & vacinity Chickasaw nation June 8th 1868 by Dr. E. Palmer M.D.

239 boggey holes on praria openings white bloom red Dotts base of upper petal June 8th [216, 230 p.p.]
240 boggey spots in praria openings great abundance June 8 [251]
241 boggey spotts praria openings June 8th [317] [349, 351]
242 sandy openings praria near woods June 8
243 seccond bottoms of sand Creek June 8
244 rich bottoms among grass June 8th
245 rich bottoms among grass, towards timber June 8 greenish white mimosa [122]
246 Dwarf shrub edges of Wooded hills white showey June 8 [54]
247 grassey hills near woods violet upper petal lake white lower lobe [101]
248 grassey hills near woods June 8 blue [99]
249 rich bottoms near woods among grass June 8
250 grassey hills near woods very showey in bunches whiteish purple deep purple center June 8th
251 Phlox grassey hills near Woods pinkish red blueish eye—blueish petal white eye [191]
252 Yucca sandy ridges 1½ to 2 feet greenish yellow in side lighter (white organs) very scattering near Cherokee town June 9 [333]
253 Cactus outer part of petal corn color middle or a vein brick red June 9
254 passion flower showey climber under brush edges of woody raveins purple & White June 10 [143, p.p.]

255 short climber edges of woods upper petals yellow lower corn color June 10 [110]
256 petals orange, base dark brown river bottoms and edges of woods June 9
257 among grass under trees June 10 pink stripes radiating from white center [107, p.p.]
258 damp bottoms among grass June 10
259 Stramonium edges of woods purplish white deep purple middle June 11 [211]
260 verbena purplish red large strong grower edges of woods June 11 [247, p.p.]
261 boggs, succulent small white bloom greenish yellow eye June 9
262 grows among grass—near wood and raveins white by night by day change pink June 9 [127]
263 grows in many branches round a common stem white but by morning is pink June 9 2 bottoms near woods [137a]
264 damp localities in bunches June 9
265 Grows in marshes outer rim petals purple inner row blue upper one base white two purple & 2 white Dotts leaves above water [344]
266 edges of woods and raveins yellow June 10 [113]
267 open spots in wood and raveins rich moist soil greenish yellow June 9 (–4 feet [161]
268 shady woods, red bloom June 9th
269 raveins & shady woods June 9 bloom white organs yellow [214]
270 shady woods light purpleish white June 10 [27, p.p.]
271 shady woods yellowish green light green eye June 9th [213]
272 shady raveins and woods June 9 [151] [153]
273 violet color gravely spots in woods June 9
274 small white rose by age often of pinkish tinge wooded hills June 9 [70]
275 shady raveins June 9 [296] [310, p.p.]
276 damp bottoms along grass very showey pink green eye yellow anthers June 9 [189]
277 mint like smell delately white shady purple lower lobe dotted red blooms surrounded by a whirl of purple leaves wooded hills June 9
278 grassey hills pink [85]
279 [missing—omitted from series.]
280 among underbrush moderate climber, milkey

281 damp bottoms June 9 violet color, river sides [139, p.p.]
282 moist grassey bottoms bright pink June 10 [75]
283 blue yellow eye June 9 moist grassey bottoms [346]
284 grassey 2nd bottoms and edges of woods June 8
285 royal purple (eye greenish corn color June 9 openings among woods [208, p.p.]
286 white, marshes, June 9 [223] [331]
287 shady woods 2 river bottoms June 10 greenish yellow
288 open spots in shady woods, yellow with green eye radiating in five lines up the petals June 11 [214a]
289 shady woods June 11
290 violet color eye corn color anthers yellow June 11 gravelly spotts among woods [208, p.p.]
291 same discription as 290
292 old fields and open rich spots among woods white anthers yellow June 11 [207a, p.p.]
293 among underbrush pink June 12
294 shady damp raveins June 12

Plants collected by Dr. E. Palmer

295 cactus on the rockey hills near Mill creek Chickasaw nation July 2
296 grows on edges and divisions of rocky hills Chickasaw Nation near Mill creek July 2 crimson [39, p.p.]
297 white eye lower lobe violet upper petal Delacate yellow shaded violet and darker striped by age turns light nankeen grows on grassey hills Penington creek Chickasaw Nation July 2 [73]
298 climbs among grass and low bushes rich soil Penington creek Chickasaw Nation July 2 (Pink, eye white
299 grows upon rockey ridges Penington creek Chickasaw nation July 2 an offensive piney smell [83]
300 edges of hills (oak) a very delacate pink shaded blue by age or in drying change deeper blue June 27 Choctaw nation
301 rockey ridges July 1 Chickasaw nation [44]
302 grows among grass wood openings blue river Choctaw nation June 27 a very Delacate pink, shrivels up after the heat of hand touches it [330]
303 trailing plant edges of praria raveins holes and grassless spots yellow sensative plant June 28 Chickasaw nation [125]
304 a grass very gummey in bunches hills Chickasaw nation June 26

305 edges of woods and praria openings (white July 1 Chickasaw nation [149] [212]
306 Prarias & skirtings of woods a very Delacate blue Choctaw nation June 27
307 among grass edges of woods bloom white Penington Creek Chickasaw nation June 26 [107, p.p.]
308 shady woods near creeks Choctaw nation June 30 uper petal red lower white
309 edges of woods & prarias yellow as soon as the [sun ?] is hot the petals curls under June 26 boiling spring Chickasaw nation
310 edges of woods and raveins white bloom Chickasaw nation July 2 [124]
311 damp spots by creeks and praria raveins yellow July 2 Chickasaw nation [21]
312 edges of creek and shady woods (white) Penington creek Chickasaw nation July 1 [222]
313 Praria raveins and hollows Chickasaw nation July 1 [302]
314 grassey dry spots in woods blue river June 1 [i.e. July 1] Choctaw Nation [288]
315 grassey openings among woods yellow July 1 Chickasaw nation [126]
316 a curious grass grows in bunches on prarias July 1 but soon as dry falls appart Chickasaw nation
317 edges of most creek banks and raveins Penington creek Chickasaw nation July 1 blue
318 fine showey plant Prarias Chickasaw nation July 1 violet color upper inner part of tube very dark [221]
319 edges of woods Choctaw nation June 30
320 Prarias Chickasaw nation July 1 white
321 showey plant praria openings among woods boggey Depot Choctaw nation June 29, buds yellowish white blooms white but by age and drying turns red [115]
322 showey yellow praria openings among woods Boggey Depot Choctaw nation June 29 yellow [128]
323 yellow base of petals greenish Bogey Depot Praria opening among woods June 29
324 woods of choctaw nation (white bloom June 27 [32]
325 Praria openings among woods Boggey Depot Choctaw nation June 29 (yellow

326 Praria openings among woods June 29 yellow base of petals brown (Boggey Depot—Choctaw nation
327 sage like smell (white) grassey openings among woods Blue river Choctaw Nation June 30 [309]
328 low shrub in woods compact grower in great numbers together Chickasaw Nation June 1 [i.e. July 1] bloom greenish yellow red outside [158]
329 very light purple but lower petal irregularly marked dark re[d]ish purple woods near raveins and river sides July 2 Chickasaw nation [240]
330 grassey openings in woods Boggey Depot Choctaw nation June 29 white mint cented [234]
331 white, yellow organs old fields road sides and wood openings Chickasaw nation July 1 [207a, p.p.]
332 woods Boggey Depot Choctaw nation 4 ft delacate pink base of upper petal slightly marked red then green—by age the blooms fade to greenish yellow June 26 very stickey—
333 damp spots grassey openings among woods Boggey river Choctaw nation June 26
334 shady spots by water Choctaw nation blue river July 1
335 damp holes in woods blue river Choctaw nation June 30—pinkis red
336 delacate pink white eye grows abundly in light rich opening in woods Chickasaw nation June 25 [162]
337 irregular bushey shrub 5 ft blue river Choctaw nation July 1 peculiar smell [46]
338 blue river Choctaw river July 1 edges of woods greenish yellow milky exudations when cut [311]
339 edges of woods, blue river Choctaw Nation bloom light blue July 1 [242]
340 moist spots praria raveins blooms white strong grower two to 3 feet [123]
341 Shumac, dwarf shrub bogey rivers Choctaw nation June 30 yellow green cast anthers orange [56]
342 flat rock creek Chickasaw nation July 2 grows dry openings in woods
343 rockey hills flat rock creek Chickasaw nation July 2 yellow resinous smell of which it is full
344 rockey hills Penington creek stickey plant (orange color July 2 [142]

345 slender plant grows among springs and by creeks Chickasaw nation light blue cented as peneroyal [237]
346 grows upon rockey hills Pennington creek Chickasaw nation July 1 [314]
347 Dry openings in woods Choctaw nation June 27 [20]
348 river bottoms Lagoons June 25 Chickasaw nation [345]
349 wooded hills boggey rivers Choctaw nation June 26 yellow grows scattering [22]
350 shady woods June 24 Choctaw nation
351 prarias near woods fine royal purple Chickasaw nation June 25 [243]
352 loose growing shrub 5 to 6 feet showey blue, enterence to mountains, Fort Smith road Choctaw nation, July [i.e. June ?] 27 [100, p.p.]
353 shady raveins in woods yellow Choctaw nation June 25 [138]
354 showey half climbing rose near streams and moist openings in woods Choctaw nation June 26 fine rose color by age fade to dirty white
355 moist raveins and damp opening in prarias Chickasaw nation June 24
356 rockey raveins hills Rileys Mills Choctaw nation June 26
357 bulbous root rockey pine hills Rileys Mill Choctaw nation (pink June 25
358 Salvia Rileys Mills Choctaw nation June 25 by raveins showey blue, tube white extending two thirds up the lower petal [241]
359 pink, grows among grass wooded hills Rileys Mills Choctaw nation June 25 [74]
360 bloom white, Praries Chickasaw nation July 1 [147]
361 loose growing shrub 6 ft by creek, white, June 24 Chickasaw nation
362 purple bloom among grass & brush skirting timber Chickasaw nation June 24 use in tea for feavers—burgamot centet (234a, p.p.]
363 bloom white burgamot cented (among grass and underbrush Chickasaw nation the only plant seen June 24 [234a, p.p.]
364 edges of woods in praria Chickasaw nation June 26 [293]
365 grows upon post oak and used by the people of Texas to dye brown
366 grows near creeks, hills round Rileys Mills Choctaw nation, redish brown

367 grows in praria raveins near woods Chickasaw nation Scarlett mottled white June 24th [192]
368 Rileys Mills among oaks only plant seen lavender base upper part of petal light salmon June 25 [248]
369 Rileys Mills Chocktaw nation June 26 oak openings, white, red dotts sage smell [233]
370 woods Rileys Mills Choctaw nation June 26 [91]
371 in bunches woods of Rileys mills Choctaw nation June 26
372 a fine hansome compact growing tree 6 feet woods Choctaw nation June 27 [268]
373 praria opening woods near Rileys Mills Choctaw nation June 27
374 low grounds and creek sides Choctaw nation July 1 [318] [319] [352]
375 rockey ridges Chickasaw nation June 25
376 grassey edges of creeks Chickasaw nation yellow bloom June 24 [108]
377 rockey ridges white bloom in bunches Pennington creek June 27 [29]
378 rich grassey river bottoms Washtaw river June 24
379 boiling spring Chickasaw nation June 24 yellow black dotts [219]
380 white piney smell grassey hills Chickasaw nation June 24 [88]
381 grassey praria edges of woods boiling spring Chickasaw nation June 25
382 among grass wood openings, Chickasaw nation Penington creek, white June 25
383 edges of raveins near woods Chickasaw nation June 24 [300]
384 Pine trees of Rileys Mills Choctaw nation June 27 trees average 75 feet makes fine timber little resin no notts—one tree measured 6 feet counted 130 rings [316]
385 Sassafras very scarce for During the Confederate war it was nearly all dug up found Rileys Mill by Mountain brook June 25 [36] [256]
386 White Malvia grassey Praria hills Chickasaw nation June 22
387 grassey praria openings among woods Choctaw nation July 1 petals royal purple middle of lower petal black, lower lobe white [120, p.p.]
388 Prarias Chickasaw nation exudes a milkey juice (white July 2 [136]
389 Prarias Chickasaw nation (pink) July 2
390 showey purple road sides Chickasaw nation July 1 large bunches [247, p.p.]

391 among grass 2 river bottoms white, only three plants of this color seen June 24 Chickasaw nation [188, p.p.]
392 grassey openings among woods edges of timber July 1 Blue river Choctaw Nation
393 A very showey bunchey plant grows upon rockey hills of a bright yellow July 2 Chickasaw nation near Penington creek [131]
394 road sides and bare grassless spots flat rock creek Chickasaw nation July 2 [303, p.p.]
395 Love vine the negroes of the Chickasaw nation have a superstition that if you think a woman in love with you the way to find it out is to take a peice of this vine fasten it to a nother plant if it grows she is in love if not your suspicions are at fault. [202]
396 grows upon grassless spots clay loom near creeks or raveins Cherokee town orange bloom 1 to 6 feet [19]
397 Prarias Chickasaw nation June 24—(white) milkey juice exudes when cut [304]
398 climbing plant among underbrush showey white bloom red inside of tube July 1st Penington creek Chickasaw nation [199]
399 Delacate pinkish white Deeper pink eye rocky hills Penington creek Chickasaw nation July 2 [163]
400 sas [i.e. same ?] as 399 only white color
401 bare gravelly spots among hills Penington creek Chickasaw nation July 2 pink closes by day
402 Rockey hills of Penington creek Chickasaw nation July 2 fine showey pink [187]
403 half climber edges of woods by raveins strong grower July 3 white bloom some what resembles the grape vine [51]
404 Prarias by raveins & road sides, white, milkey Chickasaw nation July 2
405 shady woods Chickasaw nation July 2 [297]
406 edges of woods and raveins Boiling spring Chickasaw nation July 2 creamy yellow and covered with insects [82]
407 a soft succulent rooted plant wood openings among timber [crossed out] grass (white, fleshy bloom difficult to dry Chickasaw nation June 25 [323]
408 Climber Rileys Mill Chickasaw nation June 27 [190]
409 Blue river bottoms Choctaw nation July 1 [250]
410 hansome small gracefull regular growing trees 5 to 10 feet Boggey rivers Choctaw nation June 30 [66]
411 fine showey climbs among small plants in woods Choctaw na-

tion July 1 fine light purple, white base tube upper petal striped dark redish purple above which it is white an fan shape to near top of petal [109]

412 a loose growing plant upon sandy spots and stoney ridges Penington creek [102]

413 moist spotts on prarias and in wood openings Choctaw nation June 28 light purplish white with redish purple stripes [7] [139, p.p.]

414 rockey ridges near woods Boggey river Choctaw nation July 1 pinkish purple with red dotts [238, p.p.]

415 creek sides Rileys Mill Choctaw nation June 27 (white [150]

416 strong growing plant Prarias of Choctaw nation June 25—bloom white [120, p.p.]

417 by creeks & swampy river banks white [230, p.p.]

418 climbs among under brush along creeks and edges of woods white July 2 Chickasaw nation [289]

419 found growing aboundantly on swamp elms sometimes on oaks Chocktaw nation June 28 [254]

420 edges of woods raveins & creeks—white a decoction made from the root of this plant is used by the Indians to cure ague [244]

421 yellow woods of Rileys Mill Choctaw nation June 25

422 small shrub 2 to 5 ft Stoney hills of Rileys Mill Choctaw nation June 27

423 wood openings boggey river Choctaw nation June 29—yellow

424 woods of Rileys Mills Choctaw nation June 27

425 by sides of creeks Choctaw nation June 29 edge of petals yellow then Deep orange and then brown

426 a thick wide spreding small tree 10 ft creek sides Rileys Mill June 27 [155]

427 Wood openings Choctaw nation—orange, July 1

428 light loose soil rockey hills bright showey thistle like plant Lilac color Penington Creek Choctaw nation July 2

429 moderate climber among underbrush Choctaw nation June 27 [50]

430 white mottled purple sage cented a decotion is made of this plant and used in feavers it is also used to wash the skin to cool it June 26 moist spots in wood and by raveins boiling spring to Rileys Mill [239]

431 orange color Mill creek Chickasaw nation edges of woods June 24

432 woods of Rileys Mill June 27 Choctaw nation (orange) [96] [104]
433 Prarias of Chickasaw nation June 24 yellow & brown
434 swamps of the Chickasaw nation June 23 [284]
435 yellow bloom wood openings close by night, Choctaw nation June 30 [45]
436 light spots—among rockey ridges Penington creek Chickasaw nation June 25—white [203]
437 creamy white bloom offensive piney smell grows in sandy soil flat rock creek Chickasaw nation July 2 [84]
438 trailing verbena purple white eye road sides Chickasaw nation June 24 [245-6, p.p.]
439 orange bloom Wood opening Penington creek Chickasaw nation June 25
440 edges of woods pinkish white deeper pink towards edge of petal June 23 Chickasaw nation [97]
441 grassey moist spots bottoms of blue river Choctaw nation June 29

collected at Cherokee town

442 small climber among underbrush old field & shady woods bloom Greenish yellow Cherokee town July 12 [144]
443 edges of woods upper lip of Calax red upper petal pink lower white July 10
444 small plant—sandy loom wood openings light purplish white bloom July 11 [217]
445 plant strong grower 4½ feet old fields, woods river bottoms orange blooms July 10 [77]
446 shady woods & old fields July 10 [310, p.p.]
447 July 10 old Fields and roadsides [295]
448 Iron weed high dry woods Majenta Color July 10
449 fine violet color—seccond river bottoms 3 ft high July 9
450 pink bloom low spots river bottoms July 13 [286]
451 2nd river bottoms purple bloom July 10 [209]
452 woods the root is bulbus and pounded moistened is a cure for snake bites July 12
453 grass edges of Dry raveins near rivers July 12
454 blue white cast center of lower petals 2 river bottom July 12 [236]
455 tall climber shady woods July 9 white bloom very milkey
456 a strong climbing grape grows on Washata river ripens July 12th

at Cherokee Town pleasant taste but small, black abundant bearer [49, p.p.]

457 thin skin, pulp clean from pit and skin fine pleasant taste after the gage Dark scarlet tapering to point slight Depression to curve of stem bush lose grower slim rather pendent. [64, p.p.]

458 fine round clear looking fruit of bright yellow thickly studied with corn colored Dotts—by age becomes more opaque the specks nearly disappearing and assumeing a redish shade more or less over the fruit with redish specks as it approaches to decay rather tough skin flesh adhere to pit fine sweet some what like the magnum bonum plum—upright grower compact [64, p.p.]

459 small round fruit flattened on sumit eye depressed more depressed on one side with mark to stem Dark Cherry red, thin skin thickly studdied with small white specs some pulp adhere to pit firm pulp of medium tart and sweet—wine sower tree stiff, upright grower [64, p.p.]

460 light cherry when first ripe, darker specks throu skin by age become Dark scarlet sumit has a small black spine small depression with a mark to stem—tough skin pulp adhere to stone of a mealy agreeable taste (largest of all) [64, p.p.]

Thes plums grows up the banks of the Canadian river and sandy ridges to the Arkansas river from 2½ to 4 feet

461 dwarf branching plant, woods, Chickasaw nation July 10 eye white petals light lilac lower petal center of much Darker [90]

462 woods high hills West of Canadian river Chickasaw nation bright pink July 19 [188, p.p.]

463 grows on sandy banks of Canadian river Chickasaw Nation July 19 pink with Delacate purple tinge [86]

464 grows in mire edge of Lake near little river Semonole nation July 18 Corn color, transparent—

465 trailing plant sandy spots Canadian river Choctaw nation July 19 lilac color [87]

466 high rockey wooded hills of little river Semonole nation bloom light orange color 3 to 4 feet branching [228]

467 high wooded hills W of Canadian river Chickasaw nation July 20 yellow very showey [229]

468 grows in lake near little river Semonole nation July 20—yellow lower petal center of is orange

469 black raspberry strong grower river bottoms and rich depressions between hills very productive 6 feet July 19 Semonole nation [67]

470 grassey hills of Cherokee town Chickasaw nation July 10
471 grassey hills Cherokee town July 12 bloom tube white slightly shaded pink on the outside while the inside is studdied with crimson Dotts. petals Delacate pink light green leaves [227]
472 trailing plant wood openings edges of raveins pink July 14 [112]
473 small climber July 14 creamy yellow among under brush raveins & edges of woods Cherokee town
474 Passion flower royal purple outer part of petals next rim of white then dark purple then white then dark purple then a rim of one fifth white eye pinkish red [143, p.p.]
475 grows in rich seccond bottom land very showey of a succulent nature pistil and stamens green anthers orange eye of petals irregular of a rich dark shiney lilac white radiating to rich purple upper part of petal
476 among broken ridges and raveins in woods near water courses an irregular but rather thick growing tree of 15 to 20 feet August 6th Cherokee town [197]
477 fox grape on gravelly wooded hills and raveins often but very short wood pendent to ground and unsupported by trees of a very agreeable foxey taste pulp thick rather tough makes fine preserves—[47]
478 a fine showey bulbous plant grows upon grassey plains a straight stem without leaves spring up Aug 18 [10? 20? 28?] after rains—buds redish petals outside veined the same [324]
479 Dear plum much eaten by that animal and becomes very fat turns deep cherry beginning of July but are not ripe untill last of Sep [62]
480 Large plum tree grows on post oak hills near water courses commences to change color July but ripens in Sep 10 of a sowr smell orange red, deep bloom, often covered with black more or less in flavour of wine sower plum [63]
481 an abundant productive grape black Sep 2 [48]
482 curious running bunch grass roots at every joint the bunches throws out shoots untill a great mass is formed after ponds and small streams dry up in August (31)
483 beggers lice (from the seeds sticking to passers through wood very showey abundand bloomer delacate pink base of upper petal two green lips with rays of wine red [94, 483 bis=95]
484 rose pink base of upper petal green with two divisions magenta colored rays (woods [93, 98]

APPENDIX V

Edward Palmer's Last Will and Testament

This document is filed with the Registrar of Wills, U. S. Court House, Washington, D. C., under Administration 18,023. Notations filed with the will indicate that Palmer's estate at the time of his death amounted to about $4500, including about $1000 in cash and $3500 realized from the sale of his Washington real estate. Some miscellaneous clippings were sold to F. P. Harper for $15. Palmer's two nieces received the amounts stipulated in the will, but I cannot find out that any of the remainder of the money was used either to procure portraits of Black Beaver and Major Shanklin, or to publish any of Palmer's notes. The balance of the estate was turned over to the Episcopal Eye, Ear and Throat Hospital as required by the will.

Palmer's body was buried in Rock Creek Cemetery, Washington, D. C. (Site 6, Lot 49, Section N), and a stone bearing his name was erected there some years later.

In the name of God Amen: I, Edward Palmer of the City of Washington and District of Columbia, now residing in said City and District, being of sound and disposing mind, memory and understanding, considering the certainty of death, and the uncertainty of the time thereof, and being about to set out on a journey to Mexico, and being desirous to settle my worldly affairs before starting, do therefore make, publish and declare this my last will and testament in manner and form following, that is to say.

First and principally, I commit my soul unto the hands of Almighty God, and my body to the earth to be decently buried according to the discretion of my executors hereinafter named, and after my debts and all personal charges are paid, I devise and bequeath, as follows, to wit:

As soon after my death as convenient I direct that my real estate be sold either at private or public sale as to my said executors shall appear to be most advantageous, and upon the usual times of payment, and the proceeds thereof, as well as all other property, of whatsoever kind, and all money belonging to me at the time of my death to be paid and devoted [preceding 3 words interlined, above, with marginal note: "This inter-lineation made before signing" and signature: "Edward Palmer"] by my said Executors to the following named persons and uses and no other.

First I give and bequeath unto my two nieces, Mirtle [*sic*] H. Palmer, and Jassemine [*sic*] L. Palmer daughters of my brother William Palmer late of Washington D. C. deceased, each the sum of five hundred dollars in money to be paid with as little delay as practicable after my decease.

Second. I direct my said executors to procure a picture of Black Beaver, a Delaware Indian, who once saved my life, and that of Major Shankland, an Indian Agent, and have the same pictures suitably framed and hung up in the Indian Collection of the Smithsonian Institute in Washington D. C. and the Expense thereof to be paid out of my estate.

Third. Inasmuch as I have made various expeditions to distant parts in the interest of science and have preserved notes of my observations and discoveries which are now among my effects in the City of Washington D. C. and only a part thereof have been arranged and prepared for publication, In the basement of the Seed Laboratory of the Department of Agriculture will be found nine boxes and two trunks, containing miscellaneous papers and pictures which are in part the result and fruits of my said observations and discoveries. It is my wish, and my said executors are hereby directed to consult Doctor J. N. Rose of the National Museum and Doctor L. H. Dewey of the Department of Agriculture as to the best way of utilizing the said papers and pictures in conformity with this my will.

I further direct that my said executors may in their discretion examine all of my said notes and papers, and, in their discretion, may publish the same, and for that purpose, may use of my said estate the sum of not exceeding two thousand dollars.

Fourth, I give, devise and bequeath all the rest, residue and remainder of my estate of whatever nature or kind, unto the Episcopal Eye, Ear, and Throat Hospital of Washington D. C. and to their successors forever.

Memorandum. My estate, so far as known now, consists of the following real estate, all lying in the City of Washington District of Columbia, to wit. Lots No. 22 and 23, in Bond & Schmidt Trustees subdivision of lot nine (9) in square 1,001, being Nos. 1,312, 1,314, Eleventh Street S.E. and part of lot No. 1 in square No. 766, being No. 815, Third Street, S.E. and the following Personal Estate, to wit. A Life Insurance policy in the Phoenix Mutual Life Insurance Company of Hartford Connecticut, for the sum of nine hundred and eighteen (918) dollars fully paid up, and payable at my death, to my executors administrators or assigns; the sum of about Two hundred and seventy dollars on deposit in the National Bank of Washington, District of Columbia; thirty six shares of stock in the Lake Eustis Orange Grove Company of Florida, each of the par value of one hundred dollars; two shares of stock in the new Enterprise Orange Grove Company of Florida, each of the par value of one hundred dollars, and my United States Army pension.

And I do hereby constitute and appoint Frederick V. Coville, Charles S. Bundy and John Scrivener, all of Washington, D. C. to be the executors of this my last will and testament hereby revoking and annulling all former wills by me heretofore made; ratifying and confirming this and none other to be my last will and testament. In testimony whereof I have hereunto set my hand and affixed my seal this 14th day of May A.D. 1904

[signed] EDWARD PALMER SEAL

Signed, sealed and published and declared by Edward Palmer, the above named testator as and for his last will and testament in the presence of us, who at his request, in his presence, and in the presence of each other have subscribed our names as witnesses hereto.

[signed] SAMUEL SCRIVENER, 911 U St. N.W., Washington, D.C.
[signed] VIRGIL G. WILLIAMS, 2027 T Street, N.W. Wash. D.C.

REFERENCES AND SOURCES

The following list of sources includes both published and unpublished materials. The arrangement is alphabetical by author or by institution. General references which are mentioned incidentally in this work are not in the following list, but are cited in the body of the text or in footnotes. This list of references and sources includes, as far as these have come to my attention, all major papers dealing especially with Palmer's collections, but no attempt has been made to cite all of the many works which include mention of his specimens. In the field of systematic botany, for example, almost any current paper dealing with American plants will contain citations of one or more Palmer specimens.

1. [Anonymous] "Exploration of a Mound in Utah," *American Naturalist,* Vol. X (July, 1876), 410–14.
2. ———. [Itinerary and summary of Palmer's plant collections, 1879–80]. Gray Herbarium, Harvard University, 1 p., n. d.
3. ———. "List of Plants Collected by Dr. Edward Palmer, in Southwestern Chihuahua, August to November, 1885." Gray Herbarium, Harvard University. 4 pp., n. d.
4. Allen, J. A. *List of Mammals Collected by Dr. Edward Palmer in Northeastern Mexico, with Field-notes by the Collector.* Museum of Comparative Zoology [Harvard College] *Bulletin No. 8* (1881), 183–89.
5. Arizona, University of. The University Library contains the following items from the *Merwin Catalogue No.* 549 (1914): Nos. 11, 14, 15, 16, 18, 20, 21, 22, 23, 29. (See *45* below.) These items

are also listed and described in *Catalogue No. 53* of the Arthur H. Clark Co., Cleveland.

6. Baird, S. F., T. M. Brewer, and R. Ridgway. *A History of North American Birds. Land Birds.* 3 vols., Boston, 1874.
7. Barnes, Will C. *Arizona Place Names.* University of Arizona *Bulletin No. 6 (1)* [General Bulletin No. 2] (1935).
8. Beverly, Fred [i.e. Frederick Albion Ober]. "The Ochechobee Expedition," *Forest & Stream,* Vol. II (March 5, 1874), 49–50.
9. ———. Letter to editor, *ibid.* (March 26, 1874), 105.
10. ———. "Our Okeechobee Expedition," *ibid.* (April 16, 1874), 145–46.
11. Binney, W. G. "On the Land Shells of the Mexican Island of Guadalupe, Collected by Dr. E. Palmer." *Proceedings of the Academy of Natural Sciences of Philadelphia,* (for 1879), (1880), 16.
12. Brewer, W. H., and Sereno Watson. *Botany of California* (Vol. *I: Polypetalae*). Cambridge, Massachusetts, 1876.
13. Candolle, Casimir de. "Three New Species of Mexican Plants," *Botanical Gazette* Vol. XIX (January, 1894), 39–40. Discusses Palmer's Meliaceae from Colima.
14. Carpenter, Philip P. "Descriptions of New Marine Shells from the Coast of California." *Proceedings of the California Academy of Natural Sciences,* Vol. III (1866), 207–24.
15. Cooper, J. G. "Tritonia palmeri, n. sp." *Proceedings of the California Academy of Natural Sciences,* Vol. II (January, 1863), 207. Originally read at the Academy's meeting in November, 1862.
16. Coues, Elliott. "Notes on a Collection of Mammals from Arizona."*Proceedings of the Academy of Natural Sciences of Philadelphia* (for 1867) (1867), 133.
17. ———. "List of Birds Collected in Southern Arizona by Dr. E. Palmer; with Remarks." *Proceedings of the Academy of Natural Sciences of Philadelphia* (for 1868) (1868), 81–85.
18. Dall, W. H. "Descriptions of Sixty New Forms of Mollusks from the West Coast of North America and the North Pacific Ocean, with Notes on Others Already Described," *American Journal of Conchology,* Vol. VII (November 2, 1871), 93–160.
19. ———. "A New Genus and Several New Species of Landshells Collected in Central Mexico by Doctor Edward Palmer." *Smith-*

sonian Miscellaneous Collections Vol. XLVIII (July 1, 1905), 187–94, Plates XLIII–XLIV.

20. Eaton, D. C. Thirty letters from Palmer to Eaton, deposited in the Yale University Library, New Haven, Connecticut.
21. ———. "List of Marine Algae Collected Near Eastport, Maine, in August and September, 1873 [i.e. 1872], in Connection with the Work of the U. S. Fish Commission under Prof. S. F. Baird." *Transactions of the Connecticut Academy of Arts and Sciences,* Vol. II (May, 1873), 343–50.
22. ———. *A List of the Marine Algae Collected by Dr. Edward Palmer on the Coast of Florida and at Nassau, Bahama Islands, March–August, 1874.* 6 pp. June, 1875.
23. Eckfeldt, J. W. "List of Lichens from California and Mexico, Collected by Dr. Edward Palmer from 1888 to 1892." *Contributions from the United States National Herbarium,* Vol. I (October 31, 1893), 291–92.
24. Engelmann, George. Forty-eight letters from Palmer to Engelmann, deposited in the library of the Missouri Botanical Garden, St. Louis. Also in the Engelmann Collection are copies of letters from Engelmann to Palmer, and about sixteen pertinent letters from C. C. Parry to Engelmann.
25. Ewan, Joseph. "Cantillas Canyon of Lower California: Its Geography and Botanical History," *American Midland Naturalist,* Vol. XVIII (May, 1937), 351–62.
26. Faxon, Walter. "Descriptions of New Species of Cambarus, to Which Is Added a Synonymical List of the Known Species of Cambarus and Astacus." *Proceedings of the American Academy of Arts and Sciences,* Vol. XX (1884), 107–58.
27. Fernald, M. L. "Some Rare and Undescribed Plants Collected by Dr. Edward Palmer, at Acapulco, Mexico." *Proceedings of the American Academy of Arts and Sciences,* Vol. XXXIII (October 12, 1897), 86–94.
28. Gentry, Howard Scott. *Rio Mayo Plants.* Carnegie Institution of Washington *Publications, No. 527* (November 30, 1942).
29. G[ray], A[sa]. "Florida Plants," *American Journal of Science,* Series 3, Vol. IX (January, 1875), 67–68.
30. Gray, Asa. "Contributions to the Botany of North America. 1. Characters of Canbya (n. gen.) and Arctomecon," *Proceedings of the American Academy of Arts and Sciences,* Vol. XII (1876), 51–53.

31. ———. "Botanical Contributions. 1. Characters of Some New Species of Compositae in the Mexican Collection Made by C. C. Parry and Edward Palmer, Chiefly in the Province of San Luis Potosi, in 1878." *Proceedings of the American Academy of Arts and Sciences,* Vol. XV (1879), 25–41.

32. ———. "Contributions to North American Botany. I. Notes on Some Compositae." *Proceedings of the American Academy of Arts and Sciences,* Vol. XVI (1880), 78–102.

33. ———. "Contributions to American Botany. 2. Sertum Chihuahuense." *Proceedings of the American Academy of Arts and Sciences,* Vol. XXI (1886), 378–409.

34. Harvard University.

a. Gray Herbarium. Approximately seventy-five letters from Palmer, mostly to Sereno Watson; bound volumes of *Miscellaneous Plant Lists,* (Nos. 1–3, including lists of Palmer's collections of 1874, 1875, 1876, 1877, and 1878–1879); Palmer's field notes (incomplete sets) especially those of 1896, 1904, 1908.

b. Museum of Comparative Zoology. Four letters from Palmer, and records relating to the museum's ornithological and entomological collections.

c. Peabody Museum of American Archaeology and Ethnology. *Annual Reports of the Trustees,* Vol. II, No. 1 (10th–13th) (1877–80); Vol. III, No. 1 (14th) (1881–87). Palmer's activities are discussed in several places.

d. Peabody Museum of American Archaeology and Ethnology. Fifty-eight letters from Palmer, mostly to F. W. Putnam; miscellaneous notes, and lists of collections made by Palmer including Palmer's own MS report of 104 pages on his work in 1878; references to localities and collections under Accessions 76–20, 79–14, 79–87, 80–28; Item 224 of the *Merwin Catalogue,* Call No. "N.A. Eth. P182n case 2."

e. Houghton Library (Rare Books and Manuscripts). Copy of *Merwin Catalogue No.* 549 (1914), and the following numbered items from that catalogue: 10, 12, 19, 24, 25, 27, 28, 49, 53, 57, 60a, 60b, 61, 62, 87, 88, 90, 126, 128, 137, 140, 206–11, 213, 221, 223, 254, 269, 280, 282, 283, 295, 297, 298.

35. Hawks, J. M. *The Florida Gazetteer.* New Orleans, 1871.

36. Hemsley, W. Botting. *Biologia Centrali-Americana. Botany.* 4 vols., London, 1879–88.

37. Hitchcock, A. S. "Mexican Grasses in the United States National

Herbarium." *Contributions from the United States National Herbarium,* Vol. XVII (July 15, 1913), 181–390.

38. Holmes, William H. "Illustrated Catalogue of a Portion of the Collections Made by the Bureau of Ethnology during the Field Season of 1881." *Annual Report of the Bureau of Ethnology* (1884), III, 433–89. Holmes discusses Palmer's collections.
39. Horn, George H. "Notes on the Coleopterous Fauna of Guadalupe Island." *Transactions of the American Entomological Society,* Vol. V (April, 1876), 198–201.
40. Hunter, W. D., and W. D. Pierce. *Mexican Cotton Boll Weevil.* Bureau of Entomology *Bulletin No. 114* (Washington, 1912), 62 Cong., 2 sess., *Sen. Doc. 305.*
41. McVaugh, Rogers. "Edward Palmer's Collections in Arizona in 1869, 1876, and 1877. Part 1. General Discussion; Itinerary and Sources." *American Midland Naturalist,* Vol. XXIX (June, 1943), 768–75.
42. ——. "Botanical Collections of the La Plata Expedition of 1853–1855," *Brittonia,* Vol. V (September 20, 1943), 64 79.
43. ——. "Edward Palmer's Collection in the Indian Territory, 1868," *Chronicles of Oklahoma,* Vol. XXIII (Spring, 1945), 16–21.
44. —— and Thomas H. Kearney. "Edward Palmer's Collections in Arizona in 1869, 1876, and 1877. Part 2. A Consideration of some Palmer collections cited in the 'Flowering Plants and Ferns of Arizona'," *American Midland Naturalist,* Vol. XXIX (June, 1943), 775–78.
45. [Merwin Sales Company]. *A remarkable collection of excerpts, manuscript notes, photographs, mounted cuttings from rare early American Newspapers, scientific magazines, reports, etc., etc. On Arizona Territory, New Mexico, western Indian campaigns and tribes, Texas, California, Colorado, early West, Florida, the Mormons, Cuba, Mexico, etc., etc., etc. Collected by the late Dr. Edward Palmer, U.S.A., during a sojourn of sixty years in various parts of the West*[.] *To be sold at auction Tuesday afternoon, March 3d, 1914, commencing at 2.30 o'clock, by Merwin Sales Company 16 East 40th Street, New York Telephone 1106 Murray Hill*[.] Merwin Sales Co. *Catalogue 549* (*1914*). Three hundred numbered items, with short descriptions of each. For information on the current locations of items known to be still extant, see the present bibliography under Arizona,

University of; Harvard University (Museum of Comparative Zoology, Houghton Library); Michigan, University of; Palmer, Edward (No. 88, below); Smithsonian Institution (U.S. National Museum, Division of Mammals).

Certain items from this catalogue would probably prove to be valuable sources of information about Palmer's travels and botanical collections, but it has not been possible to locate them. The most important of these, as far as can be ascertained from the titles, are as follows: Nos. 1 (Acoma Indians), 3, 4 (Alabama), 17, 26 (Arizona), 36 (Batopilas, Mexico), 37, 38 (Bermuda and Nassau), 43 (Caddoes Indians), 46–48, 69 (California), 74 (Cherokee Nation), 75 (Cheyennes and Arapahoes), 77 (Choctaw Indians), 79, 81 (Coahuila, Mexico), 80 (Coahuillas Indians), 82 (Cocopah Indians), 86 (Colima, Mexico), 105 (Durango, Mexico), 114–18 (Florida), 124 (Guadalajara, Mexico), 129 (Idaho), 161 (Kansas City to Fort Whipple), 165 (Louisiana), 171 (Mexican Indians), 173, 174 (Mexican photographs), 175, 184, 255 (Mexico, Coahuila), 180 (Mexico, Sonora), 181 (Mexico, Chihuahua), 182 (Mexico, archaeological notes), 185–88, 194–97, 199 (Mexico, various travel notes by Palmer), 202 (Mississippi), 203 (Mohaves Indians), 205 (Moquis Indians), 218 (Navajo Indians), 237 (Papajo Indians of Arizona), 239 (Paraguay), 241 (Passamaquoddy Indians), 247 (Pimo Indians), 250 (Pueblo Indians), 258 (South American), 268 (Tennessee), 271, 273 (Texas), 277 (Tonkowa Indians), 281 (Utah Archaeological), 284 (Ute Indians), 291–94, 296 (Western Manuscripts and Notes).

46. Michigan, University of. Library contains the following items from the *Merwin Catalogue No. 549* (1914): Nos. 189, 190, 192, 193, 263. Palmer's transcribed notes on his travels of 1878, 1879, 1880, 1886, and 1892, and partial or complete lists of archaeological material collected in these years; letters to Palmer from L. O. Howard, Sereno Watson, J. Duncan Putnam (2), and George Engelmann (3). This material was formerly the property of the Taylor Museum of the Colorado Springs Fine Arts Center, Colorado Springs, Colorado. The former curator of the Museum, Dr. M. A. Wilder, states that the history of the items is not a matter of record; in a letter he says: "The bundle of loose pages arrived at the Museum together with a large box of Americana miscellany. The shipment represented books pur-

chased by Mrs. Alice B. Taylor, founder of the Museum, from L. A. Krigbaum, a book dealer in Denver. There was no listing of the notes on the inventory, and in later conversation with Krigbaum, he knew nothing of their existence."

47. Millspaugh, Charles Frederick, and Lawrence William Nuttall. *Flora of Santa Catalina Island (California).* Field Museum Publications, *Botanical Series,* Vol. V (1923).
48. Missouri Botanical Garden. [See also Engelmann, George.] *Annals of the Missouri Botanical Garden.* Published quarterly since 1914 by the Board of Trustees of the Missouri Botanical Garden, St. Louis, Missouri.
49. New York Botanical Garden. [See also Torrey, John.] Two letters from Palmer to N. L. Britton.
50. Ortega, Jesús González. "Ligeros informes sobre la región de los esteros de Escuinapa y Mexcaltitán," *Memorias y Revista de la Sociedad científica "Antonio Alzate,"* Vol. XLIX (1928), 1–12, Plates I, II. Plate I is entitled "Región de Escuinapa y Mexcaltitán" and also "Exploración Biológica a la Cuenca del Río Tamazula, Escala 1:100,000," and is dated December, 1926.
51. ———. "Exploración biológica por la cuenca del Río Tamazula 6 a 26 de Febrero de 1926," *Boletín de Pro-Cultura Regional, S.C.L.*, Vol. I (2) (1929), 14–16; *ibid.*, Vol. I (3) (1929), 1–4.
52. Page, Thomas J. *La Plata, the Argentine Confederation, and Paraguay.* New York, 1859.
53. [Palmer, Edward.] "Food Products of the North American Indians." *Report of the Commissioner of Agriculture* (1871), 404–28.
54. Palmer, Edward. "Indian Rope and Cloth," *American Naturalist,* Vol. VII (December, 1873), 755.
55. [Palmer, Edward] Die Vegetabilischen Nahrungsmittel der Indianer in Nordamerika, von Dr. Edward Palmer. [Translated from English by Ludwig Wittmack.] *Monatschrift des Vereines zur Befoerderung des Gartenbaues in den Koeniglichen Preussischen Staaten,* Vol. XVII, (1874), 22–28, 76–84, 133–36, 154–75, 236–40.
56. Palmer, Edward. "The Manufacture of Pottery by the Indians," *American Naturalist,* Vol. VIII (April, 1874), 245–47.
57. ———. "The Berries of Rhamnus Croceus as Indian Food," *ibid.*, 247.
58. ———. "The Resurrection Fern," *ibid.*, Vol. IX (February, 1875), 111.

59. ———. "Martenia Proboscides," *ibid.*, 112.
60. ———. "Clay-balls as Slung Shot or Cooking Stones," *ibid.* (March, 1875), 193–84.
61. ———. "An Indian Mill Seen in the Museum of Nassau, New Providence," *ibid.* (April, 1875), 248–49.
62. ———. "The Starch of Zamia," *ibid.* (September, 1875), 509–12.
63. ———. "Manufacture of Pottery by Mojave Indian Women." *Proceedings of the Davenport Academy of Natural Sciences,* Vol. II (1877), 32–34.
64. ———. "Remarks Concerning Two Divisions of Indians Inhabiting Arizona, New Mexico, Utah, and California," *American Naturalist,* Vol. XI (December, 1877), 735–47.
65. ———. "A Review of the Published Statements Regarding the Mounds at Payson, Utah, with an Account of the Structure and Origin." *Proceedings of the Davenport Academy of Natural Sciences,* Vol. II (1878), 167–72.
66. ———. "Cave Dwellings in Utah." *Peabody Museum of American Archaeology and Ethnology Annual Report No. 11* (1878), II, 269–72.
67. ———. "Notes on Indian Manners and Customs," *American Naturalist,* Vol. XII (May, 1878), 308–13.
68. ———. "Indian Food Customs," *ibid.* (June, 1878), 402.
69. ———. "Fish-hooks of the Mohave Indians," *ibid.*, 403.
70. ———. "Plants used by the Indians of the United States," *ibid.* (September, 1878), 593–606; (October, 1878), 646–55.
71. ———. "Plants Used by the Indians of the United States," *American Journal of Pharmacy,* Vol. L (November, 1878), 539–48; (December, 1878), 586–92.
72. ———. "The Sacrificial Stone of the City of Mexico, Is It Genuine or Not?" *American Naturalist,* Vol. XV (September, 1881), 752–54.
73. ———. "Mexican Caves with Human Remains," *ibid.*, Vol. XVI (April, 1882), 306–11.
74. ———. "Texan and Mexican Plants," *ibid.* (October, 1882), inner front cover page; (November, 1882), inner front cover page.
75. ———. "Burnt Clay in the Mounds," *ibid.*, Vol. XIX (August, 1885), 825.
76. ———. "Ornaments on Pottery," *ibid.*, Vol. XXI (January, 1887), 97–98.
77. ———. "The Effect on Vegetation of the Variable Rainfall of

Northwestern Mexico," *ibid.*, Vol. XXII (May, 1888), 459–61.

78. ———. "Changes in the color of Grapes grown in Northwestern Mexico," *West American Scientist,* Vol. VI (May, 1889), 28–29. 28–29.

79. ———. "Opuntia Fruit as an Article of Food," *ibid.* (July, 1889), 67–69.

80. ———. "Palmerella," *ibid.*, Vol. VII (1890), 8–9.

81. ———. "Customs of the Coyotero Apaches," *Zoe,* Vol. I (March, 1890), 161–72.

82. ———. "The Use of Broken Pottery among Indians," *ibid.*, Vol. II (April, 1891), 73–74.

83. ———. "Chia," *ibid.* (July, 1891), 140–42.

84. ———. "Indian Method of Preparing Wool and Cotton," *West American Scientist,* Vol. VII (September, 1891), 226–27.

85. ———. "Tuba," *Zoe,* Vol. III (July, 1892), 133–35.

86. ———. "House Ants of Mexico," *Insect Life,* Vol. V (January, 1893), 196. This is an extract from a letter by Palmer.

87. ———. "Visit to a Porcupine Locality," *West American Scientist,* Vol. VIII (January, 1894), 87. This is an extract from a letter by Palmer.

88. ———. "Arkansas Mounds: Observation and Results of Excavations Made around the Mounds in Various Parts of the State: Salt Wells, Filler Mounds, Journey from Osceola, remains of Old Fortification on the Arkansas River, etc., etc., Made in Various Years," *Publications of the Arkansas Historical Association,* Vol. IV (1917), 390–448. This is Item 30 of the *Merwin Catalogue,* evidently printed in its entirety, without annotation and with a minimum of editorial change.

89. Palmer, T. S. "Notes on Persons Whose Names Appear in the Nomenclature of California Birds," *Condor,* Vol. XXX (September–October, 1928), 261–307. Contains biographical notes on Edward Palmer, pp. 290–91.

90. Parry, C. C. Approximately thirty letters and other items from and concerning Palmer, in the Parry Collection on deposit in the library of Iowa State College, Ames, Iowa. There are included some letters dated from Parry's term as botanist of the United States Department of Agriculture (1869–71) and also his field notebook of 1878 concerning plants of San Luis Potosí. See also under Engelmann, George.

91. Pollard, Charles Louis. "Plants Used for Cuban Confectionery," *Plant World,* Vol. V (July, 1902), 131–32.

92. Potts, Edward. "Fresh-water Sponges from Mexico," *Proceedings of the United States National Museum,* Vol. VIII (October 19, 1885), 587–89.

93. Powell, J. W. "Pueblo Indians," *American Naturalist,* Vol. XIV (August, 1880), 603–605. Notes that Palmer has compiled MS vocabularies of the Hopi, Zuñi, and Tewa Indians.

94. Rathbun, Mary J. "Catalogue of the Crabs of the Family Periceridae in the U.S. National Museum." *Proceedings of the United States National Museum,* Vol. XV (1893), 231–77, Plates XXVIII–XL.

95. Ridgway, Robert. "Ornithology of Guadeloupe Island, Based on Notes and Collections Made by Dr. Edward Palmer." *Bulletin of the United States Geological and Geographical Survey of the Territories* (1876), II, 183–196.

96. Robinson, Benjamin Lincoln. "A Monograph of the Genus Brickellia." *Memoirs of the Gray Herbarium,* Vol. I (February 3, 1917), 1–151.

97. Rose, J. N. "List of Plants Collected by Dr. Edward Palmer in Western Mexico and Arizona in 1890." *Contributions from the United States National Herbarium,* Vol. I (June 30, 1891), 91–116. The plants treated in this article are those collected in the vicinity of Álamos, Sonora; for others see the following references.

98. ———. "List of Plants Collected by Dr. E. Palmer in Arizona in 1890." *Ibid.,* 117–27.

99. ———. "List of Plants Collected by Dr. Edward Palmer in 1890 on Carmen Island." *Ibid.,* Vol. I (September 25, 1892), 129–34.

100. ———. "Report on a Collection of Plants Made in the States of Sonora and Colima, Mexico, by Dr. Edward Palmer, in the Years 1890 and 1891." *Ibid.,* Vol. I (January 31, 1895), 293–392.

101. ———. "Descriptions of Plants, Mostly New, from Mexico and the United States." *Ibid.,* Vol. III (December 14, 1895), 311–19. Contains 16 new species based on Palmer's collections, chiefly from Sinaloa, 1891, and Tepic, 1892.

102. Safford, W. E. [See also *No. 123b*] "Edward Palmer," *Popular Science Monthly,* Vol. LXXVIII (April, 1911), 341–54.

103. ———. "Edward Palmer," *Botanical Gazette,* Vol. LII (July, 1911), 61–63.

104. ———. "Edward Palmer," *American Fern Journal,* Vol. I (November 29, 1911), 143–47.

105. S[argent], C. S. "New or Little Known Plants: Cereus Pringlei," *Garden & Forest,* Vol. II (February 6, 1889), 64, Fig. 92. Mainly an account of Palmer's description of this species on the island of "San Pedro Martin" in 1887.

106. Sargent, C. S. Biographical footnote on Edward Palmer, *Silva of North America,* Vol. VIII (1895), 106–107. The data for this note were supplied by Palmer himself; see No. *114g.*

107. Scribner, Frank Lamson. "A List of the Grasses Collected by Dr. E. Palmer in the Vicinity of Acapulco, Mexico, 1894–95." *United States Department of Agriculture, Division of Agrostology, Bulletin No. 4,* (February 6, 1897), 7–11. Twenty-nine numbers cited; Palmer's field notes, abridged, are included.

108. ——— and Elmer D. Merrill. "Some Recent Collections of Mexican Grasses." *United States Department of Agriculture, Division of Agrostology Bulletin No. 24,* (January 9, 1901), 5–30. Based in part upon Palmer's grasses collected 1896–98.

109. Scudder, Samuel H. "Orthoptera from the Island of Guadalupe." *Proceedings of the Boston Society of Natural History,* Vol. XVIII (May, 1876), 268–71.

110. ———. "Notice of the Butterflies Collected by Dr. Edward Palmer in the Arid Regions of Southern Utah and Northern Arizona during the Summer of 1877." *Bulletin of the United States Geological and Geographical Survey of the Territories* (February 5, 1878), IV, 253–58.

111. ———. "Revision of the Orthopteran Group Melanopli (Acridiidae), with Special Reference to North American Forms." *Proceedings of the United States National Museum,* Vol. XX (1897), 1–421.

112. ———. "The North American Ceuthophili." *Proceedings of the American Academy of Arts and Sciences, Vol. XXX* (?August, 1895), 17–113.

113. ———. "The Orthopteran Genus Schistocerca." *Proceedings of the American Academy of Arts and Sciences,* Vol. XXXIV (March, 1899), 439–76.

114. Smithsonian Institution.

a. Archives. Numerous items, 1855–87, including forty-five letters from Palmer and about an equal number to Palmer (copies), chiefly from Spencer F. Baird.

b. Correspondence and Documents, Division of. Historical files and files relating to Accessions; numerous items, 1856–1911, including ninety-two letters from Palmer.

c. Ethnology, Bureau of American, Archives. Numerous items in Catalogue No. 2,400, including twenty-eight letters from Palmer; one letter from Palmer in Catalogue No. 3,317.

d. Regents, Board of. *Ninth Annual Report of the Board of Regents of the Smithsonian Institution,* 1854 (Washington, 1855); Tenth *Annual Report,* 1855 (Washington, 1856); *Annual Report of the Board of Regents of the Smithsonian Institution for the Year 1856* (Washington, 1857); *Annual Report of the Board of Regents of the Smithsonian Institution for the Year 1863,* (Washington, 1864); *Annual Report of the Board of Regents of the Smithsonian Institution for the Year 1864* (Washington, 1865).

e. U.S. National Museum, Division of Birds. Miscellaneous records.

f. U.S. National Museum, Division of Ethnology. Numerous accessions, 1864–1910, comprising records of more than 2,500 collections.

g. U.S. National Museum, Division of Mammals. Includes files from the personal collection of C. Hart Merriam, correspondence between Palmer and C. S. Sargent, 1890–91, a copy of the *Merwin Catalogue* marked by Merriam and a number of the items from this catalogue, apparently those Merriam succeeded in purchasing. The items marked were Nos. 18, 35, 44–52, 56, 57, 59 (marked: "Not got–who got?"), 65, 68, 69 ("who got?"), 80, 82, 106, 130, 147, 153, 154, 203, 204, 254, 264, 281, 283–85, 291, 294, 296. The material has been mixed so that it now seems impossible to determine which or how many items were received by Merriam.

h. U.S. National Museum Division of Mollusks. Miscellaneous records.

i. U.S. National Museum, Division of Plants. United States National Herbarium. Information on herbarium specimens, particularly those collected in 1853–55, 1863, 1869, 1899, and 1902. Approximately 145 letters from Palmer, and a copy of his notes on the trip from San Luis Potosí to Tampico, 1878–79. Miscellaneous lists, reports, field notes, and accession records relative to Palmer's collections.

115. Stearns, Robert E. C. "The Shells of the Tres Marias and Other

Localities Along the Shores of Lower California and the Gulf of California." *Proceedings of the United States National Museum, Vol.* XVII (July 19, 1894), 139–204.

116. Studley, Cordelia A. "Notes upon Human Remains from Caves in Coahuila." *Peabody Museum of American Archaeology and Ethnology Report No. 3* (1884), 233–59.
117. Thomas, Cyrus. "Burial Mounds of the Northern Section of the United States," *Annual Report of the Bureau of Ethnology No. 5* (1887), 1–119.
118. ———. *Catalogue of Prehistoric Works East of the Rocky Mountains.* Bureau of Ethnology [*Bulletin No. 12*] (1891).
119. ———. "Report on the Mound Explorations of the Bureau of Ethnology." *Annual Report of the Bureau of Ethnology No. 12* (1894).
120. Torrey, John. One letter from Palmer; Palmer's botanical field notes of 1868; and partial list of determinations made by Torrey. All in Torrey Collection at the New York Botanical Garden, New York.
121. ——— and Asa Gray. "A Revision of the Eriogoneae." *Proceedings of the American Academy of Arts and Sciences,* Vol. VIII (1870), 145–200.
122. Underwood, Lucien M. and William R. Maxon. "Notes on a Collection of Cuban Pteridophyta, with Descriptions of Four New Species." *Bulletin of the Torrey Botanical Club,* Vol. XXIX (October 31, 1902), 577–84.
123. United States Department of Agriculture.
    a. Palmer Manuscript Collection in the Division of Plant Exploration and Introduction. Approximately 500 individual items, 1853–1911, of which about 240 are unique, containing information not available elsewhere. This collection was assembled partly by Palmer himself, and partly by W. E. Safford after Palmer's death, and is by far the most important single source of information concerning the collector.
    b. A book-length manuscript of 702 typed pages, by W. E. Safford, dealing with the life of Palmer, filed with the Division of Plant Exploration and Introduction. At the time of Safford's death twenty-four chapters, covering that part of Palmer's life from birth to the year 1889, had been completed. This manuscript is of importance in the present connection chiefly because Safford seems to have had access to diaries kept by Palmer during

his travels, and quotes from these in considerable detail, particularly from those of the years 1853–55, 1863, 1867, 1868, 1869, 1870, 1874, 1875, and 1888. None of the originals, except for a typed copy of the 1910 journal and a very few small fragments of others, is known to be extant. Safford also quotes from notes and remarks communicated directly to him by Palmer; these quotations are often detailed and specific, but it is usually impossible to check their authenticity. Chapters I–V, (110 MS pages) describe early life briefly and expedition to Paraguay in detail; Chapter VI (32 pp.) covers years 1855–67 (actually 1861–67); Chapters VII and VIII (48 pp.) pertain to Palmer's trip to Indian Territory, 1868; Chapters IX–XI (62 pp.) trips to Arizona, Sonora, etc., 1869 and 1870; Chapter XII (20 pp.) covers period 1872–74, mostly trip to Florida, 1874; Chapter XIII (36 pp.) Guadalupe Island, 1875 and 1889; Chapters XIV and XV (44 pp.) California and Lower California, 1875; Chapters XVI and XVII (74 pp.) Utah, Arizona and California, 1876 and 1877; Chapter XVIII (21 pp.) San Luis Potosí, Coahuila, Nuevo León and Texas, 1877–80; Chapter XIX (13 pp.) work for Bureau of Ethnology, 1881–84, and trip to Florida, 1884; Chapter XX (29 pp.) visits to Arizona and Sonora Indians, 1884–85; Chapter XXI (63 pp.) Chihuahua, and Tarahuamare Indians, 1885; Chapter XXII (71 pp.) Jalisco, 1886; Chapter XXIII (49 pp.) Sonora and Lower California, 1887; Chapter XXIV (19 pp.) California, 1888; Chapter XXV [unfinished] (11 pp.) Colonia Lerdo, Sonora, 1889.

Materials relating directly to Palmer and his travels are relatively poorly represented. In Chapter XXII, for example, approximately nine-tenths of the seventy-one pages are devoted to notes and comments on economic plants of Mexico, many of which were collected by Palmer on this particular trip. The reader of this chapter, and most of the others, may get the impression that Palmer and his expeditions were used by Safford as a framework upon which to build a book on the economic plant-products of Mexico. Facts relating to actual collections and to itineraries are subordinated in the narration, and are sometimes in need of verification.

c. Palmer's original botanical field notes, 1890–1910, filed with the Division of Plant Exploration and Introduction. The set is incomplete, but is by far the most extensive set known to be extant.

d. Office of the Secretary. Records of the Office of Personnel, beginning with the year 1889.
e. *Report of the Commissioner of Agriculture for the Year 1869* (Washington, 1870); *Report of the Commissioner of Agriculture for the Year 1875* (Washington, 1876).

124. United States Department of the Interior.
a. *Annual Report of the Commissioner of Indian Affairs, for the Year 1868* (Washington, 1868); *Report of the Commissioner of Indian Affairs, Made to the Secretary of Interior, for the Year 1869* (Washington, 1870); *Report of the Commissioner of Indian Affairs to the Secretary of the Interior for the Year 1870* (Washington, 1870).
b. United States Commission of Fish and Fisheries. I. [Report of the Commissioner for 1871 and 1872] (Washington, 1873); II. Report of the Commissioner for 1872 and 1873 (Washington, 1874); III. Report of the Commissioner for 1873–74 and 1874–75 (Washington, 1876).

125. United States National Archives.
a. Records of the Department of Agriculture. Bureau of Chemistry (Two letters from Palmer); Bureau of Entomology (One letter from Palmer); Forest Service (Two letters from Palmer); Bureau of Plant Industry (Miscellaneous correspondence and records).
b. Records of the Interior Department. Fish and Wildlife Service (Numerous letters and other items, 1871–84); Office of Indian Affairs (Numerous letters and other items, particularly with reference to Palmer's work in 1868).
c. Records of the Navy Department, especially pertaining to Palmer's service; medical journal and log of the *Water Witch.*
d. Records of the War Department. Numerous letters and other items pertaining to Palmer's army record, 1862–67.
e. Records of the State Department. Consular Records of Guaymas, Sonora, Mexico.
f. Records of the Veterans Administration. Numerous letters and other items filed with Palmer's service and pension papers.
g. Records of the Port of New York. Passenger lists of incoming vessels.

126. United States War Department
a. Bergland, Lieutenant Eric. "Preliminary Report upon the Oper-

ations of Party No. 3, California Section, Season of 1875–76, with a View to Determine the Feasibility of Diverting the Colorado River for Purposes of Irrigation." *Annual Report of the Chief of Engineers to the Secretary of War for the Year 1876,* Pt. 3 (Washington, 1876), 329–45, and map facing p. 333; 44 Cong., 2 sess., *House Ex. Doc. No. 1,* Part 2, Vol. II. This is Appendix B to Wheeler's report on the geographical surveys west of the 100th meridian.

127. Vasey, George. "Forest Trees of the United States: Centennial Collection." *Report of the Commissioner of Agriculture,* 1875 (Washington, 1876), 151–86. According to this report, "Dr. Edward Palmer made the collection for the southern portion of California, Arizona, and Southern Utah."
128. ———. "New Species of Mexican Grasses, Collected by Dr. Ed. Palmer, in S.W. Chihuahua, in 1885." *Bulletin of the Torrey Botanical Club,* Vol. XIII (December, 1886), 229–32; continued in *Bulletin of the Torrey Botanical Club,* Vol. XIV (January, 1887), 8–10.
129. ———. "Special Uses and Properties of Some Mexican Grasses." *Bulletin of the Torrey Botanical Club,* Vol. XIV (May, 1887), 98–100. Based entirely upon Palmer's Mexican notes, 1879–86.
130. ———. "New or Little Known Plants. Uniola Palmeri," *Garden & Forest,* Vol. II (1889), 401–402.
131. ———. "Uniola Palmeri. A New Grass of Economic Importance." *Report of the Secretary of Agriculture,* 1889 (Washington, 1890), 393–94. Specifically in the report of the botanist.
132. ——— and J. N. Rose. "List of Plants Collected by Dr. Edward Palmer in Lower California in 1889." *Proceedings of the United States National Museum,* Vol. XI (1889), 527–36.
133. ———. "Plants from Southern California." *Contributions from the United States National Herbarium,* Vol. I (June 16, 1890), 1–8.
134. ———. "List of Plants Collected by Dr. Edward Palmer in Lower California in 1889." *Contributions from the United States National Herbarium,* Vol. I (June 16, 1890), 9–28.
135. ———. "List of Plants collected by Dr. Edward Palmer in Lower California and Western Mexico in 1890." *Contributions from the United States National Herbarium,* Vol. I (November 8, 1890), 63–90.
136. Verrill, A. E. "Review of the Corals and Polyps of the West Coast

of America." *Transactions of the Connecticut Academy of Arts and Sciences,* Vol. I (1868–70), 377–546. Fascicle 65 (pp. 519–34) dated November, 1870, deals with Palmer's collections at Guaymas.

137. ———. Report on the Invertebrate Animals of Vineyard Sound and the Adjacent Waters, with an Account of the Physical Characters of the Region. United States Commission of Fish and Fisheries [Report of the Commissioner for 1871 and 1872] (Washington, 1873), 295–778.

138. Watson, Sereno. "Additions" [to the Catalogue of Species in the Botany of the King Expedition]. *Report of the Geological Exploration of the Fortieth Parallel,* Vol. V (1871), 416–26.

139. ———. "Botanical Contributions. II. List of a Collection of Plants from Guadalupe Island, Made by Dr. Edward Palmer, with his Notes upon Them." *Proceedings of the American Academy of Arts and Sciences,* Vol. XI (February, 1876), 112–31.

140. ———. [Advertisement of Palmer's plants of 1875; see also p. 67], *American Naturalist,* Vol. X (1876), 235.

141. ———. "Contributions to American Botany. I. Revision of the North American Liliaceae." *Proceedings of the American Academy of Arts and Sciences,* Vol. XIV (1879), 213–88.

142. ———. "Contributions to American Botany. 1. List of plants from Southwestern Texas and Northern Mexico, Collected Chiefly by Dr. E. Palmer in 1879–80.—I. Polypetalae." *Proceedings of the American Academy of Arts and Sciences,* Vol. XVII (August 10, 1882), 316–61.

a. ———. "Catálogo de las plantas del Norte de Mexico y sudoeste de Texas, colectadas principalmente por el Dr. E. Palmer en 1879–80—I: Polypetalae." *La Naturaleza,* Vol. VI (1884), 152–70, 221–44. This translation into Spanish is by Sr. Manuel Urbina, according to a note in the index of the volume.

b. ———. "Contributions to American Botany. 1. List of Plants from Southwestern Texas and Northern Mexico, Collected Chiefly by Dr. E. Palmer in 1879–80—II. Gamopetalae to Acotyledones." *Proceedings of the American Academy of Arts and Sciences,* Vol. XVIII (August 15, 1883), 96–191.

143. ———. "Contributions to American Botany. 1. List of Plants Collected by Dr. Edward Palmer in Southwestern Chihuahua, Mex-

ico, in 1885." *Proceedings of the American Academy of Arts and Sciences,* Vol. XXI (June 2, 1886), 414–45.

144. ———. "Contributions to American Botany. 1. List of Plants Collected by Dr. Edward Palmer in the State of Jalisco, Mexico, in 1886." *Proceedings of the American Academy of Arts and Sciences,* Vol. XXII (June 25, 1887), 396–465.

145. ———. "Contributions to American Botany. 1. Upon a Collection of Plants Made by Dr. E. Palmer, in 1887, about Guaymas, Mexico, at Muleje and Los Angeles Bay in Lower California, and on the Island of San Pedro Martin in the Gulf of California." *Proceedings of the American Academy of Arts and Sciences,* Vol. XXIV (January 31, 1889), 36–82.

146. Wheeler, Louis C. "The Type of the Genus Lepidospartum," *Rhodora,* Vol. XL (August, 1938), 320–23.

INDEX